Good Food in
YORKSHIRE
and HUMBERSIDE

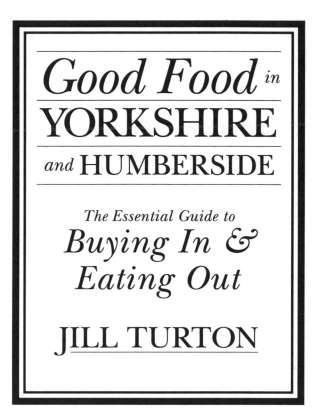

Good Food in
YORKSHIRE
and HUMBERSIDE

The Essential Guide to
Buying In &
Eating Out

JILL TURTON

FIG
TREE

First published in 1995 by Fig Tree Press
PO Box HP 88
Leeds LS6 4XR
W. Yorkshire

British Library Cataloguing in Publication Data
A catalogue record for this book is available from the British Library.

ISBN 0 9524714 0 X

Cover illustration by Brian and Lizzie Sanders
Cover design by Town Group Consultancy

Food for cover illustration: bread and cakes by Betty's of Harrogate;
organic vegetables by John Brooks of Badsworth; game by Country
Butchers of Harrogate; cheese by Farm Dairy of Knaresborough;
York ham by Hutton's of Knaresborough; pies by R. J. Lodge of
Meltham; fish by Ramus Seafoods of Harrogate; jam and cakes by
W.I Market, Otley.

For permission to use the quotation from A Local Habitation by
Richard Hoggart the author acknowledges Chatto and Windus. For
George Orwell's The Road to Wigan Pier, the author acknowledges
the estate of the late Sonia Brownell Orwell and Martin Secker &
Warburg. For permission to use the quotation from J.B. Priestley's
The Good Companions, the author acknowledges Peters, Fraser &
Dunlop. Grateful acknowledgement is made to those authors and
publishers who kindly gave permission for items to be reprinted.
While every effort has been made to trace the copyright holders of all
the quotations reproduced in this book, the publishers sincerely regret
any oversights that may have occurred.

Printed and bound in Great Britain by Smith Settle, Otley, W. Yorks
Distributed by Smith Settle

Although every effort and care has been made to ensure the accuracy
of the information contained in this publication the publisher cannot
accept responsibility for any errors it may contain.

About the author:

Jill Turton is a freelance journalist and television producer based in
Yorkshire, specialising in food, health and social issues, and a regular
contributor to Yorkshire Television, the Yorkshire Post, the Guardian
and numerous food magazines.

Contents

Introduction

'Holbeck Feast . . . the unmistakable fairground smell: hot engine oil, clinkers, toffee apples, brandy snap, mushy peas, cockles and winkles with vinegar. All in all, a dreadful compound but still more than any other mixture of smells, instantly evocative of English working class life, as powerful to us as the smell of some herbs must be to an Italian peasant.'

Richard Hoggart, A Local Habitation

That whiff of Leeds in the 1930s may still be recognisable but so too nowadays is the smell of Italian herbs. A revolution is taking place. There's never been a better time to relish good food in Yorkshire and Humberside. There's never been a more exciting range of restaurants to visit nor a wider choice of quality produce to bring home. Certainly, it's a happy time for this book to be published. I hope it will be used as a practical companion for food lovers. It is designed to let you know what's locally available wherever you are in the region. It should help you find those Italian herbs or just an honest loaf of bread.

My researches for this book underlined first the privilege of eating out in Yorkshire and Humberside today. We have Winteringham Fields, one of the top four restaurants of England according to the Good Food Guide. There's a Michelin star holder in Bradford. You can eat a Japanese feast in a private house or have a wholefood lunch in a church crypt. We have the world's finest fish and chips (even a drive-in or a Halal chippie if you want). We have Britain's best value curry houses. We have, in the Betty's chain, a still inimitable set of tea rooms.

Village inns are confidently reproducing the latest metropolitan cuisine. The heat of bistro and brasserie competition in Leeds, York, Harrogate, Sheffield and Kirklees is intense. Less so, unfortunately, in Middlesbrough and Humberside. Obviously, there are plenty of depressing eateries at every rung of the market but the overall standard at the top has never been higher and it's still improving.

Our region's food is also greatly blessed with tradition and natural resources. There is timeless excellence among the home baked cakes of the W.I. and a striking renaissance in Dales farmhouse cheeses. Yorkshire has made an unparalleled contribution to famous British confectionery. Our brown crab, white pigs and red grouse are world beaters; our rhubarb and liquorice have unique histories. If you want to experience York ham at its best, the purest honey from Europe's finest heather moors, a soft slipper oatcake from its last northern outpost or one of Ampleforth's 58 different English apples, this guide will make the connection.

Let's recognise, too, the best ethnic diversity in food outside London with Jewish, Polish and Scandinavian sources as well as the more visible Chinese, Afro-Caribbean and Asian restaurants and shops. We have excellent wholefood shops, superb vegetarian cafés and restaurants and even a village tofu maker.

I want to share all sorts of discoveries: the stately home which makes exquisite vinegars, the mucky fat queue at Dewsbury market, the all-woman samosa factory and sources of alternative ice cream for children with dairy allergies. I want to help the serious food lover find their way to the priceless collection of historic cookery books at Leeds University, to amuse the browser with old stories of gull's eggs from Flamborough or more modern ones like the Malton butcher selling rooks for pies less than a decade ago. More simply, I hope from here you'll find and use your best local butcher, baker, fishmonger and greengrocer.

Of course, we nearly all use supermarkets for speed, convenience and choice. I am no exception. The biggest stores fly in year round African vegetables, Pacific fish and South American fruit. Their hygiene and freshness is exacting; their information on diet and health can be positive. But they receive no listings in this book. They can look after themselves well enough.

The supermarkets may pay occasional lip service to expensive organic greens, free range meat and regional cheeses from small producers but they are also driving the engines of agri-business in the Third World and harsh animal husbandry on our own doorstep. Their independent high street competitors have been decimated. Now, their suppliers are frankly terrorised by the terms of trade imposed. Happier news is that the select butchers, fishmongers and greengrocers that have survived have invariably done so by raising their standards. Specialist farmers and growers, delicatessens, ethnic stores and individualistic market stalls all flourish in Yorkshire. The selective consumer is becoming the winner.

This book celebrates the best food producers. The terms of inclusion are simply that they must be distinctively good and care about what they serve. I hope that food lovers will provide them with prosperity (or just survival) and enjoy better eating in return. One of my personal gains in researching this book has been an organic vegetable grower near Pontefract. As I am lucky enough to be in range of his weekly delivery round, I have rediscovered a wonderful range of English vegetables at their purest, freshest and seasonal best.

In fact, I've never eaten better nor appreciated food more than during the research for this book. I've bought perfect asparagus from a farm shop, reawoken to the taste of real meat and savoured unique breads and cheeses. I've sampled the world as brought to Yorkshire and I've met more independent people committed to quality produce and cooking than I ever imagined existed in the region. I know, too, that there are further rewarding finds to be made. Above all, I would like this book to be a positive influence towards still higher food standards. I hope you'll make new discoveries, support the deserving and, most importantly, taste the difference.

Jill Turton
Headingley 1995

Acknowledgements

Whether farmer or grower, fisherman or chef, it is the commitment and expertise of the food producers of Yorkshire and Humberside that have made this book possible. In my travels across the region, I have met with hundreds of people who have given freely of their time and knowledge for the crucial information that underpins the guide. I thank them all most warmly for their generosity.

My particular thanks go to Sue Argent for her advice on organic food and farming; to Judy Bell, who spent long hours in her farmhouse kitchen explaining the finer points of cheese production; to John and Andrew Green who were on hand to answer queries on meat and butchering; to Chris Ramus, a tireless advocate of fish; to Nick Finnis, Brian Sanders and Tim Worsnop for their anglers' wisdom; to Charlie Flynn for his practical experience with game; to Man Chiu Leung, Irna Imran, Filip Cieslik, Jonathan and Chika Barnett and Abu Maumoniat for their detailed pointers on ethnic food. Thanks also to Richard Whiteley and Adrian Budgen for sharing their knowledge of the region and to Peter Gordon for his many suggestions and splendid appetite for all good food.

Nobody researching the historical background to food and eating in Yorkshire and Humberside can fail to pay tribute to the writings of Marie Hartley and Joan Ingilby and the scholarship of Peter Brears, formerly of Leeds City Museum. Martin Wainwright's Guardian features on regional food traditions were also particularly helpful. Further sources are acknowledged in a select bibliography.

Although all the restaurants have been visited independently, I would not have found my way to some of the most essential without Robert Cockroft finding them first. As food editor of the Yorkshire Post, his incisive monitoring of the food scene is a great force for good in the ever improving standards of the region. The Good Food Guide is the most discriminating and thorough of the annual national restaurant guides and a valuable benchmark.

Being publisher as well as author, I must also thank those who have guided me through the pitfalls of desk top enterprises. The work of Roger Ratcliffe, editor and publisher of Leeds Fax, has been most influential and he has been notably kind and supportive. Sally McKenna, author and publisher of the Bridgestone Irish Food Guide, gave generous advice in the early days. Ken Smith of Smith Settle has been calmly professional. Thanks to Valerie Austin who has tirelessly checked names, addresses and opening hours. On a more personal note, I thank my husband Grant McKee, who has not only eaten his way through this book but whose input and criticism have been invaluable. Without his support it would never have been written.

How to Use this Book

Organisation

The first half of the book is divided into broad food categories, with eight chapters covering fish, meat, fruit and vegetables, cheese, baking, preserves, sweets and wholefoods. Then, two further chapters cover particular kinds of food shopping, including markets, delicatessen, grocers, ethnic stores and farm shops. The second half of the book reviews cafés and restaurants.

Geography

Yorkshire and Humberside, for the purpose of this book, comprise traditional Yorkshire, as defined by the Ridings, and South Humberside, as defined by the 1974 local government map. There are exceptional forays into Derbyshire, Lancashire and County Durham where the journey over a boundary is short and the reward is significant.

Listings and Index

Within each chapter, entries are organised alphabetically by city, town or village. A separate gazetteer lists every city, town and village and its own good food listings. Thus, it should be equally easy to track down specific products or to find what a given place has to offer. If there is any ambiguity as to whether a community is listed in its own right or has been covered under a larger place, double check in the gazetteer. The index lists all entries by name. Where a name appears in bold type in the main text, it means it has a separate entry in its own right elsewhere in the book.

Opening Hours

Every effort has been made to give accurate opening times. However, shops, markets, cafés and restaurants are constantly changing their hours at short notice. In addition, small producers and farmers are not always on hand to deal with customers and they often ask that customers telephone ahead. Businesses often move, change hands or even close down. It is always worth checking opening hours and other details before setting out.

Prices

Prices, particularly in restaurants, change frequently. No sooner are they published than they become out of date. There are an almost infinite number of variables within a restaurant menu. Lunches are usually cheaper than evening meals; there are often fixed price or 'early bird' menus; there may be supplements on certain dishes. Service may be included or left to the diner's discretion. There may be a cover charge. Then there is the wine list. No two restaurant bills are ever really comparable so no attempt has been made to price a typical meal. The great majority of establishments listed in this book are moderately priced, in the way that anyone with reasonable experience of eating out will understand. Where an establishment is notably cheaper or dearer than the broad norm, this is specified in the main text.

Entries

All entries in this book represent a wholly independent and personal selection by the author. Such a guide does not claim to be exhaustive and there is no suggestion that any business not listed is below the standard for inclusion. There is no payment, advertising or sponsorship associated with the entries. There were no free meals. Every listing has been visited or sampled at first hand; all eating places visited without prior identification. If there are omissions, errors or recommendations please write to Fig Tree Press at the address on page 4.

1

Fish & Seafood

There's a long history, an enduring fascination and a rich bounty in the fish, seafood and crustaceans to be found in the waters in and around Yorkshire. Princess Aelfleda of Whitby Abbey put out to sea in a fishing boat in 654 AD and the last pike in the Abbey pond perished in a drought in the 1980s. In the highest moorland reaches of the River Wharfe there are still crayfish (albeit protected) to be found. Off the Yorkshire coast a big fish angler once hooked a 700 lbs tunny which took him five hours to land and hauled his rowing boat 12 miles in the process. In the 18th century thousands of whales were harpooned among the icebergs to be landed in Yorkshire ports (along with sea horses and polar bears). Tons of salt cod are still exported to Portugal and South America from Hull's cod farms and Grimsby is now the European headquarters of the fish finger and the ocean stick.

Wild salmon are present in six Yorkshire rivers, even spawning through the industrial soup of the Tees. It is possible to buy salt-marsh samphire in Settle and live cuttlefish on Leeds market. Markets remain a prime source for the fish shopper but too many high street fishmongers offer little more than tired cod fillets or dyed yellow haddock. Those that aspire to something better should be nurtured. Unless there's such a caring specialist or a passing fish van within decent range, the supermarket is sometimes the better bet. Even then, inexperienced staff make it a hit and miss affair. The dearth of fishmongers can't all be blamed on a natural conservatism when even middle of the road bistros can now offer blackboard menus full of fresh and interesting varieties. Certainly, the range and quality of fish cooked in Yorkshire restaurants has never been better.

FISHMONGERS

BEDALE

Carrick's

The majority of mobile fish vans that tour the region's villages, housing estates and outdoor markets offer fish that is fresh enough but uninspiring. Fine for cod, haddock and plaice, but what about the rest? Brothers Peter and David Carrick provide the answer with their big green van which does the rounds of the North Yorkshire markets. It's packed with ice and crammed to the gunnels with hake, halibut, ling, coley, Dover sole, smoked fish, crab, lobster, mussels and more. Every morning Peter and David make an early morning dash from their base at Snape near Bedale to Whitby or Hull where they buy their fish. The hours between 5am and 6am are spent gutting, skinning, boning and filleting before they put up the sign: 'Guaranteed no bones.' 'We're proper blockmen,' says David Carrick. A blockman is a fishmonger who is skilled in preparing fish. It's labour intensive work but their popularity is due reward. Packing up, driving home, cleaning and washing the van amounts to a 15 hour day, six days a week. On Sunday, when David Carrick might be expected to put his feet up, he jumps on board a trawler or Whitby coble and goes fishing.

Bedale Market, Tue
Leyburn Market, Fri
Northallerton Market, Wed, Sat
Richmond Market, Sat
Ripon Market, Thur

BEVERLEY

Peck & Son

A fishmonger who creates a window display using a very large and very ugly monkfish must have admirable confidence in his wares. Alan Peck certainly should have. He has been around fish literally all his life, having been born upstairs at this family fish shop in Beverley's charming Wednesday Market. He usually has at least 15 varieties on sale. Monkfish, halibut, skate, coley, salmon, mackerel, east coast crabs and the ever popular haddock are regulars. Smoked fish comes from his own smoking cabinet.

7 Wednesday Market,
Beverley, N. Humbs
☎ *01482 881582*
Mon-Fri 9am-4.30pm
Thur & Sat 9am-12 noon

BRIDLINGTON

Arnold's Fisheries

Arnold sounds like a stout Yorkshire name but actually belongs to Arnold Applequist, a Swede who ran away to sea, turned up in Bridlington and married a local girl. His granddaughter Pam Applequist runs the shop today, selling prawns, cockles, winkles, whelks, tiny shrimp, a selection of fresh fish and, above all, crab. Pam measures out her summers dressing crabs – one every four minutes, she calculates, and with sales peaking at 140 a day, that's going some. What could be more natural than rounding off a day trip to Brid with a freshly boiled crab to take home but Bridlington, despite being the centre of the East coast crab trade, is surprisingly hard up for reliable outlets and this is probably the best of a mediocre bunch.

33 Queen Street,
Bridlington, N. Humbs
☎ *01262 672277*
Open: Mon-Sat 8am-4pm
Sun 9am-4pm

Blue Lobster

Although best known as a restaurateur, the larger than life figure of Mike Baron looms large in Bridlington. He is a long-time campaigner for native British shellfish, claiming that cheap Canadian imports are ruining the trade in British and particularly east coast shellfish. If he's still in business he will sell you a lobster or a crab from his restaurant and shop overlooking Bridlington harbour but Mike Baron announced in 1994 that he plans to sell up.

West End Pier, South Cliff Road,
Bridlington, N. Humbs
☎ *01262 674729*
Open: summer Mon-Sun 8am-5pm winter Mon-Sat 10am-4pm
Orders taken through the restaurant Mon-Sun 11am-11pm

BRIGG

Brigg Seafoods

There is a decent selection of fish in this small shop just off the High Street. It includes monkfish and undyed haddock.

College Yard, Brigg, S. Humbs
☎ *01652 657850*
Open: Tue, Thur, Fri 9am-4pm
Wed & Sat 9am-2pm

FILEY

Haxby's Wet Fish

Lobster, sea trout and wild salmon are available here in the decidedly un-nautical outskirts of Filey at much below the price of metropolitan fishmongers. Crabs are usually in plentiful supply and one of their more unusual offering is small whole haddock, precisely one serving size. The Haxby's are a fishing family through and through The men – Jim Haxby, his son and his nephew – catch the fish in the east coast's inshore waters. The women – Val Haxby and daughter Mandy Gage – run the shop close to the railway station.

1 The Brigg, Station Avenue, Filey, N. Yorks
☎ *01723 512041*
Open: summer Mon-Fri 9am-5pm Sat 9am-4pm winter Mon-Fri 9am-4pm Sat 9am-2pm

Jim Smith

The best of Filey is a pleasant time-warp of white-washed Victorian hotels, municipal putting greens and donations to the lifeboat. Jim Smith's wooden kiosk on Coble Landing maintains the unchanging seaside feel. He sells the occasional local lobster at the keenest of prices, 50p bags of juicy shrimp, the freshest of fresh crabs, and the most ominous looking of hyper-pink ocean sticks (more crab colouring and pollack than crab). Pull up a chair on the front, munch a no frills, no nonsense crab sandwich and watch the world go by: fishermen still at work on nets and pots and a rusty tractor still hauling real cobles up Coble Landing.

Coble Landing, Filey, N. Yorks
No 'phone
Open: summer 9am-10pm

GRIMSBY

Jack Smith

Grimsby fish shoppers remain privileged. The survival of Fish Docks as one of the great crossroads of the fish distribution business ensures a consistent choice of fresh and interesting seafood at the weekday wholesale market. Andrew Coulbeck runs the Jack Smith wholesale operation on the quayside. At its best, early in the morning, it is kaleidoscopic, an exotic United Nations of fish: strawberry grouper from Africa, red snapper from the Seychelles, rope-grown mussels from Scotland and fresh water crevettes from Thailand. There are lobsters from Canada

and crabs from Mablethorpe; wild salmon, own brand smoked salmon, fresh sardines and tuna. Smith's supply shops and restaurants across Humberside and Lincolnshire, notably the much praised **Winteringham Fields**.

Wharncliffe Road, Fish Docks, Grimsby, S. Humbs
☎ *01472 355217*
Open: Mon-Thur 7.30am-3pm Fri 7.30am-2pm

Superior Seafoods

The family firm of Superior Seafoods has survived the dreadful 20 years haemorrhage of Grimsby's fishing industry by acting as distributors. They transport fish to all corners of the British Isles but their retail shop near the fish dock also sells a wide range of fish, exploiting the wealth of overland arrivals from Peterhead and Brixham for the early morning market and the local landings by foreign boats. Naturally, prices are often well below those in town.

1 Riby Street, Grimsby, S. Humbs
☎ *01472 362881*
Open: Mon-Fri 8am-5pm Sat 8.30am-1pm

HALIFAX

Doyle's

Glistening trout are fanned out over crushed ice. Aberdeen haddock, halibut and hake sit in neat rows amid fresh lemons and

parsley. The timeless pride of a quality fishmonger in a fine display of fresh fish is epitomised by Mark Doyle's spotless kiosk. It is appropriately top of the row of nine open-fronted cabins alongside the Victorian market hall. His rivals may be good for shellfish but the queue confirms the winner. Doyle's may be able to accommodate only two customers at a time but the rest appear happy enough to wait on the pavement outside and study what's on offer. Mark's grandfather worked at the famous Piece Hall in the days when it was 'dirty but lively' and there were 19 fish wholesalers trading there. Mark followed his grandfather into the wholesale business until he could afford to retail on his own but he still puts in three hours every morning working for a wholesaler before opening up in Albion Street. His fish comes direct from Grimsby or Aberdeen or from the wholesale markets of Huddersfield and Manchester. Most days will see cod, haddock, plaice, mackerel, trout, undyed oak-smoked haddock and Manx kippers. Mark will take orders for more unusual fish or occasionally test the adventurousness of his customers. Look out for sea bass, red snapper and black-banded bream.

3 Albion Street, Halifax, W. Yorks
☎ *01422 321351*
Open: Mon-Sat 9am-5pm

FISH KETTLES

*Cooking a whole fish can be difficult without a fish kettle. The fish can be wrapped in foil and baked in the oven or alternatively there is the dishwasher. This radical method comes untried and untested but wrapped in foil and protected by a well sealed plastic bag, a salmon is reputed to cook to perfection on the normal wash cycle – omitting the soap – of a dishwasher. If all this sounds too risky, good fishmongers usually have a selection of fish kettles which they will loan or hire. **Ramus Seafoods** of Harrogate, **Cross** of York and **Crookes Fisheries** of Sheffield can all supply them.*

GRIMSBY v HULL

'Rising high above Grimsby docks is a 312 ft tower of Moorish design built in the 1850s to provide hydraulic power to open the lock gates to the Royal Dock ... reproduced on postcards that celebrated Grimsby as the biggest fishing port in the world. It is an even more appropriate symbol of the fish dock now – both are massive and useless.'

John Goddard and Roger Spalding, Fish 'n' Ships, 1987

Just as there was once fierce rivalry between Grimsby and Hull for the title of the biggest fishing port in the world, it is now a close call as to which has suffered the most drastic decline. The proud Moorish tower mocks an empty North Wall; Hull's mighty St. Andrew's Dock was filled in for a cinema and bowling alley complex. At their peak during the 1930s, 500 vessels sailed out of Grimsby on a single tide and Hull landed six million cwt. of fish. Even as recently as the mid-1970s both ports were landing 120,000 tons of fish in a year. It has all but gone. Like the other great regional powerhouses born of the Industrial Revolution, fishing out of the Humber sprang from nothing to a world beater and back to nothing within 150 years.

When Brixham fishermen discovered the sole infested Silver Pits off Dogger Bank in 1843, the starting gun was fired for a gold rush. Hull and Grimsby smartly invested in the railways and caught the wave. In their heyday 22 fish trains pulling 800 wagons steamed out daily. Fish and chip shops became a national institution. The trawler company barons took over from owner/skippers to become millionaires. They plucked 12 year old apprentices from the workhouses and paraded their deserters in chains through the streets. In 1878 the Grimsby Observer reported an apprentice being thrown overboard and towed along behind. They sent their fleets north to Bear Island and the Barents Sea; south to Morocco and the Falkland Islands. There was work in Grimsby alone for 5,000 fishermen and 28,000 in support industries but the flip side of the Klondyke revealed appalling conditions, poverty, strikes, lay-offs and a terrible succession of drownings at sea from the 1,000 Grimsby fishermen lost in the Great War to the 36 Hull men missing in the Gaul tragedy of 1974. 'It's no fish ye're buying,' wrote Sir Walter Scott long ago. 'It's men's lives.'

The post war years brought more boom times for both the fishing and ancillary industries. There were ice-making companies and equipment suppliers, fish filleters and processors. Fish offal was converted into fertiliser, cattle food and that beloved childhood medication – cod liver oil. Hull supported a large 'cod farm' for the salting and drying of cod and 50 smokehouses established the town as the kipper capital of Britain. There was little thought to over-fishing as record catches were again tipped onto the fish docks. But in 1958 came the first of three Cod Wars which stretched Icelandic fishing limits from 12 to 200 miles. The Common Market and conservation followed fast. The fleets were scrapped. The smart owners moved into frozen food but few crewmen saw redundancy pay. The tide was out.

Today, Hull and Grimsby support diminished inshore fleets but both towns still have big wholesale fish markets. Container lorries drive through the night from ports in Scotland and Cornwall. Imports are peacefully landed by the old antagonists of Europe and Iceland. Fish fingers march out in record numbers from Grimsby factories in whose honour the world's greatest fishing port now dubs itself Europe's Food Town.

HARROGATE

Ramus Seafoods

However often shoppers drop into Ramus it is still hard to grasp that just behind the back wall swims the nation's greatest inland congregation of full grown, live lobsters: 8,000 of them, all the way from Nova Scotia, clacking away in their watery drawers and shelves, kept at a constant temperature in a dank, dark atmosphere, studiously attended by men in white coats. Chris Ramus is no ordinary fishmonger. His is a multimillion pound retail and wholesale business. Those lobsters are not part of some weird science fiction experiment. They are just passing through at the rate of up to 12,000 a week, en route to the hollandaise and thermidors of the 400 restaurants on his regular order book. It is a long way from his beginnings in the lucrative but dangerous business of freelance scallop diving in Scotland. Surviving the temptation to dive too deep and too long, he returned safely to his native Yorkshire in 1973 and started supplying fish to local restaurants, quickly winning prestige contracts at the likes of the **Box Tree** and **Pool Court**. His stated philosophy is to buy on quality before price and he has trampled all over some sacred British sensibilities in the process. He went on television to damn poor practice and hygiene at Billingsgate. He upset the east coast lobster fishermen of Bridlington 50 miles away by placing his vast weekly order in Canada 5,000 miles away, steadfastly insisting that the fishermen in Canada handle and manage their catch better. He acknowledges, too, the contribution made by the sometimes controversial trout and salmon farms: 'Farmed salmon has saved our industry,' he claims. 'Scottish fish farms are now producing excellent quality

salmon and trout at really good prices.' His salmon remains a consistent best seller at prices that would make market traders blush. Ramus staff will bone it, fillet it and even cook it if required. Buy a whole salmon and there's a fish kettle for hire. Whole sides or just a few slices are available smoked over oak. Each May, there are limited supplies of wild salmon – at a price. Even a committed farmed salmon enthusiast like Chris Ramus will admit that the first wild salmon he caught as a sportsman was the best he ever tasted. Meanwhile, his agents sweep the nation's fish markets: 'If there are storms on the east coast and no fish, it may be all right on the west.' He favours the inshore fleets of Whitby, Brixham, Aberdeen and Peterhead where boats go in and out each day so the fish can be on his slab within 48 hours. When the wholesaling and campaigning is done, Ramus remains an excellent fishmonger for the public, serving up to 300 customers a day. The Ramus slab might offer Dover sole, lemon sole, squid, sardines, eels or whiting. There are Baxter's potted shrimps 'By Appointment' from Morecambe Bay, kippers from Loch Fyne, Seahouses or the Isle of Man. Rope-grown mussels come from Scotland and Wales, oysters from Scotland and Devon. But the ultimate special treat buy from Ramus must be their seafood platter – lobster, peeled prawns, mussels, cockles, smoked salmon, crevettes, dressed crab and caviar, all beautifully arranged on platters, ranged by price, on your own plate if required. It's an annual best seller for those in retreat from the Christmas turkey.

Ocean House, King's Road, Harrogate, N. Yorks
☎ *01423 563271*
Open: Mon-Fri 8.30am-5.30pm
Sat 8.30am-5pm

HEDON

Swain's Fish Van

Jim and Glynis Swain's market fish van has one of the few slabs outside Hull and Grimsby to sell cod cheeks two tiny morsels of tender cod that are found, as one would expect, in the cod's head. The army of fish processors who clean and fillet the fish from the auctions of Hull and Grimsby, often remove these tender pieces and sell them as a perk of the job. Gently fried in butter and garlic, they are well worth snapping up. Besides cod cheeks, the Swain's buy daily from Grimsby's wholesale market and bone and fillet themselves. Their range includes pollack, ling, sea bream (known here as red fish), monkfish, lemon sole, Scarborough woof, megrim (a flat fish) and, sometimes, squat lobster. Glynis is happy to advise on the cooking and quaintly does her sums with chalk on a piece of slate.

Hedon Market, Wed
Hull, Willerby Road Market, Thur
Market Weighton Market, Fri
Pocklington, Tue
Withernsea, Sat

HUDDERSFIELD

Winn's Fresh Fish

The best thing about the bland 1960s Queensgate Market Hall is Winn's Fresh Fish where every day there is a dazzling multinational presentation and queues and excitable business to match. There are species like trevally (a West Indian favourite) and pegello that defy the fattest food encyclopaedias. Then come croaker, silver pomfret, grouper, red mullet, pandora snapper and Malabar snapper, again all warm water or Mediterranean specialities. Finally, there is a tremendous range of more familiar names to British waters and plates: hake, grey mullet, whole salmon, monkfish, squid, skate wings, lemon sole, whole coley, herring roe, oysters, whelks, winkles, Arbroath smokies, natural smoked haddock, Finnan haddock, John Dory, herring fillets and smoked salmon.

Queensgate Market, Princess Alexandra Walk, Huddersfield Mon-Sat 9am-5.30pm Weds 9am-1pm

HULL

Blades Newland Fisheries

Blades is the glorious exception to the golden rule that Hull, of all places, has invariably been a lousy place for the buying public to find good fish. It probably dates back to the days when everyone knew someone who worked on the fish dock and who could be relied on for 'a fry of fish' – a newspaper parcel from under the counter, handed over with a nod and a wink and fried up for tea. In those days no one would dream of actually buying fish from a fishmonger. Now that the fish dock is just a memory and a 'fry' is harder to come-by, we can be thankful for Blades Fisheries where Les Watson who has spent a lifetime in the industry has recently taken over the running of the shop from long-time owner Jim Brocklesby. One hundred different varieties of fish regularly pass across the counter, sourced across the length and breadth of the British

Isles. From Newlyn to Ullapool, there will usually be cod, whiting, monkfish, pollack, brill, coley and ling on the slab. From further afield comes swordfish, shark, tuna, wrasse, red mullet and sardines. Shellfish includes spider crab, langoustine and squat lobster – tiny lobsters with succulent flesh in the tail, rather like langoustine. There are free range eggs and poultry and in autumn the shop stocks fresh game that includes grouse, wild duck, teal, guinea fowl and 36,000 pheasants direct from shoots on the Burton Constable estate.

28 Cottingham Road, Hull, N. Humbs
☎ 01482 42167
Mon-Fri 9am-5.30pm
Sat 8am-1pm

Mark Hartley

Manchester Street is something else. Between the great artery of Hessle Road and emasculated St. Andrew's Dock, the once great home base of the Hull trawling fleet, Manchester Street is still alive, still full of the whiff of fish. It's neither quaint nor romantic but the tangled maze of small industries of fish filleters and processors is the last surviving link to Hull's halcyon days. Filleters can still be seen in open workshops filling buckets with heads and innards. Trucks bustle in and out. To find Mark Hartley's you'll have to ask –

there's no name-plate, no number – but his unpretentious crab, whelk and lobster business is worth finding. 'I don't buy anything dead or cooked,' says Mark, who trades daily in hundreds of live crabs and lobsters, delivered to him alive and kicking, straight from the boats. More than 30 boats routinely supply Mark Hartley with all they can catch, giving him a working day to make a landlubber shudder. After boiling in great stainless steel vats, the shellfish are despatched through the night to Billingsgate or to wholesalers across the British Isles but there are still plenty left for the casual caller who wants a fresh crab or one of the lugubrious lobsters swimming about in the sea water tanks.

Manchester Street, Hull, N. Humbs
☎ 01482 25918
Open: summer Mon-Sun 4am-8pm

Swain's

See Hedon entry.

Willerby Road Market, Hull, Thur

LEEDS

Granvin's

The city's first quality fishmonger outside **Kirkgate** market for years. Selling unfamiliar fish to a region reared on battered haddock can't be easy but Franco

---

— YORKSHIRE CRAB —

The rocky shoreline from Filey Brigg to Spurn Point provides some of the best brown crabs in the world. Bridlington harbour is the centre of Yorkshire crabbing. Every day throughout the spring and summer a fleet of self-employed fishermen take out their little boats to collect the crabs from inshore pots at depths of up to 100 feet. If there's a worry about their continued star billing, it's nothing to do with intermittent algae scares which contrary to common belief do not affect crab or lobster but whether over-fishing has denied the crabs their proper scavenging diet and made them watery and less dense. Nevertheless, Yorkshire's east coast crabs are still so highly regarded that Spanish vivier trucks transport them live across the continent as prizes for the markets and restaurants of Madrid. Available year-round. Best between April and December.

and Jane Vinci have never shied from a challenge. After running a Leeds restaurant (the late Da Vinci's in Shaw Lane, the Bermuda Triangle of Leeds restaurants), they moved into the wholesale business, supplying fresh fish to the likes of **Leodis** and **Sous le Nez.** Their latest venture brings us a shop well stocked with native British fish but their initial calling card is the more esoteric (and expensive) varieties: red snapper, parrot fish, blue marlin, swordfish, fresh tuna. The price of sea bass, Dover sole, brill, turbot and sea bream can hit home hard, too, but you are separated from your money with charm, enthusiasm and, in Franco's case, genuine expertise. The Vinci's continue to supply the restaurant trade which should guarantee they continue to stock a wide range for their retail customers. The fish is complemented by a small range of delicatessen: smoked salmon, olives, anchovies, quails eggs and wild mushrooms but it is the overdue arrival of good fish to this part of north Leeds that is primarily so welcome.

469a Otley Road,
Leeds, W. Yorks
☎ *0113 261 3420*
Open: Tue & Wed 9am-4pm
Thur & Fri 9am-5pm
Sat 9am-1pm

LEYBURN

Carrick's
See Bedale entry.
Leyburn Market, Fri

MARKET WEIGHTON

Swain's
See Hedon entry
Market Weighton Market, Fri

NORTHALLERTON

Carrick's
See Bedale entry.
Northallerton Market, Wed, Sat

POCKLINGTON

Hailey's
See Skipton entry.

Swain's
See Hedon entry.
Pocklington Market, Tue

RICHMOND

Carrick's
See Bedale entry.
Richmond Market, Sat

RIPON

Carrick's
See Bedale entry.
Ripon Market, Thur

ROBIN HOOD'S BAY

Bay Fisheries
John Brown is one of Bay's last natives with a connection to the sea. Like an Esk salmon, he went round the world before coming home to sell lobster and crab from his own pots and wild salmon caught at sea. Buy some fish and he'll tell you where to net the best local brown shrimp for free, irresistible for children of all ages.

The Dairy, New Road,
Robin Hood's Bay, N. Yorks
☎ *01947 880665*
Open: Mon-Sat 9am-4pm

ROTHWELL

Hailey's
See Skipton entry.
Rothwell Market, Sat

SEDBERGH

Strickland's Fish Van
Ralph Strickland cuts a lonely figure on Sedbergh's much reduced market. Cod, haddock and plaice are the mainstays but he buys whatever looks good on the quayside at Fleetwood: monkfish, rainbow trout, dabs and Manx kippers.
Sedbergh Market, Wed

SHEFFIELD

Crookes Fisheries
Dressed in a bright yellow sou'wester, Frank the fisherman takes up his position every day on the pavement in Crookes. 'He's the best thing we ever bought', says owner David Maleham. Frank, when he's not being kidnapped in student pranks, is a life-size model that makes Crookes Fisheries difficult to miss. If Frank doesn't attract attention then the 200 lb halibut that regularly makes up the window display, surely will. From a smart blue and cream tiled shop, David Maleham is one of Sheffield's best fishmongers and his dramatic displays include not only halibut but turbot, Dover sole, fresh marlin, tuna, swordfish, sailfish and black banded bream. It's not all so rarefied. The familiar fish are here too, as fresh as David can get them: 'Anything landed at 11 o'clock in Cornwall can be on my slab the next day,' he promises. His salmon comes from Ireland, where he believes the fish are less cramped and bred in fewer numbers than on the big Scottish farms. In summer he regularly has crab, live lobster, sea trout and wild salmon and whenever he goes diving in the Scilly Isles he's liable to return with a crate of crawfish. Standbys include garlic smoked mackerel, undyed Finnan haddock and anchovies in olive oil. David Maleham is an indefatigable advocate of fish. 'We offer people recipes, lend them books, hire out fish kettles, anything to get them to try something different. They never go out with what they came in for.' A first-rate fishmonger.

205 Crookes, Crookes,
Sheffield, S. Yorks
☎ *0114 266 0966*
Open: Tue 9am-4.30pm
Wed-Fri 9am-5pm
Sat 9am-4pm

GONE FISHING

'I believe the grayling the most beautiful fish in the world. Where Kilnsey Crag stands up like a rampart below Hatton Gill there is a stone bridge over clear water, running over pebbles white as mushroom tops, spotted with water snails black as ebony. In the swift places of the water the grayling rests, a fish of silver and pearl, fanning the stream gently with fronds of bronze silk . . . I hate to give you the recipe for cooking him.'

Dorothy Hartley, Food In England, 1954

No fish tastes better than the one you caught yourself and Yorkshire provides the angler with edible fare from sea, beach, estuary, river, canal, drain, reservoir, gravel pit, lake, pond and fish farm. Probably no county can match Yorkshire for its sheer range of fishing – and eating – opportunities.

Sea angling: the Tuna Club of Great Britain is still based at Scarborough but forget Hemingway and big game fishing. The classic Wakes Week holiday at Bridlington would be incomplete without a day at sea with a coble party for around £20 (rod and bait included). Harbour skippers include **Peter Jowitt ☎ 01262 605545, Frank Ridley ☎ 01262 605855** and **Paul Dallos ☎ 01262 674954,** a Hungarian ex-miner. There are similar deals at Whitby. Hope to catch cod, whiting, ling, dab or at least mackerel. For beach angling – no licence needed although anything down to the mid point between high and low tide theoretically belongs to the Queen – the best spots for sea bass and plaice are reckoned to be Redcar and Filey Brigg. A small fleet of shrimpers once worked the Humber Estuary commercially from the village of Paull. You can still shrimp effectively off pier or boat and with a child's net at Robin Hood's Bay. Whiting frequents harbours and there are flounders in brackish estuary waters. Subject to localised algal pollution and a trusted guide, east coast cockles, winkles and even razor shells and sea urchin can all be found and eaten. Mussels are also to be seen clinging to the rocks, but since they are particularly subject to pollution and consequently to shellfish poisoning they should be approached with special care.

Coarse fishing: far more of Yorkshire's abundant coarse fish is worth eating than even the average angler appreciates. A good rule is to run cold water over the fish to reduce its earthy flavour. Coarse fish are also helped by spices and marinades. Pan fry a perch and poach a pike in a fish kettle. As carnivores, all should be fine. Carp is so popular on the continent that it is farmed commercially and is the Christmas turkey of Poland. Eels are plentiful in the Humberside canals (some lock-keepers will even jelly them for you) and their superior cousin the lamprey is back in Yorkshire freshwater, in the Ure at Ripon and in the upper Swale. Roach is undeniably bony but good enough for **Winn's** to sell in Huddersfield Market. No one recommends the bottom feeders bream and tench. Yorkshire anglers are appalled to hear that gudgeon is regarded by the French as a delicacy. Dace is too small; barbel, chubb and rudd inedible. But the best coarse prize is grayling, as eulogised above by the doyenne Dorothy Hartley. Without chauvinism, there is no better grayling than Yorkshire grayling. Similar to trout in appearance and taste, it frequents the higher reaches of moorland rivers and can still turn up occasionally in Dales pubs. It should be eaten as soon as possible. Pack it with thyme. Grill or, on high authority, micro-wave.

Game fishing: the Wharfe at Burley is the prestige location for Yorkshire trout, the preserve of 'by invitation only' fly fishing clubs and the connoisseurs of corporate hospitality. It was an exclusive club on the Wharfe that infamously banned locals from joining because of their local knowledge. As wild salmon return up the Humber and the Ouse, there are viable pools at Naburn, Newby Hall and Boroughbridge but salmon licences (let alone a ghillie to tie your fly on the Esk) are prohibitive. Trout fishing is generally more democratic. There are river beats in parallel with grayling in higher, cleaner water, stock ponds of reservoirs and gravel pits and ultimately there are trout farms, where the game lies in failing to catch your rainbow trout.

Trout farms: there are numerous fish farms, private and public, across the region. **Lindholme Trout Fishery, Sandtoft, Nr. Epworth, S. Humberside ☎ 01427 872015** stocks brown and rainbow trout. The National Rivers Authority's **Moorland Trout Farm, Newton Road, Pickering, N. Yorkshire ☎ 01751 73101** is not particularly attractive but is a key stocking source for angling clubs and associations. Trout fisheries in Nidderdale, meanwhile, stand accused of letting rainbow trout escape to dominate the Nidd's native wild brown trout. Yorkshire's most celebrated trout farm is **Kilnsey Park Trout Fishery & Fish Farm, Kilnsey, Nr. Skipton, N. Yorkshire ☎ 01756 752150**. In the heart of Wharfedale, Kilnsey Flush is a Site of Special Scientific Interest. An area of fenland and limestone springs supports an exceptional range of herbs, grasses and rare orchids, which can be studied by appointment. More accessibly, there is an adventure playground, a museum of rural life, a Vietnamese Pot Bellied pig and 30 tonnes of rainbow trout a year. Trout is always available from the shop. Large trout (5–12 lbs) should be ordered in advance. Trout comes hot-smoked (60-80°C) ready to eat, or cold-smoked (20-30°C) which requires cooking. There's frozen venison, pheasant, grouse, rabbit, wood pigeon and guinea fowl. Fly fishers can buy day or half-day tickets on Kilnsey's two small lakes which are lifting with trout. They trap 85,000 visitors a year.

All freshwater belongs to someone and not always the rich. It is compulsory to hold a National Rivers Authority licence, available from Post Offices, before acquiring a permit from the owner or tenant of the water. Any of Yorkshire's many angling clubs – Barnsley A.C. is the most successful match team in Britain – and tackle shops will advise. **Bennetts of Sheffield, 1 Stanley Street, Sheffield, S. Yorkshire ☎ 0114 275 6756** is one of the biggest and the best. **The National Federation Of Anglers, 2 Wilson Street, Derby, Derbyshire ☎ 01332 362000** acts as a national clearing house for most clubs and associations.

The condition of Yorkshire's rivers remains unhappy. Stretches of the Sheaf, Don, Rother, Dearne and Aire simply cannot support life. Major recent scandals have seen industrial chemicals discharged into Huddersfield Broad Canal and the Calder, killing a 15 mile stretch of the latter. The Yorkshire Water Authority coolly puts polluters on its board and bans the Press from its meetings. **The National Rivers Authority, Olympia House, Gelderd Road, Leeds ☎ 0113 244 0191,** the official guardian of freshwater fish, is worthy but too weak. We can cheerfully celebrate the improbable presence of crayfish in the lake at Harold Park, Bradford but we should also mourn the last known burbot in Yorkshire, caught in the river Derwent in 1954. No one can re-stock an extinct species.

SKIPTON

Hailey's

George and Sandra Hailey have been selling fish for over 15 years. The choice is basic but sound. Grimsby cod and haddock are supplemented by whatever looks good and fresh when they buy from Grimsby's wholesale market. Apart from George's van, Sandra has a stall in Grimsby's Freeman Street market every day except Tuesday when she does door-to-door delivery in Otley, Ilkley and Embsay.

Skipton Market, Fri
Pocklington Market, Tue
Rothwell Market, Sat

WAKEFIELD

Wood's

Pushing 70 years of age, Mick Wood is nevertheless still going strong in his clogs and long white apron on Wakefield market. His stall is the star of the Fish and Meat hall with a huge range of fish that might include lemon sole, Dover sole, monkfish, oysters, hoki, skate wings, herrings, small whole haddock, redfish, mussels, smoked sprats, turbot, brill and squid. In the summer fresh crab comes from Bridlington, Withernsea or Skipsea.

Wakefield Fish & Meat Market
Teal Street, Wakefield, W. Yorks
Mon-Sat 9am-5pm
Wed 9am-1pm

WHITBY

Noble's

A highly dubious but commendable legend has it that an over-indulgence of Mrs Noble's dressed crabs gave Bram Stoker the nightmares that inspired his famous work, Dracula. Certainly the Noble family would have been around when Bram Stoker took his holiday in Whitby. They have been catching and selling

fish in Whitby for well over a hundred years. Then, the Noble men sailed south to the rich herring grounds off Yarmouth while their women pickled and kippered the hundreds of thousands of herrings they brought home. Today, the Noble family are all shore-based, selling crabs, kippers and fish from a shop at the top of Church Street. High above the harbour, the Nobles' smoke house has one of the finest views in Whitby. With a wan October sun setting behind the headland, Eric Noble, his fishing days over, talked about the demise of the industry, the imposition of quotas, and swore he could dress a crab in three minutes – a fisherman's tale or a Yorkshire record?

113 Church Street,
Whitby, N. Yorks
☎ 01947 601555
Open: summer Mon-Sat
8am-5pm Sun 9am-5pm
winter Mon-Sat 8am-4.30pm
Sun 9am-4.30pm

WITHERNSEA

Swain's

See Hedon entry.

Withernsea Market Sat

YARM

Danby Fish

Derek Sanderson opened Danby Fish in a small shopping arcade off the main street in 1993, a brave move outside a major conurbation. He has an excellent range: oyster, king prawn, large, ready cleaned squid and, unusually, smoked cod. Turbot, too, is often difficult to find in fish shops, since it is usually snapped up at the wholesale markets by restaurateurs but Derek Sanderson says he buys it whenever he can. His turbot, helpfully cut into manageable steaks, was perfect.

Danby Wynd, Yarm, N. Yorks
☎ 01642 790051
Open: Tue-Sat 9am-5pm

YORK

Cross of York

John Kenny began learning about fish at nine years old. Standing on a box he could earn a shilling a week wrapping fish for Mr Cross, the fishmonger on York market. Twenty six years on, infused with optimism and ambition, he now owns Mr Cross's market stall and runs a shop in Clifton. Between them, they provide just about the best fish in York. Oysters from Ireland, rope-grown mussels from Scotland, crab and lobster from Flamborough and salmon from the Outer Hebrides dominate the sophisticated end of their sales but haddock and cod remain the local favourites and take some beating at their best. John Kenny buys from the fish auctions at Hull, where bidding is Dutch, starting high and coming down. 'It takes some skill,' says John. 'You have to assess the fish, guess the weight and make your bid. You have to be quick or you've missed it. I once had to bid on sight for 43 stone of halibut.' For 25 years John Kenny drove to Hull, three mornings a week, always bidding against the same man, who like him was after the best fish. Finally, they got together and the rival became Cross's buyer. After the auction, the fish goes straight to their own plant for filleting. Hull, claims John, still has the best filleters in the country.

90 Clifton, York
☎ 01904 624838
Open: Mon-Fri 8.45am-5pm Sat
8.45am-1pm York Market: Tue-
Sat 7.30am-5pm

Good fish stalls can be found on
the following markets:
Barnsley, Bradford, Dewsbury,
Doncaster, Grimsby,
Guisborough, Leeds, Rother-
ham, Scunthorpe and Sheffield

ESK SALMON

'Oh! most divinely beautiful lady, my lady of the Esk, thou knowest it is no exaggeration for me to say that I have loved thee and worshipped at thy shrine all my life, with the ardour of an ancient Briton's reverence for his rover's goddess.'

T.H. English, The Yorkshire Esk Fishery Association, 1923

One of the most remarkable sights in the natural world is that of a salmon leaping the rapids of a fast flowing river, returning, having spent between two and four years at sea, to the river of its birth. In Yorkshire, that river is principally the Esk although spawning salmon and sea trout have been found in the Wharfe, the Ure, the Swale and the Derwent. Their survival is perennially fragile.

The salmon gather at the mouth of the estuary in July. With each rising tide the fish migrate into the estuary and upstream in the Esk, as far as Ruswarp. If the water is low at Ruswarp Weir the salmon will drop back to the sea again and fail to breed. An artificial 'staircase' has been built to help them up. Salmon and trout fishing is allowed in the non-tidal stretch of the river Esk above Ruswarp Weir.

Most of the 29 miles of the river Esk are privately owned. Day fishing is permitted on a short stretch owned by the Egton Estate. A licence is required from the National Rivers Authority (available from the Post Office) and permits are issued by the Egton Estate. Prices range from £10-£20 a day depending on the season. Glaisdale, Grosmont and Danby Angling Clubs lease stretches of the river and the old established Esk Fishery Association, formed in 1864, lease an 11 mile stretch of the Esk. They have 65 members who subscribe around £400 a year and employ a full time bailiff who is involved in hatching, rearing and restocking the Esk. Only 11 salmon were taken legally from the Esk in 1993, making them the most expensive in England.

Poaching is no joke. Whitby locals and organised gangs net fish from both river and sea. Teams of inspectors regularly patrol the Yorkshire rivers and poachers face heavy fines. If it were not policed, say the National Rivers Authority, the total salmon and sea trout population could be lost. The fishermen of Whitby and the villages of the east coast have, for generations, relied on salmon and sea trout as a means of supplementing their income during the summer months. Today, salmon fishing at sea is heavily regulated and only 17 drift nets and 25 fixed net licenses are issued by the N.R.A. for a stretch of coast that runs from Holy Island to the Humber.

Prior to 1959, salmon and trout fishing catches had a negligible effect on stocks but as bigger nets with smaller meshes were introduced, stocks became depleted. The 1986 Salmon Act restricted salmon and sea trout fishing at sea to bona fide fishermen who earned their living from fishing. Since then, no new licences have been issued and once a licensee retires or dies, the licence is lost with him. Not surprisingly it is an unpopular piece of legislation with fishermen who claim their livelihood is being jeopardised for the sake of the sportsmen. While you still can, buy sea caught wild salmon from local fishmongers on the east coast or eat the excellent home made gravadlax at the **Mallyan Hotel** in Goathland.

Egton Estates Company, Estate Office, Egton Bridge, N. Yorks ☎ 01947 85466
Esk Fishery Association, 2 The Shallows, Stamford Bridge, York ☎ 01759 372272

FISH SMOKERS

GRIMSBY

Alfred Enderby

Across the derelict skyline of Grimsby Fish Dock one chimney still smokes. It belongs to Enderby's, the last smoker in town, still flourishing after 60 years despite the annihilation of so much of the fishing industry around. Richard and George Enderby, sons of the founder Alfred, smoke cod, herring and salmon but their speciality is authentic Finnan haddock – a haddock that has been headed and split is cleaned and then salted. It is hung on 'speats' or rails before going into the smokehouse where piles of oak shavings and sawdust are lit and allowed to smoke slowly and gently through the night. Fresh fish comes from the quay every morning where a busy wholesale market still operates. Although principally wholesalers, Enderby's will sell to callers and are happy to show visitors the smokehouse.

Fish Dock Road, Fish Docks, Grimsby, S. Humbs
☎ 01472 342984
Open: Mon-Fri 8am-4pm
Some Sat 8am-11am
Please 'phone ahead

WHITBY

Fortune's

No trip to Whitby is complete without a pilgrimage to Bill Fortune's ramshackle and blackened smokehouse for a pair of Fortune's newspaper wrapped kippers. Taciturn Bill Fortune can't say when he first began working in the family craft: 'As soon as I could hold a knife' is as far as he's prepared to go but one Fortune or another has been kippering in Henrietta Street for over 120 years with the Abbey above and the North Sea below. At their height they split and smoked 3,000 kippers a day. Now it's down to around 4,000 a week. They're sold in pairs, just as they've always been, but Bill Fortune complains that his mail order trade has been curtailed by EC regulations. Good fat herrings are needed for kippering. The oil in the fish helps to keep them moist. Poor herrings badly smoked can come out looking and tasting like a bit of old tree bark. Some Yorkshire fishmongers nowadays recommend Manx kippers as the best around. Sadly, Whitby landed herrings, once the mainstay of the town's inshore

fleet, have long since been overfished and Bill Fortune now gets his from Iceland. Split and salted, the herrings are fastened to long poles on tiny hooks known here as tenter hooks. Smoking over sawdust takes between 12 and 30 hours, depending on how near the fish are to the smoke. Bill Fortune uses a mixture of hard wood for the smoky flavour and soft wood for a rich, dark colour. It would be sacrilegious to note that the woody taste of a recently purchased pair of Fortune's kippers suggested too much soft wood in the Fortune recipe. It must have been an aberration for here is a Whitby institution as sepia and revered as a Frank Meadow Sutcliffe photograph.

22 Henrietta Street,
Whitby, N. Yorks
☎ 01947 601659
Open: Mon-Fri 9am-4pm
Sat 9am-3.30pm
June-Sep as above plus Sun 9am-12 noon

---

*Shops that smoke their own fish include **Coniston Hall** at Coniston Cold, **Noble's** of Whitby and **Peck & Son** of Beverley.*

THE TEESDALE TRENCHERMAN

Johnny Cooke-Hurle goes under the robust title of the Teesdale Trencherman. It's a name that well befits the meat, game and fish smoked in a smokehouse converted from an old farm building in the grounds of Startforth Hall just over the Yorkshire border at Barnard Castle. He smokes chicken, pheasant, duck and venison over oak chips. Quail is marinated in orange and lemon juice and smoked over hickory chips. He rarely smokes his own fish but smoked salmon, trout, mussels and prawns are supplied by the excellent Loch Fyne Oysterage. Johnny Cooke Hurle also offers his smokehouse to customers with their own produce and will have a go at most meats. So far he has successfully smoked lamb, wild boar, gammon, goat, goose, sausage and conger eel. He makes regular fortnightly deliveries to Durham, Northumberland and North Yorkshire. Everything is available by mail order and there are frequent additions to his list including York ham, Cotherstone cheese and fresh oysters.

The Teesdale Trencherman, Startforth Hall, Barnard Castle, Co. Durham ☎ 01833 38370

2

Meat & Game

Roast Yorkshire grouse, Nidderdale lamb and Denby Dale pies, York ham and Barnsley chops. Yorkshire has an enduring love-affair with meat. We eat just about every conceivable part of every conceivable creature. It's only a decade since rooks were sold for pies in Malton. Today, goat is on offer at a Michelin-starred restaurant as well as on Afro-Caribbean menus. Yorkshire farms husband deer and wild boar. Market stalls offer cowheel, windpipe and garlic black pudding. Clearly, it is not yet compulsory to be a vegetarian in Yorkshire and it's easy to believe the claim that there are more pigs than people on Humberside. Sadly, too many of them are brought up in pig units akin to battery chicken regimes, producing pork that is tasteless and bacon that boils in the pan. BSE and dietary concerns have also led to a decline in red meat sales. But there is an alternative – animals reared outdoors on old fashioned feeds have more flavour. But organic farmers can rarely persuade butchers to take their meat: 'No call for it' is the glum response. Meanwhile, 10,000 independent butchers have closed in the last decade and organic farmers are obliged to set up shops on the farm. There *are* good butchers. The best will tell you the breed, the source, where it was slaughtered and how long it has been hung. The long queues and healthy trading of such shops bear witness to the fact that the discerning customer can still recognise a decent piece of meat.

BUTCHERS

BARNSLEY

Albert Hirst

Yorkshire's black pudding king was, of course, Albert Hirst who won fame not only in England but in the international Black Pudding Competition in Mortagne-Au-Perche in France. Albert Hirst also made the Barnsley chop famous by serving up a one and a half pound cut of loin of lamb to the Prince of Wales to mark the opening of Barnsley Town Hall in 1933. In his heyday the late Albert's empire ran to seven shops in Barnsley, five delivery vans and a wholesale business. Now the shop in Charter market is the last redoubt. The hardship of the year long miners' strike and the virtual extinction of the coal-fields have taken their toll. Still, Albert Hirst Jnr. has plump rings of shiny black puddings piled up high on poles on his counter. In post-modern Barnsley they come with apple and cream, garlic or fat free. To his amazement, Albert is selling them to smart restaurants as starters; a renaissance, one suspects, that is some way from a revolution. Also: fresh meat, sausages in natural skins, boiled feet, pig's chap (face), boiled pigs' tails, polony, savoury duck, potted beef, brawn (pig's head), pork dripping, 12 dozen pork pies every week and the legendary, if over-rated,

Barnsley chop. With two more Albert's in the male line, the inheritance is secure.

14/17 Meat Market, Charter Market Hall, Barnsley, S. Yorks
☎ *01226 289258*
Open: Tue, Wed, Fri & Sat 8am-5pm

BEDALE

Cockburn & Son

Strategically located between the Dales and the North York Moors, Cockburn's are long established as one of the biggest and best game dealers in the region. Known as a 'processing house' in the trade, Cockburn's normally dress and pluck 20,000 grouse from Yorkshire's heather moors every year, making them one of the principal grouse suppliers in the country, a reputation that was particularly difficult to sustain in 1993 when barely a single grouse was shot on Yorkshire's moors. Ten days of continual rain during the hatching season literally made it a washout, disastrous not just for the dealers but also for the beaters who rely on work from the shoots. In more temperate years Bryan Cockburn's staff are on the moors by noon on the Glorious 12th of August to take delivery of the first grouse of the season. Sons Mark and Jonathon dash down the A1 to London with 500 grouse to grace the din-

ner tables of the Café Royal, Dorchester, Hilton and the Ritz. Another trip to the moors at 5pm allows for the first grouse to be delivered to the **Nag's Head** at Pickhill and the **Blue Lion** at East Witton. While there are some who swear the grouse is better for long hanging, Bryan Cockburn recommends two or three days at the most. Pheasant is at its best and cheapest in mid November. Partridge and mallard are available from October and woodcock from December. The shooting season ends on February 1 and it is illegal to sell game after February 14. Cockburn's put anything left over to good use in game pies and patés, part of a stock list that runs to 220 different items. Bryan Cockburn, who has been butchering in Bedale for 33 years, also farms his own Highland Cattle. These hardy long haired beasts come from a single suckler herd and are fed on grass and hay, reared slowly and naturally without the use of concentrates. They reach the shop in September and this wonderful home reared beef, properly hung for two to three weeks, is available for only two months. The rest of Cockburn's meat comes live from local markets, which, says Bryan Cockburn, provide some of the best lamb and beef in the country. He stocks wild venison, wild boar and a popular own cured York ham. 'Every farmer in the Dales used to cure their own ham, including my grandfather who was a butcher in Bainbridge. I'm glad that my two sons know how it's done.' Dry cured with salt, saltpetre and brown sugar and matured for three to four months, this is York ham made in the time honoured way. Few enough other butchers manage it. Cockburn's are members of the Na-

---

THE Q GUILD

The Q Guild (Q for quality) was established in 1987 by the Meat and Livestock Commission to set standards of quality, service and hygiene for independent butchers. Members pay a fee of £800 and inspections are carried out by the MLC. Thirteen regional butchers qualify. A similar 'Shop with Assurance' scheme is run by the National Federation of Meat Traders.

tional Federation of Meat Traders 'Shop with Assurance' scheme.

12 Market Place,
Bedale, N. Yorks
☎ *01677 422126*
Open: Mon-Sat 8am-5.30pm

BOSTON SPA

Wilkinson's Butchers

George Wilkinson, a Boston Spa mainstay for 28 years, has his beef and lamb delivered weekly from the Scotch Premier Meat Company, a farmers' co-operative which guarantees meat free of additives and animal by-products. Pork is bought locally. Sausage, pies and hams are cooked on the premises.

136 High Street,
Boston Spa, W. Yorks
☎ *01937 843340*
Open: Mon-Sat 8am-5.30pm

BRIDLINGTON

Charles E. Ayre

Once upon a time a proper pork butcher was complemented on using every part of the pig except the squeal. Mr Ayre still fits the bill. Today, when paté has replaced potted meat and people choose chorizo rather than polony, there are few specialist pork butchers who can still make everything themselves. Appropriately, the Chapel Street shop looks set in a different era with its traditional green and yellow ceramic tiles, business-like meat hooks and old mirrors. In the window are crisp, golden pork pies and rings of red polony. Little tubs of brawn sell for just a few pence, remarkably cheap after the laborious effort that goes into simmering the pig's head with herbs and spices, mincing then mixing with jellied stock. There is collared head, a slicing brawn, belly pork with crisp crackling that comes hot at lunchtime (10.30am on Sat), and boiled pigs' trotters at 10p each

on Mondays and Wednesdays. 'A gentleman takes six every week', says one of the ladies behind the counter. Charlie Ayre's little shop is a reminder not just of traditional British food but also of a generation which grew up with war time rationing and learned to make ends meet.

5 Chapel Street,
Bridlington, N. Humbs
☎ *01262 672439*
Open: Mon-Thur 9am-5pm
Fri-Sat 8am-5pm

DEWSBURY

Cross's

It's difficult to miss Cross's kiosk on Dewsbury market. There are the queues; the staff working at break-neck speed, miraculously dodging each other without a pause in their high spirits and chatter; the Union Jack emblazoned across the back wall, celebrating Cross's black pudding win at the Prix D'Excellence in 1970 and the sign that claims 'Established in the reign of Queen Victoria'. Keith Cross proudly boasts that his daughter Joanne is the fourth generation to join the business since the family set up on Dewsbury market in 1899. The unfailing attraction of Cross's is old fashioned northern food that is cheap and satisfying – roast pig's feet, brawn, polony, haslet, ham shanks, spare ribs, roast pig cheek, pork pies still warm from the bakery and a favourite traditional spread for a Yorkshire

breadcake: 'mucky fat', dripping infused with rich, meat gravy. At 10.55am the queue has swollen to 30 or more, snaking round the shop (no doubt to the frustration of Richmond's next door, 'Pork Pie Champions' though they may be), but a Dewsbury ritual is about to begin. At 11am sharp a van arrives and tray after tray of sweet smelling roast belly pork is carried shoulder high into the shop with full drama and sense of ceremony. A whiff of panic ripples through the queue. Will there be enough for everyone? Some make a dash for Cross's other stall but the queue there is just as long. Half pound pieces of hot roasted belly pork are oozing with meat juices and melting fat, the skin baked until it is definitively crisp and salty. No one would claim any of this is a paragon of healthy eating. After Glasgow and Wigan, Dewsbury is the heart disease capital of Britain. The double decker 'Health Bus', a mobile advice centre laid on by the Department of Health, makes a precarious three point turn: 'Eh, mind you don't get knocked down by 'ealth bus', calls out one joker. The bus stands devoid of customers all day. Someone should tell them they're all round the corner at Cross's buying mucky fat and a nice bit of pork crackling for tea.

Dewsbury Market,
Cloth Hall Street,
Dewsbury, W. Yorks
Open: Wed-Sat 9am-5pm

HORSE MEAT IN LEEDS

'The Horse Meat Shop in the stew of tumbledown premises at the side of the Market was always a draw, principally because it took very little imagination to visualise the unappetising purplish joints and lumps of yellow fat in the window as horse, and partly because its frontage was painted in a vivid red, like blood; I liked to hear my mother tell me, as she often did, that it had to be painted this colour by law, to distinguish it from ordinary butchers' shops.'

Keith Waterhouse, City Lights, 1994

GRIMSBY

Pettit's

A grandly decorated boar's head, crown roast and guard of honour form the centrepiece of a stunning window display. Giant coils of Cumberland sausage and kebabs of pork, kumquats and sweetcorn make up the supporting cast in the tableau. Here is a butcher that makes a spectacle out of a humdrum piece of shopping. Inside, dry cured bacon and York hams hang from steel hooks. The fine old Victorian tiles are intact and sepia photographs from the 1930s show a proud tradition of display although the serried ranks of hung game are now barred by hygiene regulations. Pettit's have had a butcher's shop in Bethlehem Street for 100 years. Where once they delivered from a fleet of six horse-drawn vehicles they now franchise their sausages in the U.S.A. and supply Selfridges and Harvey Nichols. Grimsby shoppers have ten varieties to choose from including Lincolnshire pork, Toulouse and cider and apple. The delicatessen counter has Parma ham, Westphalia ham, Scottish black puddings and haggis. Not bad for a fish town. John Pettit jealously refuses to discuss his sources and refers instead to his advertising literature. So here it is: 'The company is well known and respected for Prime Scotch Aberdeen Angus Beef, fresh poultry and game from Lincolnshire and Norfolk and Pork from the Royal Smithfield Champion Herd.'

Bethlehem Street,
Grimsby, S. Humbs
☎ *01472 342724*
Open: Mon-Fri 7am-5pm
Wed & Sat 7am-1pm

GUISBOROUGH

Munro's

When Munro's opened 13 years ago on Guisborough's attractive main street there were – and still are – six other butchers within half a mile, so Munro's decided that the only way to compete was on quality. The queues and the Q Guild recognition are the vindication at this solid all-rounder especially as Stuart Hodkinson accepts that it's the dearest in town. Meat comes from the farm of owner Stuart Munro, supplemented by meat bought live from farms at Ruswarp, Whitby and Stokesley.

41 Westgate,
Guisborough, N. Yorks
☎ *01287 636509*
Open: Mon-Sat 8.30am-5.30pm

Seatory's

As well as fresh meat, Seatory's have a wide selection of old fashioned delicacies: saveloys, polony, black pudding, white pudding (a sausage of oatmeal, stock and leeks), savoury duck (a herb and breadcrumb mixture, cooked and cut into squares) and a Scottish fruit pudding which even in Scotland is now something of a curiosity. It is a mixture of bread, currants, raisins, sultanas and spices stuffed into a sausage then fried and served with bacon and eggs for a blood curdling breakfast.

7 Market Place,
Guisborough, N. Yorks
☎ *01287 610343*
Open: Mon-Sat 8am-5pm

HARROGATE

Country Butcher's

With its vivid exterior paintings of the animals to be found less recognisably within, Country Butcher's is a familiar landmark on the route in and out of South Harrogate. It also stocks one of the biggest selections of game and poultry in the district. There's rabbit, wood pigeon, hare, mallard, goose, corn-fed chicken, free range and Norfolk black turkeys. Wild venison is from the estates at Kilburn and

Ripley. With a few days' notice the staff will supply and prepare almost anything, including a bird stuffed inside another bird inside a turkey, reminiscent of the Victorian Yorkshire Christmas pie (see p37). Peter Buck also owns **Hutchinson's** of Ripley.

11a Leeds Road,
Harrogate, N. Yorks
☎ *01423 502582*
Open: Mon-Sat 7.30am-5.30pm
Fri until 6pm

HEBDEN BRIDGE

Maskill's

The tiles in Stephen Maskill's spotless butcher's shop hark back to an earlier incarnation as the Co-op greengrocer. There's greater continuity in the Maskill's themselves. They've been farming in Lincolnshire and Yorkshire for 200 years and Stephen's own 70 acre farm run by his father at Sowerby Bridge is the shop's dependable supplier of top quality meat. Although not registered as organic, the Maskills do not use artificial fertilisers on their land. The sheep and cattle are raised on grass in summer and traditional feed in winter. 'We buy at the right age, we know how the animals are cared for, and we hang the meat for ten to 15 days, a little less in summer', says Stephen Maskill.

9 Crown Street
Hebden Bridge, W. Yorks
☎ *01422 842411*
Open: Mon-Wed 8am-4.30pm
Thur, Fri 8am-5.15pm
Sat 8am-1pm

HELMSLEY

Nicholson & Son

The onward march of Helmsley market square as a tourist mall rather than, well, a market square is bound to pressurise a traditional family butcher. Nicholson's have side-tracked into fruit and veg, pies, pastries and prepared dishes of lasagne with

Bolognese sauce. As with other Q Guild butchers, they have a penchant for value-added meats. Their prize offering is 'Slavink', belly pork stuffed for roasting with seasoned minced pork. They do stir fry preparations and bespoke burgers but are at their best when at their simplest: a country butcher's buying all their meat including Yorkshire spring lamb from local farms and turning up their hygienic nose at anything factory farmed or fed.

Market Place,
Helmsley, N. Yorks
☎ *01439 770249*
Open: Mon-Sat 7am-5pm

HOLMFIELD

S & C Meats

Free range organic meat is sold by specialist butchers in up-market locations to middle class customers who can afford to pay the high prices. Well, that's the myth. A different reality, in West Yorkshire at least, lies in the remarkable background to S & C Meats of Holmefield. The shop looks like any other suburban butcher, on a busy main road in a nondescript suburb, a few miles from Halifax. Its cheery proprietors Steve Holmes and Chris Argent are born and bred Yorkshiremen, no trendier than the surroundings. But their meat is extra special. It comes from Far Isle Farm, high up in the Pennines above Oxenhope, one of West Yorkshire's most unforgiving locations and exposed to the very worst weather. Not only has this farm outlasted its neigh-

bours – nearly all the other farms on the hillside were sold to incomers long ago – but for nearly 50 years, long before it was fashionable, long before the word was even applied to farming, Far Isle has been wholly organic. Steve Holmes's parents, Frank and Marjorie came to the farm in 1947. There was no running water or electricity. There were no headlines then about B.S.E. and salmonella either but from the outset the Holmes's set out to farm cleanly and simply, in harmony with the environment and controlled by the seasons. In the early days Frank Holmes' expertise was in poultry production. He incubated and reared chicks and ran a local egg round. When battery hen production was introduced he refused to compete, convinced it was wrong and vowing no good would come of it. The Holmes's have retired next door but their daughter Sue, married to butcher Chris Argent, carries their torch at Far Isle. Today, although not registered as organic, the sheep and cattle are free-range, organically reared on 130 acres of land that has never been touched by chemical sprays or artificial fertiliser. Hardy cross bred cattle graze in natural hay meadows of many different species including nitrogen-rich clover. When they come inside for the hardest winter months they live on nothing but hay. 'Only the smaller ones are given extra feed, an old fashioned ration of barley, flaked maize, pea meal, oats and linseed', says Sue. 'They are fin-

ished on rough grazing where they can develop slowly and naturally and provide meat of good quality and flavour'. Sue plans to use Rosie, a pedigree heavy horse, to do some of the work of the tractor to preserve the land. 'It has been difficult', Sue admits. 'Public response has been very slow but things are looking much brighter now because people are starting to question what they eat. I'm proud of the animals and the way we've done it.' Brother Steve Holmes now farms across the valley and together with brother-in-law Chris Argent they run this friendly butcher's shop selling superb Far Isle free range meat without fuss or pretension at prices comparable to conventional butchers.

259 Shay Lane, Holmfield,
Halifax, W. Yorks
☎ *01422 244859*
Open: Mon-Fri 9am-12.30pm
& 1.30pm-5pm
Thur & Sat 9am-12.30pm

ILKLEY

Clayton's

Tom Jackson (entry p200), trades union thunderer turned Ilkley epicure and second hand cookery bookseller, nominates Clayton's as his favourite sausagemaker. Check out the Toulouse sausage in their refurbished shop in Brook Street. They're made of pure pork and their Cumberland sausage is a coarse-cut herb mixture. In keeping with the times, much of Clayton's meat is butchered and prepared, ready for the Ilkley set Agas: lean strips of beef for Stroganoff, rolled and stuffed beef olives, crown roast. There is game in season. Meat is local except beef which, whenever possible, is Aberdeen Angus.

35 Brook Street, Ilkley, W. Yorks
☎ *01943 608015*
Open: Mon-Fri 8.30am-5.30pm
Wed 8.30am-1pm
Sat 8.30am-4pm

CHATSWORTH FARM SHOP

Excellent fresh meat and game come from the Q Guild butchers at Chatsworth Farm Shop in Derbyshire (entry p120).
Stud Farm, Pilsley, Bakewell, Derbys
☎ **01246 583392 Open: April-Oct Mon-Sat 9am-5.30pm**
Nov-Mar Mon-Sat 9am-5pm Sun 11am-5pm Tue from
9.30am

——— REAL MEAT ———

'I was invited, as I frequently am, to visit one of the farms supplying these free range chickens [sold in supermarkets at £1.40 per lb]. I said I would be delighted to do so and that I would also like to visit one of the farms supplying the 39p per lb bird. That request was refused.'

Frances Bissell, The Real Meat Cookbook, 1992

It was the war and serious food shortages that compelled successive post-war governments to make Britain self sufficient in food. Farmers were encouraged to produce meat that was plentiful and cheap. Mixed farms gave way to specialist units. Battery production now provides us with poultry that almost everyone can afford but nobody is allowed to see during life. The Holderness peninsula supports the highest pig population in the world, mostly reared intensively indoors. Lamb remains overwhelmingly free range but much beef now comes to us from cows fed on powdered milk and concentrates containing growth promoters, again living indoors until sent to slaughter at twelve months or less. Artificial insemination and cloning have come out of the laboratory and into the farmyard. The Rare Breeds Survival Trust has had to launch an accreditation scheme to support farm shops and butchers who sell breeds that would otherwise be extinct.

Up until 1988 slaughterhouse waste from sheep, pigs and cattle went into animal feed but outbreaks of *bovine spongiform encephalopathy* (BSE) in cattle, thought to come from infected feed, led to a government ban. Cases are only now slowly beginning to fall but the causes of BSE and the effect on humans is still unclear, a serious cause for concern. Small wonder that vegetarianism is booming and that more farmers now believe that intensive production is not sustainable; that salmonella and BSE are the inevitable consequences of factory farming. They are increasingly rearing cattle traditionally, in family groups, first on their mother's milk, then outdoors on rough pasture, wintering indoors on quality silage before being 'finished' on lusher, summer grass.

In 1994, the RSPCA launched the Freedom Food label, for farm animals brought up free from fear, distress, pain and disease. Critics claim the RSPCA standards are not high enough and that organic production provides the only truly reassuring conditions for livestock. The United Kingdom Register of Organic Food Standards (UKROFS) was begun in 1987 to set compulsory standards. Certification is carried out principally by the the Soil Association.

To be classed as organic, animals must be fed an organic diet from land untouched by chemical fertilisers and synthetic pesticides. They must have adequate living and bedding space and access to open pasture. Mothers should be allowed to rear their offspring. Growth promoters are not allowed and emphasis is placed on avoiding stress and keeping animals naturally healthy. Modern veterinary medicines are allowed in emergencies. A quarantine period is required before slaughter if antibiotics have been used so that residues can be flushed from the system. There should be careful management of transport and slaughter. Animal protein, such as meat, bone and feather meal, has been prohibited by the Soil Association for many years. For decency to the living animal, safety from disease and the sheer taste of the meat, organics make incontrovertible sense.

Longbottom's

Ilkley's 'Dickensian Day', held each November, sees Brian Longbottom with a long apron across his ample frame and be-whiskered in full Pickwickian trim, barbecuing 12 different kinds of sausage to tempt the passing shoppers. For the rest of the year, more conventionally dressed, he can offer one of the widest range of meats in town. There is usually veal, duck, quail and all the seasonal game, including pheasant, mallard and grouse. But what's all this tripe? Is the trend for peasant English food sweeping the spa? Not quite. Longbottom honeycomb, he admits, is usually bought for the family pet.

17 The Grove Promenade,
Ilkley, W. Yorks
☎ *01943 607649*
Open: Mon-Sat 8.30am-5.30pm
Wed 8.30am-1.30pm

KNARESBOROUGH

Hutton's

'Don't come to me if you want bright red meat', says Trevor Mudd who for 37 years has been selling his own farm-reared meat from this splendid shop off the market square. Hanging it for two weeks accounts for the colour. He puts the flavour down to home grown feed and traditional husbandry. Lamb, pork, free-range chickens and, at Christmas, free-range geese and turkey come from the farm near Driffield run by son Phillip. Stocks are supplemented from local farms at Scriven. Trevor, with his second son Steven, keep shop in Knaresborough where they also dry and brine cure their own bacon. It is a well honed operation that includes their own EEC approved abattoir 'so we know the meat's not mucked about with', says Trevor. They sell a wide range of game from local shoots at Plumpton Hall and Goldsborough: pheasant,

hare, partridge, pigeon and wild duck. Grouse comes from North Yorkshire's heather moors and they take Yorkshire's own wild venison.

Castlegate,
Knaresborough, N. Yorks
☎ *01423 863122*
Open: Mon-Fri 7am-5pm
Sat 7am-4pm

LEEDS

Wilson's of Crossgates

The city's only Q Guild butcher is a fair step away from most of the good food locations in Leeds. Good luck to Crossgates. It has few enough gastronomic treats and Wilson's is clearly cher-ished, as witnessed by the seriously long queues which are thankfully processed with great gusto. Every High Street could support a Wilson's because there's no magic to the formula. The supermarkets have closed down Britain's butchers as much through the indolence of the trade as its customers but the Green family, who took the shop in 1985, have bucked the trend simply by selling quality meat at fair prices. It costs more than Bradford market where Robert Green once had three shops in a price war with 32 other butchers, but now the beef comes direct from local farms near Ilkley and his Yorkshire spring lamb is the best from Malton. It's all well hung and skilfully butchered. Free range chickens and bronze feathered Christmas turkeys are supplied by a specialist producer in East Anglia. If any of this starts to sound elitist, there is also a huge choice of cheap, good value cuts: shin of beef, brisket, oxtail or prepared dishes of marinated chicken in garlic. Kebabs, burgers, sausages and pies are made on the premises. Sons John and Andrew Green drive the impressive machine. Their great-grandfather ran a but-cher's shop in Morley but if he

was a good butcher he was a lou-sy gambler, to the extent that he lost his shop on a number of occ-asions. Happily, the Green's are back butchering in Morley, another **Wilson's of Crossgates.**

38 Austhorpe Road,
Leeds, W. Yorks
☎ *0113 264 5448*
Open: Mon-Sat 7.30am-5.30pm
Fri 7.30am-6pm

MORLEY

Wilson's of Crossgates

The Green family opened their first shop in Morley market four generations ago. Now they're back in a bright white and green shop that was totally refitted in 1994 to match the style of their sister shop in Leeds. Manager Steve Curtiss sells the same quality meat and poultry and runs a popular cooked meat counter. The pork pies are reg-ularly sped across town from the shop at Crossgates.

62a Main Street, Morley,
Leeds, W. Yorks
☎ *0113 253 4813*
Open: Mon-Sat 7.30am-5pm

NORTHALLERTON

Trueman's

Anyone who mourns the decline of the independent butcher should go to Northallerton where there are five butchers on the High Street alone, although even that healthy number is a drop from the eight shops serving a smaller population in the 1950s. The Trueman family who have been butchering in Northallerton for 36 years are one of the best. Andrew, who runs the business with his father Steve, buys well hung, top quality meat from the same local farms each week. Although today's best sellers are mince and chicken pieces, there is still a demand for large joints especially for the shooting parties: 'There are lots of shoots round here. One lady comes for eight ribs of beef', says Andrew. Testimony to the quality of their meat is the Londoner who enjoyed Trueman's beef so much during a holiday in Yorkshire that he arranged to have their joints sent down on the King's Cross train.

85 High Street,
Northallerton, N. Yorks
☎ *01609 773502*
Open: Mon-Sat 8am-5.30pm

NORTON

Fletcher & Son
Peter Hogg is a most particular butcher, one of the dwindling band of high class independent butchers who still buy meat on the hoof. Despite Malton auction mart being sited round the corner, he still prefers to make the 40 mile round trip to Seamer where he buys from small farmers with good quality suckler herds. The carcass is brought back and hung for ten days. For further reassurance, a blackboard in the shop lists the farms that have supplied the meat that week. Buying the whole animal means that he must put every bit to good use. The head, feet and shanks make 60 lbs of brawn per week. The jellied stock goes into the pies. There are old fashioned cuts such as oxtail and thin rib of beef. He has his own dry cured bacon. His joints are beautifully marbled and full of flavour. Peter Hogg first began working here at the tender age of 12 and has been sole proprietor since his father retired two years ago. Fletcher's is a registered Q Guild butcher.

2 Commercial Street, Norton,
Malton, N. Yorks
☎ *01653 692217*
Open: Mon-Sat 8am-5.30pm

RIPLEY

Hutchinson's
Run by Peter Buck of **Country Butcher's** in Harrogate, Hutchinson's supplies the same quality meat and game from just off the village green of this model estate village.

Ripley, N. Yorks
☎ *01423 770110*
Open: Mon-Fri 8am-5.15pm
Sat 8am-1pm

ROOS

Melbourne's
It is said there are more pigs in Humberside than people, so naturally Q Guild butcher David Archer buys locally. Most, he says, are free-range but he can't always guarantee it. Nevertheless, after a lifetime in the meat trade, he reckons he knows a decent piece of pork when he sees one. Beef and lamb come not from Humberside but from the well respected Scotch Premier Meat co-operative of Inveraray who supply beef free of additives and recycled animal waste. The Archer's also run a small bakery making bread proved slowly without the use of additives and improvers, sweet and savoury pies and a popular selection of cakes.

Melbourne House,
Roos, N. Humbs
☎ *01964 670241*
Open: Tue-Fri 7am-5.30pm
Sat 7am-12 noon

SHEFFIELD

Ashton's
Ashton's have made their reputation from their well hung beef (14 days), which comes weekly from the Scotch Premier Meat company of Inverary, a co-operative of 700 farmers, who supply meat guaranteed free of additives and recycled animal waste. Sheffield butchering colleague Colin Crawshaw of the **Crawshaw's** chain, recommended to Ashton's their seam butchering technique where meat is separated muscle by muscle to provide lean mince and stewing steak. Ashton's sausages have collected awards at the Yorkshire Show and commendations from the Guardian newspaper's 'Sausage Quest'. Choose from minted lamb and tomato, pork and chives, pork and onion, honey roast, Cumberland and classic pork sausages. They dry cure their own bacon. Cheaper buys include chitterlings, tripe, pork spare rib joints and rabbit. It is the tiniest of butcher's shops but business is brisk enough to provide a living for Mr and Mrs Alan Ashton and their sons Keith and Andrew.

48 Greenhill Main Road,
Greenhill Village,
Sheffield, S. Yorks
☎ *0114 237 7315*
Open: Mon & Thur 8.30am-1pm
Tue & Wed 8.30am-5pm
Fri 8.30am-6pm Sat 8.30am-4pm

Crawshaw's
Crawshaw's is the top butcher's chain in Sheffield. Their shops in Meadowhall, Hillsborough and the mother ship at Stocksbridge satisfy more than 10,000 South Yorkshire shoppers every week which is encouraging proof that discerning customers still abound. It's an enthusiastic family show with Colin running Stocksbridge and John at Meadowhall but with Mr Crawshaw Senior taking the key role of buyer. He selects only grass-fed English beef direct from the wholesaler. 'Very few butchers choose their own meat these days,' says Colin. 'They get it delivered by a wholesaler and so are dependent on what he brings. We go ourselves so that we can get the best choice. We look at hundreds of beasts but we only buy about 10% of what we see.' What they are looking for is colour, size, conformation, texture and what Colin Crawshaw describes as 'general appeal'. 'After years of experience you just learn to recognise a good beast when you see it.' Pigs come from a collective in Cambridge which does not use feed

with animal by-products. Crawshaw's use this source for dry-curing their own bacon. They practise seam butchering, the continental system that involves taking the meat apart muscle by muscle. Once it has been separated from the bone, the fat can be easily cut off. Butchered this way there is no fat or gristle running through the meat. The price per pound for beef might look expensive but it's lean meat with no waste. Joints, meanwhile, are well hung with enough fat to provide tenderness and flavour. 'You need fat on roasting joints,' says Colin, 'but lean meat for mince and stew.'

518 Manchester Road,
Stocksbridge, Sheffield, S. Yorks
☎ 0114 288 3548
Open: Mon-Sat 8am-5pm

Unit 25, The Barracks,
Hillsborough, Sheffield, S. Yorks
☎ 0114 285 5200
Open: Mon 8am-5pm
Tue 8am-5.30pm Wed 8am-6pm
Thur 8am-7pm, Fri 8am-8pm
Sat 8am-5.30pm

11 Market Street,
Meadowhall Centre,
Sheffield, S. Yorks
☎ 0114 256 8054
Open: Mon-Thur 8am-8pm
Fri 8am-9pm Sat 8am-7pm
Sun 11am-5pm

Funk's

Hot roast pork sandwiches with plenty of crackling are an irres-istible best buy in this busy little pork butcher's. Besides convent-ional cuts, there is everything else produced from a pig: home cured ham and black pudding, rolled belly pork, haslet, pig's trotters and tails. Their tomato and garlic sausage have won them glory at the Yorkshire Sausage Championships, awarded by the **Thomas Danby Catering College** and it almost goes without saying, too, that Funk's make their own pork pies.

65 Middlewood Road,
Hillsborough, Sheffield, S. Yorks
☎ 0114 234 3506
Open: Mon 10am-5pm
Tue, Wed, Fri 9am-5pm, Thur
9am-4pm Sat 9am-4.30pm

SLEIGHTS

Radford's

Radford's, which has been in the same family for five generations now, is a splendid institution, particularly notable for its hams. Dry cured or steeped in Guinness and molasses for the Admiral Ham, they hang for up to six months before being sold. One dependable customer is the Grosvenor, a London pub where expatriate Yorkshire palates devour two hams a week. All meat at this attractive Q Guild butcher's is reared locally and hung for at least two weeks. As well as the usual cuts they produce a wide range of cooked dishes such as stew and dumplings and marinated cuts ready for grilling. The delicatessen counter is expanding with olive oils, their own patés and cooked meats, pies and own-baked bread. Seasonally, there is wild duck, grouse and pheasant from the North York Moors which begin just outside the front door. The first week of December finds Peter Radford bidding for the champion beast at Ruswarp fat stock market. After taking its place in the window, it is hung in time to be sold as a prize-winning roast at Christmas, when Radford's also sell some 200 farm fed turkeys and 40 local geese.

81 Coach Road, Sleights,
Whitby, N. Yorks
☎ 01947 810229
Open: Mon-Sat 8.30am-5.30pm

THORNTON DALE

Hill's

Charles Hill is the epitome of butcherdom. Plump and jolly, dressed in the regulation blue and white striped apron, he dispenses sound advice and good cheer in equal measure from his charming butcher's shop in the picturesque village of Thornton Dale. Outside, beautiful blue and cream tiles spell out the name of a former butcher, A. Hill, no relation. In spite of a refit, Charles Hill has thankfully retained the original sash window from where in the old days the butcher served his customers. The practise would not be permitted under today's stringent hygiene regulations where even the traditional butcher's block is considered a health hazard. Charles Hill, like his friend and colleague, Peter Hogg who owns **Fletcher's** at Norton, buys his meat on the hoof from Seamer auction mart. He also has pies from **Botham's** of Whitby, dry cured bacon, his own brawn and black puddings. He makes four types of sausage:

THE GREAT CAWOOD FEAST

The biggest recorded banquet ever held in Yorkshire took place at Cawood when George Neville was appointed Archbishop of York in 1465. What they were about to receive comprised 1,000 sheep, 100 oxen, 6 wild bulls, 304 calves, 2,300 pigs, 204 kids, 500 deer, 5,500 venison pasties, 400 rabbits, 4,000 teals and mallards, 2,000 chickens, 2,000 geese, 1,000 capons, 2,400 fowls, 1,000 egrets, 4,000 pigeons, 204 cranes, 204 pheasants, 204 bitterns, 400 swans, 400 storks, 500 partridge, 400 curlews, 104 peacocks, 1,200 quails, 600 pike and bream, 12 seals and porpoises and may the Lord have made them truly thankful . . .

GAME

'The Marquis of Ripon, born in 1867, and probably the finest shot of the period, recorded the greatest total of game ever shot by a single man: 556,000 birds, including 241,000 pheasants; and he died, appropriately, in his butt on the grouse moor, taking his fifty-second bird on the morning of 22 September 1923.'

K. Middlemas, The Pursuit of Pleasure, 1977

Y ou can see the Marquis' gun in the billiards room at Newby Hall. The man was a complete bounder, confides a lady attendant. For generations, both rich and poor have enjoyed the benefits of Yorkshire's excellent game – with due hierarchy. In the 19th century, the game account for one week at stately Wentworth Woodhouse, near Rotherham, amounted to 69 partridges, 37 pigeons, five pheasants, four hares and two quail. Sparrow pie, meanwhile, was popular among the neighbouring mining communities. According to the former curator Peter Brears, the bird specimens in Leeds Museum include water rail, corncrake, plover, curlew, finches, black headed gull, blackbird, brambling, jackdaw and redshank, all bought at Leeds Market in 1880. It was still possible to buy rooks for pie making in Malton as recently as 1987.

Rabbits were often farmed in large warrens on estates in the Wolds and Howardian Hills. Up to 800 rabbits would be strung in pairs across a pole and taken by cart to the markets of the West Riding. In York, the rabbit man would tie them to his belt skinning each one there and then as he sold it. The myxomatosis outbreak in the 1950s killed 60 million rabbits and wiped out demand for the next 30 years. Today, farmed rabbit is available in supermarkets and wild rabbit from butchers in rural areas.

The ordinary countryman or farmer usually goes rough shooting. This is done on foot with a dog and gun, usually for a mixed bag of wild pheasant, duck, hare, pigeon and rabbit. Driven shoots take place on managed estates where teams of beaters drive the game toward the guns. Most are private but the common land of Ilkley Moor supports a licensed grouse moor where a syndicate leases the shooting rights from Bradford Metropolitan Council for six shoots per year. Public access must be maintained.

But it is on the 21 private estates across 185 square miles of heather covered North York moorland that the world's most exclusive and expensive grouse shooting takes place. Driven grouse in Yorkshire is said to be superior to the best of Scotland. On old established shoots where people return year after year it is virtually impossible to get a gun. Without access to a private shoot or membership of a syndicate, wealthy aristocrats and American and Japanese businessmen are obliged to join a commercial shoot. Eight guns hosted by the Duke of Westminster in a recent year shot 1,400 birds at a cost of £21 a bird – a cool £30,000 for a day's shooting. In the local butcher's shop, a brace of pheasant was selling at £5 and grouse at £8.

The popularity of shoots and the limited demand for game also means that it remains one of the best value meats around. The birds spend the majority of their life in the wild in conditions that would no doubt be the envy of their cousin the battery chicken. Yorkshire shoots can also provide snipe, woodcock, mallard, teal and widgeon. Many butchers in the region hold a game licence which will be displayed in the shop. It is illegal to sell game after February 14.

Grouse   Open season: August 12-February 1

The pure wild red grouse has resisted all attempts to breed in captivity. It relies on heather for both diet and shelter. Flying fast and low, the grouse is the finest and most expensive sport. It is hung for three to ten days and is considered best in the first few months of the season. The North York Moors are arguably the best grouse moors in Britain but even they can be unpredictable: 1992 was the best grouse year in history. In 1993 there were virtually no birds at all. The season opens on the Glorious 12th, ceremonially attended by the shooting classes, the saboteurs and the Gentlemen of the Press.

Pheasant   Open season: October 1-February 1

Although pheasants are often seen roaming wild, most will have been reared on game farms to satisfy the huge demands of commercial shoots. Birds are released into the wild to acquire the characteristics of wild birds. Only about half will actually be shot but that's still 12 million per year in Britain. Much of the meat goes to the continent.

Partridge   Open season: September 1-February 1

Like pheasant, partridge are usually reared and hatched on a game farm then released into the wild. In recent years they have been affected by pesticides. They are usually shot as part of a pheasant shoot and are rated best early in the season.

Pigeon   Open season: all year

Destroyers of crops, pigeons are so prolific that despite hiring professionals to shoot them farmers wage a year round battle against the birds. They are best for eating in spring and summer. Young birds are known as squabs.

Quail   Open season: not applicable

Wild quail is a protected species. Farmed quails are reared much like battery chickens.

Guinea Fowl   Open season: not applicable

Generally reared commercially on factory farms although some free-range birds may be reared on shooting estates or by individual farmers.

Rabbit   Open season: all year

Farmed rabbits are reared in conditions similar to battery hens. In the wild, a doe can produce 20 offspring with up to six litters. They cause extensive damage to crops.

Hare   Open season: all year but selling prohibited March-July

A few years ago the brown hare was in decline but has returned to prominence in recent years under cover of hedgerow and woodland.

Duck   Open season: September-February

A great deal of wildfowl is protected but mallard, teal and widgeon are legitimate quarry.

Deer   Open season: varies with type

With no natural predators, roe deer have expanded enormously over the last 25 years and are found in many Yorkshire woods and moors – even on the outskirts of Leeds. Deer attack trees and crops and for this reason and to maintain healthy stocks, they are culled by authorised stalkers. Wild venison is available from many Yorkshire butchers.

pork with fresh garlic and parsley, or with garlic and mushrooms, Lincolnshire and Cumberland. He also keeps an excellent range of cheeses, including pasteurised Red Leicester, Brie and Appleby's Cheshire.

Maltongate,
Thornton Dale, N. Yorks
☎ *01751 474223*
Open: Tue-Sat 8.30am-12.30pm
& 1.30am-5.30pm
Mon & Sat 8.30am-4pm

WALSHFORD

Walshford Farm Shop

There was a time in the 1970s when Britain went freezer mad. People who normally bought a joint for the weekend were suddenly investing in half a cow or lugging home a lamb. Butchers and farmers rubbed their hands and lapped it up. Then came the backlash. There were the dubious bits that no one really liked or even knew what to do with. There were scare stories of horse meat. Butchers went back to conventional selling and farmers closed down their farm shops but Walshford, under the management and now the owner-ship of master butcher Jeff Sharp, survived. He attributes its

strength as much to its location on the A1 as to the quality of the meat. One third of his customers are indeed regulars of the Great North Road. But Jeff Sharp has an eye for quality, purchasing animals that have been fed trad-itionally from local farmers. His loyal buyers know him and trust him. Most of the meat is frozen and comes in a variety of packs. The Beefeater pack contains mince, braising and rump steak. A Connoisseur's pack has topside, sirloin and rump. Just like a conventional butcher there are also individual fresh and frozen joints as well. While prices compare with other butchers they do come down in winter. Buy a whole rump between February and April and the price should be down by one third. As well as beef, lamb and pork, there are chickens, free range eggs and farmed venison. Whether it's pork fillet or pig's kidneys by the dozen, they're all here.

Walshford, Nr. Wetherby,
W. Yorks
☎ *01937 586166*
Open: Jan-Apr Tue-Sat 8.30am-
5pm Sun 11am-4pm May-Dec
Mon-Fri 8.30pm-5pm
Sat 8.30am-5pm
Sun 11am-5pm

YORK

Scott of York

Hams have been cured here in the shadow of York Minster for well over 100 years, one of the surprisingly few outlets for auth-entic York ham. Stephen Bailey's shop is all spotlights and sparkling tiles these days but behind the counter is a world the public never sees: a magical warren of rooms and doors with dangerously low lintels. Ancient wooden floors creak and bow, staging a rare vision of hams hanging from hooks in the ceiling, hams side by side in the curing rooms, hams sparkling in their salt-encrusted glory. Authentic York ham like Scott's, is dry, coarse and fairly salty, It is a rustic ham available in joints from two to 50 lbs The newly refurbished shop with its temp-erature controlled, refrigerated cabinets may belie the centuries old tradition of ham curing that goes on behind the scenes but Stephen Bailey has successfully embraced both old and new. He sells fresh meat, his own pork pies and sausages and even Yorkshire curd tarts.

81 Low Petergate, York
☎ *01904 622972*
Open: Mon-Sat 7am-5pm

YORK HAM

*Legally, York ham has to be cured within two miles of the city walls to qualify for the name. It's all a bit daft as jambon de York is a widespread European shorthand for mild cured, pink ham while within the city walls there's hardly a butcher who cares to produce it. They can't even agree on the legend. The ideal version is that the original York ham was cured then smoked over oak from the timber offcuts and shavings used in the construction of York Minster. The kill-joys say York ham was never smoked and it isn't nowadays anyway. Its historic fame is attributed to the quality of the northern salt, more credible perhaps is the still highly rated breed of Yorkshire Large White pig. Happily, **Scott of York** is the most honourable exception to the local disinterest. Stephen Bailey cures with a mixture of salt, brown sugar and saltpetre rubbed onto joints of pork. Saltpetre or potassium nitrate is a constituent of gunpowder which has been used for centuries to kill bacteria and preserve colour. The salt draws out the water and is partially absorbed. Every other day for more than a month new salt is added and massaged into the ham. Then it's washed off and the hams are hung in a cool room for five to six months to mature fully. The resulting ham certainly bears no relation to the thin, wet, mild cured ham that has been injected with a curing solution and soaked in polyphospates to make it swell.*

FARMS

BARNSLEY

Round Green Deer Farm

Drivers heading north on the M1 could be forgiven for becoming distracted as they approach junction 37 near Barnsley. It is an unlikely place to spot a field full of red deer. This is Round Green Deer Farm, where the Elmhirst family have been farming for over 200 years. They introduced deer in 1979 and now produce farm-reared venison for meat and breeding stock. Frozen venison is available all year round from the farm shop and by mail-order despatched in special cool boxes. It is available fresh to order from September to March. They have every cut imaginable: haunch, on or off the bone, saddle, shoulder and diced for casseroles. There is smoked sliced venison, sausages and burgers. They will even sell a coat or a set of antlers for hat hooks or walking sticks. The deer are not produced organically but they are reared without the use of growth promoters. They spend their first winter inside fed on silage and calf rearing nuts and later on silage and straw. In April they are turned out to grass where they grow very quickly. Those heavy enough are slaughtered in August while the smaller ones will be kept for a further year. The farm has its own slaughterhouse and air-conditioned butchering and packing unit. Farmed venison is very lean with only about half of the fat of most red meats and because it is young it is less 'gamey' than wild venison. With only 5% fat compared to around 30% in other red meats, venison needs careful cooking to keep it moist. Jenny Elmhirst is very experienced in cooking venison and is happy to advise. Round Green venison is also available from **Windmill**

Farm, Beckwithshaw who act as distributors in North Yorkshire.

Worsborough,
Barnsley, S. Yorks
☎ *01226 205577*
Open: Mon-Sat 9am-6pm
Sun 12 noon-5pm Please
'phone ahead at weekends

BECKWITHSHAW

Windmill Farm

North Yorkshire distributors for Round Green venison.

Beckwithshaw,
Harrogate, N. Yorks
☎ *01423 503930*
Open: Mon-Sun 9am-6pm

CLAXTON

Bullivant & Daughters

Vivien and Jenny are the Bullivant Daughters. They have dedicated themselves to sustaining the purist husbandry methods of their late father who farmed traditionally at Claxton for almost 50 years. Animals graze outdoors for most of the year. In winter, the cattle are fed a heady mixture of silage mixed with black treacle while the pigs are treated to a porridge of home grown corn, barley and oats enriched with whey, a by-product of Judy Bell's cheesemaking operation at **Shepherd's Purse**. The result of all this five star love and attention is succulent beef and lamb, the sweetest pork with crackling to fight for, prime all-meat sausages and their own exceptional dry cured York ham, which is matured for six months and helps explain why York ham became famous in the first place. The daughters run the 34 acres alone, rearing 25 Aberdeen Angus cattle, 20 Berkshire/Gloucester Old Spot pigs and two dozen Friesland Cross lambs. They are quick to stress

that the farm is not strictly organic as they do use selective weed killers on the hay but they are genuinely concerned about the widespread use of chemicals and fear that pesticide residues will end up in the water supply. A farm shop sells frozen joints and sausages.

Vicarage Farm, Claxton,
York
☎ *01904 468222*
Open: reasonable hours
Please 'phone ahead

GLAISDALE

Bank House Farm

Anyone strolling in the woods above Bank House Farm could be in for a shock. Invariably, rooting about in the undergrowth will be two very big and very black pigs. These Old Black sows along with 80 Kent and Suffolk Cross lambs and a herd of hardy North Devon cattle all live on this windswept, north facing, upland farm in Glaisdale. Add to this the 'less favoured area' status and some labour-intensive organic production and you learn something of the quiet determination of the young owners, Chris and Emma Padmore. Bank House has been farmed on organic principles for 20 years, first by Mary Heron, former assistant to the charismatic founder of the Soil Association, Lady Eve Balfour, and now by the Padmore's. They took it from its unofficial status to Soil Association symbol for lamb and beef. The lambs live mostly outdoors. Cattle spend the winter inside with plenty of space on a diet of hay and a minimum use of veterinary treatments. Sadly, despite all the care lavished on their cattle the farm does not have enough land to 'finish' the animals and they have to be sold on, thus losing their organic status. The Padmore's sell their lamb to private customers and the Old Blacks produce 40 pigs a year for pork and bacon which the Padmore's cure themselves. Their pork is not officially registered as organic although the pigs virtually roam at will. For pork, bacon and lamb, contact the farm direct.

Glaisdale, Whitby, N. Yorks
☎ *01947 897297*
Open: reasonable hours
Please 'phone ahead

HARWOOD DALE

Burgate Farm
Catriona Cook began producing free-range pork from Oxford Sandy and Black pigs because they are tough enough to live outside in Harwood Dale. These attractive pigs are not organic but they are fed on home grown foodstuffs and reared naturally and slowly. They are slaughtered at around six months compared to commercial pig production which slaughters at around 16 weeks. The resulting pork is reminiscent of less scientific times when meat had more fat and more flavour. The crackling is proper crackling. Pigs are sold as a half (55 lbs) or a quarter (28 lbs), fresh or frozen. The meat can be butchered to the customer's requirements and sausages can be made as part of the order. Lamb is also available.

Harwood Dale,
Nr. Scarborough, N. Yorks
☎ *01723 870333*
Open: reasonable hours
Please 'phone ahead

HOLME ON SPALDING MOOR

Bursea Farm
Buying joints of beef here is not for the soft hearted. Just beyond the shop is the source – one of Britain's most decorated Dexter herds which customers are welcome to inspect. These engaging cows are technically miniatures and their gambolling calves no bigger than pet dogs. They are not organically reared but calves aren't weaned until six months. They mature slowly and naturally on the farm's home-grown food without the use of growth promoters, living in a family unit for two years. The success story of one of Yorkshire's largest Dexter herds springs from a raffle ticket bought 10 years ago at the Royal Show. Helena Ellis thought she'd won a car. It turned out to be a calf. She also sells lamb and pork from her own Saddleback pigs. All the meat is frozen and sells from the farm. Her beef is also available from the **Smithy Farm Shop** at Baldersby.

Howden Road, Bursea,
Holme on Spalding Moor,
N. Humbs
☎ *01430 860348*
Open: Fri & Sat 9.30am-5pm

OXENHOPE

Great Hill House Farm
'Happy to be free' is the advertising slogan used by Jeff and Wendy Wilkinson for their free range meat. If pigs could talk... Still, they enjoy a fine view from their Pennine mud before heading for the freezer. What began as a hobby, rearing a few pigs and selling them to friends, has developed into a full time job with a farm shop. Their frozen joints of venison, wild boar, organic lamb and Highland beef have, they claim, 'the taste of a bygone age'. Their own pork aside, meat comes from similar reliable enterprises around the country. They also have the rarity of a farmhouse butter from Lancashire. Mail order available.

Farm Enterprises,
Hill House Lane,
Oxenhope, W. Yorks
☎ *01535 6442296*
Open: Tue-Sun dawn to dusk

THORNTON STEWARD

Wensleydale Wild Boar Breeders
It is claimed that Ripley Castle, near Harrogate, was granted to Thomas Ingilby for rescuing the king from the path of a charging wild boar. Tony Hill of Wensleydale Wild Boar Breeders admits to one or two close shaves since he re-introduced wild boar to Wensleydale 300 years after it had been hunted to extinction. The ferocity of wild boar is legendary and boar hunting provided great sport for Richard III during his residence at North Yorkshire's Middleham Castle. Despite attempts at restocking in the 15th century, deforestation and over-zealous hunting finally led to the wild boar's extinction in Britain. Tony Hill's animals, although able to roam freely among the undergrowth, are securely fenced in and no threat to visiting royalty. These pure bred wild boar look something like a pig with their long snouts and wiry coats of black and silver. They enjoy snuffling around for roots, shrubs, grubs and worms. Tony Hill describes the meat's gamey edge: 'Wild boar is to pork, what venison is to beef.' He sells a dozen different cuts from haunch and shoulder to sausages, liver and dry cured oak smoked. The high cost of rearing wild boar means that it is more expensive than beef or venison but one pleasant opportunity to taste before committing is to call at the excellent **Blue Lion**, East Witton in Wensleydale, where it is usually on the menu. Wild boar is available direct from the farm or by mail order with carriage costs on a sliding scale depending on the order.

Heron Cottage, Manor Farm,
Thornton Steward,
Ripon, N. Yorks
☎ *01677 460239*
Open: Mon-Fri all reasonable hours. Please 'phone ahead

PIES & PIEMAKERS

MELTHAM

R & J Lodge

When the Earl of Carlisle read about Lodge's hand raised pork pies in The Times, he immediately telephoned Raymond Lodge and demanded that one be sent to him straight away. 'I'll send you an order form', said Raymond. 'I don't want an order form', bellowed the Earl: 'I want a pie'. Happily, he was more than satisfied with his pie and rang up in the same forthright tones to thank him for a taste he'd almost forgotten about. The Earl of Carlisle is not alone in saluting the quality of Lodge's pork pies. The shop, mail order service and stands at all the local shows mean that Lodge's pies are famous, approaching legendary. Yet the business remains the small scale husband and wife partnership it has always been, operating from the compact shop where Raymond began as a butcher's assistant 25 years ago. In 1991 the Lodge's decided to close the fresh meat section to concentrate on pie making and an easier life. Instead, they are busier than ever. They make five different pies – pork; turkey, ham and cranberry; game pie; wild boar with blackberry and mushroom and best of all, fidget pie: a pork pie with apple, ham and sage and onion stuffing. In contrast to the mass produced factory pie, the gentle skill of a hand raised pork pie looks positively therapeutic. Raymond first takes a ball of pliable hot water crust pastry and places it against the base of the cylindrical wooden pie mould, the other end resting on his stomach. Then, by gently turning the mould at the same time as easing the pastry up the sides, he creates the pie shell. It takes about 30 seconds to produce a perfectly even shape with no tears or holes. The shell is eased off the mould, filled, topped, trimmed and decorated. Each pie is wrapped in a greased strip of brown paper to prevent over-browning and placed in the oven to bake. Once wooden pie moulds were part of any well stocked kitchen but now Raymond has to have his specially made. The basket of antique moulds on display in the shop came from a retired baker in Keighley. As well as the pies, Janice Lodge keeps a fine range of specialist cheeses: Cotherstone, Dorset Blue Vinny, Rhodes Lancashire, Curworthy from Devon and Lincolnshire Poacher, Simon Jones's full bodied, unpasteurised cheddar-type cheese. A well kept secret amid the adulation is Lodge's fat bacon. Unlike regular bacon, this has four, yes, four inches of pure white fat above a thin layer of meat: 'Even that's too lean for some people', claims Raymond with a straight face. It comes from a small producer in Golcar who swears his pigs are fed on double cream and cabbage leaves. When grilled to a crisp, it is heart-stoppingly good and should be severely rationed. More conventionally, Lodge's sell a good dry cured bacon and a Staffordshire Black smoked ham marinated in black treacle. Success at what Raymond calls 'the pie job' has surprised him but he earnestly believes that people recognise a well made pie with good ingredients. 'My old boss used to say you can only sell rub-

---

PORK PIE APPRECIATION SOCIETY

Two hundred years ago the Yorkshire Christmas pie contained turkey, goose, chicken, partridge, and pigeon, successively stuffed within each other like Russian dolls. The crust walls were elaborately decorated and built to castle strength for the London deliveries, where the pies became all the rage. The Fawkes of Farnley Hall would send one each year to their illustrious former house guest, the painter J. M.W. Turner. Despite the long decline of independent butchers, there are still some 50 regional pork pie makers left. The Confederation of Yorkshire Butchers solemnly stage a pork pie competition at their annual conference. Most are unremarkable but the best make hand raised pies with rich and tasty crusts which inspire extreme loyalties. Indeed, every Saturday Yorkshire Pork Pie chauvinism reasserts itself when the Old Bridge Inn Pork Pie Appreciation Society meet up for a pie and a pint in Ripponden. Guest pies are marked out of ten, rejects are tossed to the ducks outside and women are wittily banned. Connoisseurs may meditate on the fact that the average commercial pork pie contains three times as much fat as protein and that the stock for the jelly is traditionally boiled up with all the pig's leftovers from ear to tail and the unmentionables in between, a far cry from the Yorkshire Christmas pie.

DENBY DALE PIE

*'A blunt-speaking Yorkshireman was guarding the door of the barn where the pie was
cooking when these men from the ministry approached and demanded admission. "As
ta 'ad thy shit tested?', he asked. They said 'What!' 'If thy 'asn't 'ad thy shit tested I've
got a paper 'ere that sez tha can't come in.' There was no answer to that, so they got back
in their cars and drove away.'*

Julia Smith, Fairs, Feasts and Frolics, 1989

The baking of giant pies is a strange Yorkshire compulsion. They've been made to
celebrate wars won, railways opened and laws reformed. If they don't collapse first
they are usually inedible, if not downright dangerous. The whole surreal enterprise of
baking the world's biggest pie has finally settled down half-way between Holmfirth and
Barnsley. Denby Dale has seen off its historic rivals. Nowhere can compete with its
glorious fiascoes and extravaganzas, most recently attended like a Cup Final by 100,000
touched souls. They should have known from the start. The first pie baked in 1788 to
celebrate the return to sanity of George III was no sooner consumed than the poor King
went mad again.

In 1815 the second pie – now two feet deep and seven feet across – celebrated the
defeat of Napoleon at Waterloo. The Repeal of the Corn Laws was marked ignominiously
in 1846 when the platform supporting the pie gave way and 15,000 hungry spectators
scrambled for the remains. In 1887 they brought in the professionals for Queen
Victoria's Golden Jubilee. That year a ton and a half of meat, game and potatoes was
cooked in batches over a number of days and then added to the pot. On Pie Day, when
the first slice was cut, the stench of decomposing meat was so bad the whole lot had to
be buried in quick lime. The London chef brought in to take charge did a runner but face
was saved by the good ladies of Denby Dale who successfully baked a 'Resurrection
Pie' within the week. With a heifer, two calves and two sheep inside, this was no mean
feat itself.

The 1896 pie, two feet bigger than the record, was back in the hands of the locals
and was safely served in the park to the accompaniment of brass bands and fireworks.
The next pie in 1928 also went well as far as most people were aware. However, the pack
of dogs chasing the procession down the street knew something. The pie was on the turn
and 'four barrow loads of meat had to be quietly carted away', a secret, only recently
revealed, according to Julia Smith's diligent researches. The 1964 pie went well enough
except for a Mr Buckley in whose barn the pie was made. In order to get it out, the barn
had to be demolished. It was 18 ft. long, defied the best efforts of public health officials
to have it banned and paid for a village hall – Pie Hall, of course.

The latest pie in 1988 was a still more sophisticated affair. There was sponsorship,
technical committees and medical tests. Everyone connected with the pie even had to
have their stools tested hence the turning away of the men from the ministry. After a
blessing by the Bishop of Pontefract, the pie set off on its procession with spectators
sinking in fields of mud, roads choked by the mother of all traffic jams and the general
cacophony of 50 floats and a funfair. Somehow 50,000 people fought through for their
£1 portions. The next scheduled bake is not until 2013. Four times per century probably
feels enough.

bish once'. In spite of their fame and orders from blustering earls, Lodge's don't forget their regulars and from 8.30am every morning there is a brisk trade in hot egg and bacon sandwiches and 'Drip T-Cakes'.

Greens End Road, Meltham, Huddersfield, W. Yorks
☎ *01484 850571*
Open: Tue-Fri 8.30am-5pm
Wed 8.30am-1.30pm
Sat 8.30am-12.30pm

NORTHALLERTON

Pepper Arden Game Pies

Pepper Arden Hall is a country house of fading splendour where Cherry Gatty and her team produce hand made game pies in one of the old dairies. The business began four years ago as a way of using the game shot on the estate and has developed into a fully fledged business making 30 dozen pies a day to a Victorian recipe that belonged to Cherry's mother-in-law. Sadly, she has had to omit the truffles from the original recipes. Pepper Arden supply **McCoy's** restaurant, **Lewis & Cooper**, Knares-

borough's **Farm Dairy** and shops and delicatessens across the region. Their stand at the Yorkshire Show always attracts long queues. Pepper Arden's walled gardens sell Pick-Your-Own soft fruits during the summer.

South Cowton,
Northallerton, N. Yorks
☎ *01325 378548*
Not open to the public
Pick-Your-Own: June & July
Mon-Sun 9am-6pm

OTLEY

Weegmann's Pork Shop

Pork pies are very personal. Everyone has a favourite made by their own special butcher and every other butcher seems to be a pork pie competition winner. Weegmann's have a strong word of mouth recommendation going for them. They have been making pork pies and sausages in Otley since 1869 so they must be getting it right.

6 Market Place,
Otley, W. Yorks
☎ *01943 462327*
Open: Mon-Sat 8am-5.30pm

SKIPTON

Stanforth's Celebrated Pork Pies

David Holmes began working at Stanforth's as a 'jelly boy', pouring hot stock into the newly baked pies. Today he presides over the production of 10,000-15,000 pies a week from this tiny shop that for many is a compulsory pilgrimage on a visit to Skipton, with queues that threaten to topple into the Leeds-Liverpool canal. As well as pies there are plenty of other traditional pork products: black puddings, polony, sausages and haslet. Stanforth's was established in the 1930s by Jim Stanforth and its blue and white painted sign suggests it has hardly changed since. However, the 14 staff involved in the bakehouse are clearly part of a well oiled production line going on behind the scenes.

9-11 Mill Bridge,
Skipton, N. Yorks
☎ *01756 793477*
Open: Mon, Wed & Thur
7am-5pm Tue 7am-1pm
Fri 6am-5pm Sat 6am-4pm

SAMOSA SISTERS

*Mrs Kalwant Kaur Virdee of **Pinky's** outside catering makes a mean home-made samosa but you won't often come across them so the accolade for the best samosas regularly available in Yorkshire goes to **Mariam's**, an all-woman kitchen tucked away anonymously down a cobbled street in a former mill in Dewsbury. Mariam Maumoniat came to England from Bombay with her family in 1962. They encouraged her to try selling the tasty samosas that she had always made at home. The venture was a success and today Mariam, her daughter Julie and eight staff make up to 3,000 samosas per day, patently proud that they are all women and doing it themselves. They are equally proud that every piece is made by hand, including the pastry. Each one is filled with good quality halal meat and/or vegetables. Mariam's principally supply a string of local Indian restaurants and takeaways in the Dewsbury, Bradford and Leeds triangle but buyers are now also coming from as far afield as Manchester as her reputation grows. One of their biggest outlets is **Maumoniat's International Supermarket** in Leeds, run by Mariam's brother in law, Yausaf. Boxes of freshly cooked samosas arrive here daily. To buy direct from Mariam's in Dewsbury you must order in bulk. A minimum 100 small samosas (£16) come uncooked and frozen and could go straight in the freezer. Defrosted and baked or deep fried, they are great for parties. Mariam's also make expert onion bhajis, shami kebab and chicken and vegetable rolls.*
***Mariam's, 9-11 Carr Street, Batley Carr, Dewsbury, W. Yorks** ☎ 01924 467576*
Open: Mon-Fri 10am-5pm

YORKSHIRE PUDDING

'The mystique about Yorkshire pudding is nonsense. Like other remembered dishes of childhood, the best Yorkshire pudding is your mother's or your grandmother's or your Aunt Mary's – and if those early puddings were soggy or burnt, no doubt that is what a Yorkshire pudding ought to be.'

Jane Grigson, The Observer Guide to British Cookery, 1984

No dish is more associated with Yorkshire than Yorkshire pudding. Supposedly, it can only be properly made by a native of Yorkshire, a conceit well punctured by the late Jane Grigson, a native of Sunderland, who cites a Yorkshire pudding competition won jointly by a Chinese restaurateur and an elderly Londoner who had never travelled north of Watford.

Probably the earliest recorded recipe for Yorkshire pudding comes in *The Art of Cookery Made Plain and Easy*, written by Hannah Glasse and published in 1747. A native of Northumberland, Hannah Glasse refers to Yorkshire pudding with an easy familiarity, suggesting it was a standard dish in the kitchens of the north of England. It seems probable that it was less well known to cooks in the south and this may account for its inclusion in her instructional book.

In Hannah's day, meat was roasted on a spit before an open fire. The dripping juices were caught in a pan beneath the meat and used to baste the joint. The pudding batter was placed in a separate tin beneath the meat and, as it cooked, the mixture became infused with the rich flavours of the roasting meat as it dripped onto the pudding. It was turned and cooked until the underside was brown and, after being drained of fat, sent hot to the table.

The spit was replaced by a succession of ovens but Yorkshire pudding retained its place on the nation's dinner table, served not just with roast beef but mutton, rabbit and even game. In many a Yorkshire household where meat was a luxury and nothing could be wasted, Yorkshire pudding was – and still is – served before the meat; the idea being to fill the family up on 'Yorkshire' so they would want less of the more costly meat. Leftover batter could be cooked and served as a dessert with raspberry jam, golden syrup or black treacle.

A quart of milk, five eggs and a pinch of salt, beaten with flour to make a smooth batter – Hannah Glasse's Yorkshire pudding recipe would be recognisable today. We might favour a lighter pudding with more eggs in proportion to flour but the remarkable feature of Yorkshire pudding is that in 250 years of cooking virtually nothing about it has changed. Not that recipe compilers have been deterred from devoting whole collections to the subject, using up every celebrity variation and inserting such aberrational items as haggis and daffodil.

For a taste of Yorkshire pudding with onion gravy served traditionally before the meat, Whitelock's First City Luncheon Bar is a perfectly preserved pub and dining room in the heart of Leeds. It won't be as good as mother's or grandmother's or even Aunt Mary's but the oak settles, blazing fires, starched white napery and old fashioned service make a setting fit for Hannah Glasse.

Whitelock's, Turk's Head Yard, Briggate, Leeds, W. Yorks ☎ 0113 245 3950

3

Fruit & Vegetables

Yorkshire's agriculture can be loosely divided by the A1. On the west, livestock predominates. The eastern side produces the arable crops: wheat, sugar beat, oil seed rape, potatoes and barley for Yorkshire's beer. The north bank of the Humber supports field crops of cauliflowers, sprouts and cabbage. Hydroponic lettuce and tomatoes are grown in computer controlled glasshouses with vents that open and shut as clouds pass overhead. Agri-business has brought us the world's food, abundant and clean, superficially fresh and cheap. Supermarkets tempt us with kumquat and lychee, mange tout and mangoes. We can have strawberries in January and broccoli the year round but scant choice in English apples. We no longer eat with the seasons, let alone remember when they are. The price of all this includes new pressures on the Third World, highly stressed British farmers too frightened to criticise the system and intensive chemical regimes on the land. Fortunately, the region also sports a committed band of growers who raise crops without artificial fertilisers, invariably on mixed farms where healthy soil can be built up using animal manure, compost and crop rotation. Sadly, not everyone has easy access to organics but there are still enlightened farmers, enterprising greengrocers and bargain market stalls who care about their produce. We have herb growers, organic deliveries, fruit orchards and city farms where food is tended by the unemployed or the disabled. Nobody need be an ideologue to support them, just a lover of good food.

GROWERS

AMPLEFORTH

Ampleforth Apple Orchard

The young men in jeans and warm sweaters, weighing out apples, may look like any other students earning some holiday cash but these labourers at Ampleforth's orchard are novitiate monks, sent out for some fresh air and hard physical labour. Eventually, they will take their 'vows for life', become full members of the Benedictine community and teach at Ampleforth's famous public school. Such a committed and no-cost labour force would be the envy of any commercial apple orchard were it not for the interruptions. At 12 o'clock, habits replace denims and the labourers stride off to mass. Ampleforth is not just the country's most northerly commercial orchard. With 58 different varieties of apple and 2,500 trees, it is the last substantial monastery orchard left in Britain, providing a year round supply of apples for the school and a surplus for sale at the farm gate. The orchard was founded in 1900 by Abbot Smith, who took to planting apple trees after being advised to take fresh air as a cure for his asthma. Six of his original trees survive. In the 1960s, the ten acre orchard was further developed by Father Edmund Hatton, whose father was founder of the East Malling Institute, Kent, the national centre for fruit research in Britain. Today's 'Keeper of Apples' Stuart Murfitt is a refugee from a chemical spray-equipment firm who became increasingly concerned about the use of pesticides: 'The machines I repaired were always covered in chemical spray. When the Alar scare blew up, I knew it was time for a change.' In the 1980s,

Alar, a growth promoter used extensively on apples, was suspected of causing cancer. A controversial campaign to ban it was led by comedienne Pamela Stephenson. Finally, in 1989, manufacturers Uniroyal took Alar off the market. Ampleforth's trees were still being sprayed every week when Stuart arrived in 1987. Now, the fruit is totally spray-free, greenfly kept at bay by the thousands of ladybirds that have taken up residence. 'We lose the equivalent of one tree's fruit a year to wasps. The secret is to pick the apples before they become too ripe.' The successive ripening of so many varieties at Ampleforth means that there are apples from late August to mid November and their natural keeping qualities allow many more to be stored until April. A protective ring of sour cooking apples at the edge of the orchard deters any potential schoolboy scrumpers, but with a plentiful supply of apples in the school, the orchard holds other attractions. 'This is why they come down here', says Stuart, kicking a discarded cigarette packet. The orchard at Ampleforth is remarkable in its range and diversity. A simple comparative apple tasting will confirm how amazingly different apples can taste. Long forgotten names like Beauty of Bath, Blen-

heim Orange or Yorkshire's own Ribston Pippin, grow alongside new varieties such as Fiesta and Jester. Fortune, Greensleeves, St. Edmund's Pippin, Irish Peach, Ingrid Marie, Kidd's Red Orange and King's Acre Pippin are rare outside this orchard. Stuart Murfitt suspects his ten trees of Red Gravenstein are the last in the country. Ampleforth also grow plums, greengages and unusually the cherry-plum. They've had bumper crops of dessert damsons and there's honey on the comb from the monastery bees.

Ampleforth Abbey,
Ampleforth, N. Yorks
☎ *01439 788485*
Open: April-September
Mon-Sun 8am-4.30pm
Honesty box at weekends

BADSWORTH

Brickyard Farm

Brickyard Farm is a first rate source for super organic vegetables at their freshest. Customers can 'phone through their order and John Brook will pick it straight from the fields ready for collection. A farm shop operates on Friday and Saturday and for customers further away there is a fortnightly delivery run within 15 miles of Pontefract. For those in range it's a great way to transform your appreciation of Eng-

---

OLD ORCHARDS

Sadly, orchards like the one at Ampleforth are in decline. The charity 'Common Ground' reports that out of 6,000 varieties of apple recorded by the National Apple Register, only nine dominate our commercial orchards: 'When old orchards disappear so do landscapes. Localities lose their distinctiveness. Nature is the poorer and so are we.' It is Yorkshire's blessing that Ampleforth's orchard remains one of the finest in all England.

lish vegetables in season and fresher than any supermarket vegetable shopping. The choice is wide: leek, calabrese, red chard, green chard, cabbage, kale, cauliflower, parsnip, marrow, tomatoes, celery, sprouts, beetroot, rhubarb, lettuce, cucumber, courgettes, beans, pumpkins, celeriac, fennel, radicchio and endive. Forget preconceptions about wrinkled vegetables and grub infested potatoes. The produce here is virtually unblemished. Rediscover carrots as sweet as nuts and spinach that packs a punch. Potatoes are another revelation with a dozen varieties including: Pentland Javelin, Red Craig Royal, Sultan's Foremost, Ulster Chieftain, Ulster Sceptre and Maris Baird, John's recommendation as his best early potato. If John and Lyn Brook don't have what you want, they are prepared to grow it to order (within soil and climatic reason). John farmed conventionally for 18 years before turning organic: 'I gradually began to feel chemicals were unnecessary. The final straw came when I went on a spray course and they gave us masks and face shields. I thought this can't be doing me or the land any good.' That was in 1984 and five years converting the 60 acre farm to fully organic brought Soil Association status in 1989. The Brook's keep a small flock of Jacob sheep, a few cows and pigs. Orders can be taken for meat which is slaughtered and sold through a local butcher. Their enthusiasm for farming and growing is transparent. John loves showing children round the farm and school parties are always welcome. The Brook's plan an open day and they often man the organic growers stand at the Great Yorkshire Show.

Badsworth Common,
Nr. Pontefract, W. Yorks
☎ *01977 617327*
Open: Fri & Sat 9am-5pm

BRIGHOUSE

Kershaw's Garden Centre

This excellent garden centre on the edge of town has five acres of fruit beds bearing raspberries, gooseberries, redcurrants, blackcurrants and rhubarb available on a Pick Your Own basis. The rhubarb season begins in late May and the rest of the fruit is usually ready from mid July to the end of August. Prices are below shop averages and everything is grown 'as near to organic as possible', meaning that they use only organic fertiliser but will occasionally administer spot treatment with pesticides if any of the fruit is threatened with greenfly. Kershaw's also sell organic compost from West Riding Organics and a wide variety of vegetable plants, herbs and fruit trees, including vines, peaches, tayberries, blueberries, apples, plums and pears.

Halifax Road,
Brighouse, W. Yorks
☎ *01484 713435*
Open: Mon-Sat 9am-6pm
Sun 10am-4.30pm

COWTHORPE

Goosemoorganics

Committed environmentalists Alex Marsh and Arnold Warneken grow organic fruit, vegetables, salad crops and herbs at their farm near Wetherby. They also run programmes in horti-

culture for adults with learning difficulties and mental health problems. Produce is wholesaled to shops but is also available from the farm gate or by the box. Groups of families can order a £3 or £5 box of vegetables, delivered every Thursday. There is a minimum order of £15. The system relies on groups of families agreeing to a regular order, with a free box going to orders of £30 and more. They also supply free range eggs and wholefoods.

Warfield Lane, Cowthorpe,
Nr. Wetherby, W. Yorks
☎ *01423 358887*
Open: by appointment

FADMOOR

Newfield Organics

Howard Wass farms the land he was born on and after half a lifetime he realised that he was farming to suit a chemical regime rather than his land. So in 1980 he began converting to an organic farm. It took 12 years of working seven days a week and the planting by hand of 85,000 plants but by 1993 he had doubled his turnover and achieved a record harvest. Successful growing of organic produce also needs effective marketing and Newfield Organics are fortunate in being able to sell much of their produce to organic wholesaler Mike Sellers at **Standford Hall Farm**. For produce direct from the farm, Howard and

---

SOIL ASSOCIATION SYMBOL

Organic food is food that has been produced without the use of artificial fertilisers, pesticides, growth regulators and livestock feed additives. European legislation stipulates that food sold as organic must be registered and must be subject to an annual inspection. The Soil Association is the largest organic certification body in the UK. It is a registered charity which besides carrying out inspections and certifications aims to promote organic food and farming. It is the best guarantor of organic quality.

The Soil Association, 86 Colston Street, Bristol
☎ **0117 929 0661**

WHEELBARROW FOODS

Marketing is the perennial headache of organic growers who invariably find themselves locked into a system whereby greengrocers don't want their produce in case it highlights any possible shortcomings in the conventional produce while supermarkets make such stringent demands in grading, distribution and packaging that it becomes uneconomic for a small-scale organic producer. But a small group of organic growers in South Humberside have pioneered a scheme that successfully links growers to customers. No fortunes have been made, it doesn't even provide a decent living for any of the growers but as Wheelbarrow Foods enter their ninth year, they can stop digging for a moment to congratulate themselves on a scheme founded on admirable principles and plain common sense.

It is the brainchild of Betty Whitwell who was concerned about the decline in local services to rural areas. Under the Enterprise Allowance scheme she set up a small business growing organic produce on a quarter acre plot in her back garden and selling a selection of wholefoods from her pantry at the back of the house. But she soon found she could not grow enough to meet the demand so she encouraged other local growers to get involved. Their small co-operative now consists of four growers and uniquely they hold a joint Soil Assocation symbol.

What happens next sounds complex but has a beautiful logic. It works here and it is a system which is slowly being adopted elsewhere: a group of local families agree to buy organic produce on a regular weekly basis; the growers supply Betty with a list of their produce; Betty passes that to the organiser of the families; their total weekly order is passed back to Betty and on to the growers; the order is prepared and delivered to an agreed meeting point. Customers are rewarded with a wide variety of fresh organic produce, picked on the day of delivery at regular greengrocers' prices. In return the growers get a better price than wholesalers will pay and a guaranteed market for everything they grow. Everybody's happy but it's a system that takes commitment and organisation. The growing, claims Betty Whitwell, is the easy bit.

On her own plot she grows apples, plums, pears, blackcurrants, raspberries, strawberries, peppers, aubergines, fresh basil, herb plants, most of the conventional vegetables, Cara potatoes and rears free range chickens. From her small pantry she runs what must qualify as the region's smallest shop. She keeps a range of wholefoods including dried fruit, juices, nuts, seeds, pasta, pulses, flour including **Mount Pleasant** organic stoneground from the mill at nearby Kirton in Lindsey, Traidcraft tea and coffee, dried herbs and spices, cheese and olive oil and, of course, fruit and vegetables from her garden. Nobody has to belong to the scheme to buy from the shop and Betty Whitwell is open for business to any interested callers.

Although the four members of the Wheelbarrow Foods co-operative sell their produce through the scheme, **Chris Clark Organic Vegetables** and Joan and Alan Gould of **Woodrising** have smallholdings at Goxhill and sell produce direct from their home. Between them they grow a vast range of seasonal fruit and vegetables. For full details of their produce see the individual entries.

Wheelbarrow Foods, 3 Thorngarth Lane, Barrow on Humber, S. Humbs
☎ **01469 530721 Open: Mon-Sun 9am-9pm**

Rosemary Wass run a locally popular Friday afternoon shop from their barn on Fadmoor's picture postcard green. April to August is usually best. They sell at least four varieties of potato, three cabbages, carrots, parsnips, swedes, onions, leeks, and sprouts.

The Green, Fadmoor, N. Yorks
☎ 01751 431558
Open: Friday 3pm-5.30pm
Telephone orders taken for collection any time

FOSTON ON THE WOLDS

Foston Growers
A beautiful white-washed house with neat lawns and herbaceous borders is the home of Jenny and Tim Webb and the delightful location of organic Foston Growers. A small pond, shaded by willows, is full of fairground goldfish that have thrived and multiplied. A bigger pond has reeds and water lilies with benches to sit and watch for a heron or a kingfisher. Tucked away at the far end of this naturalistic garden (created by Tim Webb, a professional gardener and forester) are three quarters of an acre of second-hand glasshouse where Jenny Webb grows organic vegetables. She studied protective cropping for three

years at Bishop Burton College of Agriculture and her tomatoes, winter lettuce and celery are grown without chemicals or artificial fertilisers. For three years Jenny rose at dawn to pick the produce, drive to a collection point and then return to put in a full day's work. Marketed through Eastern Counties Organic Produce (ECOP) and distributed by Geest, her organic food eventually ended up in the nation's supermarkets. But disillusioned with the supermarkets' rejection rate for misshapen tomatoes or slightly damaged lettuce, Jenny Webb pulled out of ECOP in 1993 and now sells from the farm gate and through conventional wholesalers. She constantly experiments with new crops but usually has early carrots, beans, courgettes, tomatoes and peppers, all lovingly packaged.

Foston on the Wold,
Nr Driffield, S. Humbs
☎ 01262 488382
Open: Mon-Sun
All reasonable hours

GOXHILL

Chris Clark Organic Vegetables
Chris Clark describes himself as a fed-up teacher. His first love is the two and a half acre vegetable

plot he has cultivated in the corner of a farmer's field where he grows fruit and vegetables for the **Wheelbarrow Foods** co-operative. His ambition is to be a full time grower but until he can afford that he will continue the day job. His small holding supports carrot, potato, swede, onion, brassicas, salad crops, gooseberries, blackcurrants and a rhubarb bed. In his garden he has planted a small orchard of apple and pear trees. The produce is available at the gate of his neat bungalow in Goxhill or through Wheelbarrow Foods.

Dilfield, Thornton Road,
Goxhill, S. Humbs
☎ 01469 531872
Open summer Thur-Sun 9.30am-6pm winter Sat & Sun 9.30am-6pm

Woodrising Organic Produce
Joan and Alan Gould's timber house was built by a former railway worker and this long, low bungalow with its bay windows looks as if it has been transplanted from a country railway station. Surrounded by two acres of organic garden, mature trees, a pond and great drifts of daffodils in spring, it's hard to believe that 15 years ago the house and garden were almost derelict. It's now a haven for wildlife and their biggest problem is what to do about the badgers who have already eaten three beds of best beetroot. The organic movement always beckoned to the Gould's. Dairy farming was their living but in 1978, well into middle age, they determined to aim for self-sufficiency and from an advert in Exchange & Mart they found Woodrising. Today, the garden provides a huge range of food which supports not only themselves but supplements their pension with sales from the garden gate and through the **Wheelbarrow Foods** co-operative. In spring, every flat surface is cov-

ered with seed trays and they can name at least 40 different kinds of fruit and vegetable grown from seed each year. They pick their produce at the very last possible minute, which in summer usually means at first light and 4.30am.

Thorn Lane, Goxhill, S. Humbs
☎ *01469 530356*
Open: Mon-Sat all reasonable hours

HALIFAX

Bracken Farm

Bracken Farm has held the Soil Association symbol for organic vegetables for the last 15 years but now the Osbourn's have decided its time to retire from commercial growing apart from the soft fruit still available to those willing to Pick Your Own. Although the Osbourn's have allowed their Soil Association symbol to lapse, their fruit is still grown as it always has been – organically. There are raspberries, strawberries, gooseberries and blackcurrants from mid-June to mid-August.

Priestley Green, Norwood Green, Halifax, W. Yorks
☎ *01422 205578*
Open: mid June-mid August Mon-Sun 10am-7pm

HAREWOOD

Hawthorne Farm

Organic potatoes, grown to Soil Assocation standards, are produced by Patrick Snowden, brother of Michael Snowden, who farms next door at **Wharfedale Grange.**

Dunkeswick, Harewood, Leeds, W. Yorks
☎ *0113 288 6254*
Open: all reasonable hours

Wharfedale Grange

Interested in mizuma or baby pak choi, pousse epinard or mooli? Specialist wholesalers may supply them to the country's smart-

est restaurants but the home cook normally never gets a sniff. Fortunately, Yorkshire has a wonderful resource in Wharfedale Grange, just off the Leeds to Harrogate road. Peaking for six short weeks every summer, here is soft fruit in abundance and an esoteric range of baby leaves, miniature vegetables, herbs and edible flowers. The father and son partnership of Michael and Richard Snowden began as conventional growers but were persuaded into exotic vegetables by Yorkshire wholesaler Alan Porter in the days when he travelled through the night to Paris and Rungis Market to buy the continental produce sought by demanding restaurateurs. Although Porter eventually moved out of fresh produce to concentrate on cheese and chocolate, the Snowdens still supply restaurants with continental leaves and miniature vegetables. Certain chefs even visit the farm to wander through the chervil beds or hand-pick a strawberry variety. Conventional vegetables are grown year round for restaurants and wholesalers. But it is in high summer that the public gets its look in. The Pick Your Own fruit operation includes nine varieties of strawberry and six of raspberry. There are gooseberries, blackcurrants, redcurrants, tayberries and blackberries. What could be saner on a

sunny evening than ducking out of the commuter chase of the A61 to spend 10 minutes picking a pound of summer fruit still with its bloom and as fresh as can be? If that's too much effort, there is usually something ready picked for sale. The farm shop also sells those chic miniature salad leaves and exquisite little carrots, fennel, parsnip, beetroot, squashes, nasturtium and courgette flowers. Herbs, bunched or pot grown include dill, chervil, coriander, basil and parsley. Fruit and vegetables are not organic although sprays are kept to a minimum. Many crops receive no spray at all. As a grower, Richard Snowden has strong views on the seasons. 'People expect to have year round supplies of everything. They are surprised when we don't have baby carrots in January.' The Wharfedale Grange season begins in early May with asparagus. Richard Snowden sells 4 lb boxes: 'It comes in different sizes, ready trimmed. People have it with butter the first night, then in soups and salads after that. It's delicious fried with bacon.' The asparagus finishes on June 20, the longest day, when the crowns must be left to reproduce again for next year. The first strawberries are usually ready with the asparagus and the salad leaves by early July. The season continues

---

ORGANIC WINE

Synthetic fertilizers and pesticides are used just as much in wine as food. Organic wine is grown without additives, pesticides or synthetic fertilisers and must conform to EEC specifications. One of the largest importers, wholesalers and retailers of organic wines, beers and ciders are Vinceremos run by Jerry Lockspeiser and Jem Gardenar who are extremely knowledgeable about organic drinking. Wines are available by mail or can be ordered and collected personally from their Leeds warehouse. There is no retail outlet.

Vinceremos, 65 Raglan Road, Leeds, W. Yorks
☎ *0113 243 1691 Open: Mon-Fri 9am-5.30pm*

to build steadily until the middle of August.

Wharfedale Grange, Harewood, Leeds, W. Yorks
☎ *0113 288 6320*
Open: June-mid August Mon-Sun 9am-6pm

HEMLINGTON

The Larchfield Community
Like **Botton Village** in Danby, North Yorkshire, Larchfield is part of the Camphill Village Trust. Its aim is to develop employment opportunities for mentally handicapped adults and training schemes for local people with special needs. The farm and gardens are managed bio-dynamically, without the use of pesticides and chemical fertilizers. As well as being a source of unusual vegetables the quality is generally superb. Seasonally available should be kohlrabi, Swiss chard, aubergine, pumpkin, corn salad, celeriac and all the regular vegetables. They often have potted plants, medicinal and culinary herbs and old cottage garden flowers and native wild bluebell bulbs from their own wild flower garden. Larchfield run a bakery and coffee shop at Hemlington and their produce is sold at **Guisborough Market** every Thursday. Wholemeal bread with molasses and sunflower seeds, cakes and biscuits made with organic

flour all sell well, so well that they are often sold out before 3pm.

Stokesley Road, Hemlington, Middlesbrough, Cleveland
☎ *01642 595143*
Open: produce Thur & Fri 1pm-4pm Sat 10am-1pm Coffee shop Mon-Fri 10am-1pm

LEEDS

Meanwood Valley Urban Farm
The site of a Victorian rubbish tip between a drab council estate and the aptly named Meanwood Road is probably the right place to locate an urban farm. These are no Elysian Fields and yet from a 1980s sea of mud, a pair of leaking caravans, a bad dog and a ring of bed-frame fencing rose Meanwood Valley Urban Farm, a working farm on 13 acres of land a mile and a half from Leeds city centre. The aim of the farm was to introduce children to farm animals and provide training for people with learning difficulties. From such unpromising beginnings has emerged a working farm, with its own flock of sheep, two pigs, a cow and hens which are currently producing nine dozen eggs a day. The farm is open seven days a week and all the produce is for sale. Last year 12,500 children visited the farm and took part in some of

the education workshops. There are bug hunts where children learn about the food chain, mud workshops which explore the soil make-up and an incubator where children can watch chickens hatch. City children, some of whom have never seen a goat before, can try milking. The farm also runs an adult literacy scheme and a return-to-work programme for 35 long term unemployed men and women, many of whom are learning horticulture with Sandy Middleton. In her characteristic woolly cap, Sandy has turned this once depressing site into a flourishing market garden and has qualified for a Soil Association symbol for organic produce. Volunteers to help out in the garden are always welcome. Wherever possible, food is picked while you wait. Leeks and beetroot come with rich damp soil still attached and as fresh as you like. The standard is excellent, nothing is allowed to hang around for long and anything that doesn't sell goes to feed the animals. There is no organic premium and prices are reasonable. There are bargains to be had like fork damaged potatoes at 10p a pound or ripe tomatoes at 50p a pound. As well as fruit and vegetables (though not carrots, they've had problems with carrot fly), there are fresh herbs, garlic, chillies, fresh and dried flowers.

ORGANIC HERBS

There are 10 different lavenders and 40 different varieties of thyme and the national collection of santolinas at Carole Starr's Herb and Heather Centre south west of Selby, which has become a tourist attraction as well as a garden centre. On a six acre plot she cultivates over 500 organically grown medicinal and culinary herbs, from comfrey to lemon scented basil and the same number of heathers, conifers and evergreens. Most plants are available by mail order. There are pot-grown herbs for sale on site and Carole will cut fresh culinary herbs to order for her customers. As well as talks, educational visits and guided tours of the garden, Carole has a tearoom featuring her home baking, with such 'herb lunch' specials as 'Herbie sausage rolls'. There are additive-free honeys, preserves, chutneys and mustards for sale. Her gardening shop concentrates on organic and bio-friendly products.

Herb & Heather Garden Centre, West Haddlesey, Nr Selby, N. Yorks
☎ ***01757 228279 Open: Mon-Sun 9.30am-5.30pm closed Wed***

Growing is seasonal. This is not the supermarket and not everything will be available all year round. The workers too may have learning difficulties and service may sometimes be slow. Shopping at Meanwood Valley Farm means buying good fresh food at the same time as supporting a worthwhile charity.

Sugar Well Road, Meanwood,
Leeds, W. Yorks
☎ *0113 262 9759*
Open: Mon-Sun 10am-4pm

NAFFERTON

Green Growers

This is no idealised country garden, hemmed in as it is by the railway line and the unrelenting rumble of the flour mill, but Green Growers is an exemplary operation and Gwen Egginton, a soil scientist with dual degrees and a Ph.D., knows how to grow an organic vegetable and run an independent business on her one acre plot. She succeeds in offering fruit, vegetables, herbs, plants and truly free range eggs at a reasonable price to people who want their food free of pesticides and chemical sprays. Gwen delivers weekly to three or four local families and in summer keeps a stall at the garden gate. In winter, when her own produce runs out she buys in organic vegetables to maintain a supply to her regular customers. Her commitment is to small scale sustainable agriculture: skips are raided for anything that can be recycled, composted bark and manure are used instead of peat and a hot box built into the manure heap maintains a temperature around 10° above the outside temperature, an ideal environment for bringing on seedlings. Telephone orders are taken and delivered locally each week.

1 Station Cottages,
Wansford Road, Nafferton,
Driffield, N. Humbs
☎ *01377 45362*
Open: all reasonable hours
Please 'phone ahead

PICKERING

Standford Hall Farm

For the last ten years Mike and Pam Sellers have been beating the system that says supermarket power invariably grinds down alternative food distribution. Their retailing and wholesaling of organic fruit and vegetables is one of the biggest and best in Yorkshire. Produce from a network of growers is distributed to organic retailers across the region in a circuit that clocks up more than 1,000 miles a week. But the Sellers are not just distributors, they are also growers, and on singularly unpromising land of heavy soil in a low lying frost pocket, which they have nevertheless worked up to Soil Association standard. They produce 20 different kinds of vegetables, including courgettes, French, runner and broad beans, lettuce, potatoes, cabbage, cauliflower and cucumber – all sold from their farm shop. The latest addition are strawberries grown in one of their five poly-tunnels. They sell their own organically reared beef, Yorkshire lamb and free range chickens. They also stock **Botton** bread, cheese and yoghurt, free range eggs, organic mushrooms and pot grown herbs.

Westgate Carr Road,
Pickering, N. Yorks
☎ *01751 472249*
Open: Mon-Fri 9am-6pm
Sat 9am-1pm closed Tue

HARLOW CARR GARDENS

'If it will grow at Harlow Carr it will grow anywhere', says Chris Margrave, Gardens Curator at the Horticultural Society's northern base at Harlow Carr at Harrogate: 'That's our raison d'etre.' The 68 acres of gardens at Harlow Carr are a wonderful place to enjoy an afternoon stroll. but Harlow Carr is more than that. It offers a unique setting in which to learn about gardening and horticulture. Become a member (£21) and, amongst other benefits, you can share in the distribution of seeds, get free advice on problems and attend a host of workshops, demonstrations and lectures. For food gardeners, there are apple and pear trees, demonstration fruit cages and vegetable trials. Each year 20 different varieties of one type of vegetable are grown in identical conditions and results assessed. They also research cultivation techniques using cloches, mulches and various gardening products all aimed at extending the growing season for northern gardeners. They also have 150 varieties of rhubarb that make up the National Rhubarb Collection. The Vegetable Sanctuary is where rare and endangered vegetables, such as the 6ft Victorian, Champion of England pea, are cultivated and thus saved. The results of their research are published in the Northern Horticultural Society's magazine, the Northern Gardener.

Harlow Carr Gardens, Northern Horticultural Society, Crag Lane, Harrogate. N. Yorks
☎ *01423 565418 Open: Mon-Sun 10.30am-5pm or dusk*

SHEFFIELD

Heeley City Farm

Ducks, hens, turkeys, guinea fowl and goats live contentedly in this oasis of green just a few minutes outside the city centre. Apparently local residents tolerate the early morning cockerel crowing and have been known to rescue the odd stray animal. Generally, however, the farm is run by a team of volunteers with an impressive commitment to their breeds. The farm offers a spectacular hilltop view of the city and on a sunny afternoon it's a popular place for families to play, stroll in the herb garden or order snacks in the mainly vegetarian café. Soup and savoury dishes are made with the farm's own-grown herbs and vegetables. Salads are collated from their wide range of leaves: lollo rosso, lamb's lettuce, nasturtium and much more. The vegetable plots and poly-tunnels are where the serious business goes on, providing work experience for people with special needs or just the pleasure of growing for those without. Beyond the standard produce range, Heeley specialises in Chinese and Asian vegetables to meet the local demand from ethnic communities for ultra-fresh food. Pak choi, kohlra-

bi, karela or bitter gourd, okra, mooli, black radish, squash, pumpkin and melon lead a vast and colourful list. They grow all the soft fruit and around 60 pot grown herbs. Popular ones such as coriander, basil and fenugreek are sold by the bunch. Heeley's organic produce is in such demand that it barely has the chance to go on sale since customers usually pick their own as soon as it is ready. The farm runs WEA courses in gardening, bee-keeping, back yard farming and herbal health. With 120,000 visitors a year, Heeley City Farm is one of the country's most successful urban farms.

Richards Road,
Sheffield, S. Yorks
☎ *0114 258 0482*
Open: summer Mon-Sun 9am-5pm winter 9am-4.30pm
Café: summer Wed-Sun 11am-5pm winter 12 noon-4pm
Open every day during school holidays

TOLLERTON

Stark Farm

Greg Bucknill has believed in organic agriculture ever since he went collecting horse muck with his father for the family garden. He was never happy with conventional commercial methods

and is now a Soil Association symbol holder. He grows a wide range of organic vegetables under glass: tomatoes, cucumbers, peppers, aubergines, beans, courgettes and, as a lucrative cash crop, flowers which are dried in an old hay loft. Stark Farm also keeps livestock which do not hold the Soil Association symbol but are reared as close to organic as possible. These are sold primarily to friends in spring and autumn. His vegetables are more readily available from **Alligator**, York's premier wholefood shop and seven days a week at his farm gate.

Sykes Lane, Tollerton, N. Yorks
☎ *01347 838169*
Open: May-Dec Mon-Sun dawn to dusk

YORK

Brunswick Organic Nurseries

Pedal or stroll down the York-Selby cycle track and drop in on this small but admirable organic nursery, funded by York Social Services to teach horticultural skills to a small group of adults with physical disabilities or learning difficulties. Under Project Co-ordinator Adam Myers, the aim is to develop skills and at the same time provide a satisfying, worthwhile occupation for people who for whatever reason are unable to work in a conventional setting. They grow a wide range of organic produce, including spinach, beans, lettuce, tomatoes, courgettes, peppers, onions, leeks, garlic and parsnips as well as soft fruit, apples and excellent plums. They also have herbs, bedding plants and flowers. A project well worth supporting.

Appleton Road,
Bishopthorpe, York
☎ *01904 701869*
Open: Mon, Tue, Thur, Sat, Sun 10am-4pm
Wed & Fri 10am-1pm

YORKSHIRE WINE

Gillian and Richard Brown have taken home-brew from the kitchen and the demi-john to professional production in a converted flax mill on the banks of the river Nidd. Old wood-cuts of Peggy Bacon-Face, Barnaby Cheer-Up and Squire Amorous Great Hat are the distinctive labels of Yorkshire Country Wines. Elderberry, elderflower, blackberry, cherry, mead and parsnip and raisin are available at the mill or from specialist food shops throughout the region. They also serve Yorkshire cheeses and their wine from a café at the mill.

Yorkshire Country Wines, Riverside Cellars, The Mill, Glasshouses, Nr. Harrogate, N. Yorks
☎ **01423 711947/711223 Open: Wed-Sun 11.30am-4.30pm & Bank Holidays. Jan & Feb Sat & Sun only**

WILD AND FREE

Nuts, berries, seaweed, fungi – there is still a wide range of free food lurking among the Yorkshire hedgerows and on the east coast seashore. There is an undeniable satisfaction to be derived from bringing home a bag full of berries, hips and haws to make jams and jellies that cost absolutely nothing. But it has to be admitted that much free food hardly repays the effort of collecting it – outside eras of wartime hardship. It remains uncultivated and unharvested for good reason and it's no surprise that blackberries and raspberries are most people's only direct contact with wild food. Our abundant wild garlic loses its flavour as soon as it is cooked; a ripe cobnut is invariably spotted by a bird before a human; and while the prolific bladderwrack seaweed may add body and nourishment to a stew, most of us are nourished enough. The best seaweeds of caragheen moss and laver are west coast specialities. The nearest marsh samphire is from North Norfolk. We have fish and game, of course, but they are dealt with elsewhere and can be far from free to remove from the wild.

Yet, without too much trouble, the region can provide the enthusiast with crab apples and rowan berries for jelly; elderflower for sorbets or sparkling wine; sweet chestnuts for roasting. Germain Schwab of **Winteringham Fields** in South Humberside and Chris Kwiatkowski of **Partner's** of York are two chef/proprietors who find and serve wild fungi, even the rare and cherished morel. Numerous organised **Fungus Forays** will help the beginner distinguish the edible mushroom from the magic or the mortally dangerous. Rosehip syrup is still made from wild fruit collected by volunteers. It was discovered in World War II that rosehips have twenty times as much Vitamin C as oranges, leading to a dreaded school canteen partnership with rice pudding. But Yorkshire does have two genuine living traditions in free, wild food:

Bilberries: Peter Heslop of the **Mallyan Hotel** at Goathland has this little blue-black fruit supplied direct to his kitchen from a private gatherer literally combing the heather moors of North Yorkshire. His bilberry and apple pie is a Yorkshire favourite with a history that goes back to funeral teas and beyond. The apple and cream help to cut the acid of the bilberry for a delicious pie. Before the war, gypsies would be granted moorland rights for a day's picking but nobody can be picking British bilberries with serious commercial intent any more. **Hodgson's** of Settle stock imports from Poland. Enthusiasts should head for a heather moor between July until September. The berries lurk around the heather stems in miserly clumps. You will need to scour a fair sized area for a decent collection and it will involve patience and back pain.

Dock Pudding: Richard Mabey's authoritative *Food For Free* recalls how the inaugural World Championship Dock Pudding contest at Hebden Bridge in 1971 was launched in the Personal Column of The Times and still drew 50 entrants. The tradition of eating 'poor man's cabbage' has long roots in Calderdale, and Mytholmroyd is a continuing competition stronghold. The leaves of bistortum *polygonum bistorta* are boiled up with oatmeal and chopped onion, mixed with beaten egg and served hot. Or it can be allowed to go cold then sliced and fried in bacon fat. The green leaves thrive in damp upland fields and meadows. They are easily spotted when they flower in summer but the aficionado commends the spring leaves for the best taste. Supporters attribute good health and longevity to dock's iron and vitamins. Yorkshire historian Julia Smith has heard the taste compared to both caviar and cowflap.

GREENGROCERS

BEDALE

Carrick's
The Carrick name has been a fixture on North Yorkshire's markets for 64 years in five locations, a sturdy tradition but one that moves smartly with the times. Witness chanterelle mushrooms, baby sweetcorn and Kenyan beans. If John Carrick's prices are occasionally slightly dearer it's a fair trade for choice, quality and freshness. In summer he makes early morning runs for dawn-picked soft fruit which hit his stalls the same day. As a greengrocer he sets his alarm clock at 3.30am for the 100 mile round trip to Leeds wholesale market to be back and ready by 7am and still have a working day's supply of energy for market hype and extra helpings of banter. Next door, Peter and David Carrick run the family fish business.

Bedale Market, Tue
Leyburn Market, Fri
Northallerton Market, Wed, Sat
Richmond Market, Sat
Ripon Market, Thur

BEVERLEY

Good 'N' Fresh
Grower turned grocer, John Dibb offers probably the widest selection of fresh produce in Beverley. He buys daily from Hull's Humber Street wholesale market, finds some of the earliest Jersey potatoes and buys organic leeks out of no special affection for organics but because he acknowledges their quality. It's the place to find a lively selection of salad leaves such as lollo rosso, oak leaf and endive.

19 Butcher Row,
Beverley, N. Humbs
☎ *01482 881483*
Mon-Sat 8.30am-5.30pm

BRADFORD

Ahmed Foods
Khurshid Ahmed's greengrocery had been trading unobtrusively for six years on the ever changing Asian bazaar of Leeds Road until he splashed out on bold brass lamps and a royal blue paint job to highlight one of the most colourful food displays going. Every imaginable fruit and vegetable tumbles out onto the pavement. It's a happy hazard for pedestrians if not distracted motorists heading down into Bradford from Leeds. There are dates and okra. There are baby aubergines, little eddoes and Indian yams. There are big bunches of oregano and coriander at a fraction of supermarket prices and with an infinitely superior aroma. There is the drumstick (a subcontinental bean for spicing up soup) and the mysterious doodhi (a kind of squash). And there are next to no labels to help make sense of the overflowing cornucopia. Despite Khurshid's willingness to help out he admits he doesn't always know the English names for much of his less recognisable stock but he or his customers will certainly be able to tell you what to do with it and there's always a fall back of masses of familiar fruit and vegetable at bargain prices. Bradford's Asian community has preserved a culture where indigenous shopping, cooking and eating have beaten the fast-food onslaught. The bequest to the city is bread, spice, vegetables and much more that no English tradition could provide. Ahmed's is a prince of provision.

1382 Leeds Road,
Bradford, W. Yorks
☎ *01274 665239*
Open: Mon-Sat 9am-8.30pm Sun 10am-8.30pm

HARROGATE

Barber's Fruiterer's
This excellent greengrocer's sits alongside **Ramus Seafoods** and **Arcimboldo's** in a Harrogate suburb to complete arguably Yorkshire's most useful trio of good food shops virtually next door to each other yet under independent ownership. Barber's represent consistent good quality. There's a strong selection of the main fruit and veg. lines, established brand names in cans, jars and bottles and imaginative surprises that lift it well above the High Street common standard. It's self service but the check-out staff are more than helpful and won't drop a five pound weight of spuds on top of a more dainty bag of wild mushrooms.

142 Kings Road,
Harrogate, N. Yorks
☎ *01423 509609*
Open: Mon-Sat 8am-5.30pm

HEATON

Hopwood's
Out to impress his girlfriend, one of Hopwood's customers ordered caviar, foie gras and truffles from Heaton's prize greengrocer and delicatessen. Within 24 hours Angela Hopwood had successfully tracked them down but a final check with the customer revealed he'd lost faith in his local supplier and ordered his treats from Harrods. She was disappointed: 'He didn't think we'd be able to get them and he'd paid double the price.' It's not all Beluga and black Perigord at Hopwood's but Angela and her mother Sylvia have become adept at hunting down the unusual. They frequently supply anything from asparagus to sea kale to the nearby Michelin starred **Restaurant 19**. The mainstays,

EGTON BRIDGE OLD GOOSEBERRY COMPETITION

'The countenances of the group were expressive of deep earnestness and anxiety. Each man kept his box or basket close to himself and when he opened it to get out a gooseberry he did so with extreme care, lest the extent of his treasure might be seen. One would take out a monster berry, and holding it tenderly by the stalk, would place it on one of the scales, and watch it as it lay there lest it should come to harm.'

Anon, 1854

The Egton Bridge Old Gooseberry Competition has been held on the first Tuesday in August for nearly 200 years. Today it attracts journalists and TV news crews for its unchanging tradition of bucolic charm. 'This year it's Pebble Mill', says Chairman Eric Preston: 'One year we had a journalist from the New York Times.'

Gooseberry competitions have their roots in the damp cottage gardens and allotments of the industrial north where flower shows and competitions led to an enthusiasm for ever bigger and better gooseberries. In 1845 the Gooseberry Growers' Register recorded 171 shows. Now there are just two, at Holmes Chapel in Cheshire and Egton Bridge in North Yorkshire.

In the past, competitors would take their gooseberries from show to show, sometimes bringing a selection of possible prize winners, keeping them in a box to be revealed one by one at the weigh-in. In this way it was sometimes possible to keep back the heaviest specimen for another competition.

Today's show may be less secretive but it's equally competitive. The weigh-in takes place on the morning of the show at Egton Bridge's village schoolroom. Specimens are presented to the three weighmen and two judges huddled over a pair of ancient Avery scales. Using an arcane system of grains and drams, the ripe berries, swollen until nearly bursting, are weighed. The weight of two ounces is loaded with significance for the gooseberry grower. It is the Everest of the competition, the weight to which they aspire. No one at Egton Bridge has yet beaten the world record: a Woodpecker of 33 drams 2 grains, (a fraction over two ounces) grown by Mr A. Dingle of Marton in Cheshire in 1978. 'The winners usually come in at just under two ounces', says Eric Preston.

After the weighing, the visitors begin arriving. No thrills and spills, just a gentle afternoon diversion. They can inspect the berries – the heaviest red, yellow or white, the heaviest twelve or six and the supreme champion. The show has nothing whatever to do with taste or flavour. It's not a competition for gourmands. No one would dream of eating the big, fat swollen berries of Woodpecker, Lord Derby and Fur Bob. It's size that counts today although the chairman does admit to being partial to a gooseberry pie.

Prizes are modest: 'We don't want it to become a money-making event', says Eric Preston. The copper kettles and brass pans of the past have been replaced by today's equivalent of watering cans and toasters. The day ends with pots of tea and home-made cakes, a raffle and a brass band. And that's it. Winners and losers repair to the Horseshoe Hotel for gooseberry growers' tales. It's English village life, as pretty as a picture, unchanged for generations. Just the thing for the New York Times.

Egton Bridge Gooseberry Society, 58 Birch Avenue, Sleights, Whitby, N. Yorks ☎ 01947 810332

however, are good fruit and vegetables, locally made vegetarian patés and 60 or more British and continental cheeses, something they know about after eight years running Ilkley's premier cheese shop, **Burrell's.**

10a Highgate, Heaton,
Bradford, W. Yorks
☎ *01274 483108*
Open: Mon-Fri 8am-5.30pm
Sat 8am-4pm

HEBDEN BRIDGE

William Holt's

Sepia photographs bear witness to the fact that there's been a greengrocer here since the turn of the century. Owners have come and gone since the eponymous Mr Holt but for the last seven years it's been run by Robert and Caroline Garforth and their enthusiastic son Lee. Their range is impressive for a small shop. Everything is labelled by variety or country of origin. Besides the basics, there are what Lee calls 'the fancy lines', which in Hebden Bridge mean endive, lollo rosso, oyster mushrooms, celeriac, chillies, ginger and star fruit. Cod, haddock, salmon and trout come from Grimsby to meet a modest demand for fresh fish and, just as fishmongers used to do, the Garforths throw in a handful of parsley free of charge, typical of a good local shop giving good old fashioned service.

6 Bridgegate,
Hebden Bridge, W. Yorks
☎ *01422 842143*
Open: Mon-Fri 8.30am-5.30pm
Sat 8.30am-1pm

ILKLEY

Arcade Fruits

Locals recommend this attractive shop a just a few hundred yards from the main shopping thoroughfare and sure enough the choice includes some less common items: celeriac, kohlrabi,

oyster mushrooms and a decent selection of wet fish.

Victorian Arcade, South
Hawksworth Street,
Ilkley, W. Yorks
☎ *01943 602447*
Open: Mon-Sat 8.30am-5.30pm

Asquith & Son

Ilkley is well off for greengrocers but Asquith's always has something special to offer: wild mushrooms in dusty glory, baby aubergines, big bunches of fresh coriander or a display of squash and pumpkins in brilliant autumn hues. Their limited fish counter is invariably good and fresh.

4 Grove Promenade,
Ilkley, W. Yorks
☎ *01943 600600*
Open: Mon-Sat 8.30am-5.30pm

LEEDS

Barrett's of Cookridge

Headingley residents remember with nostalgia when Barrett's was their shop, a greengrocer garlanded in fur and feather now seen only in their old photographs. Rabbit, hare, pheasant and grouse took their turn to hang outside in all their autumn splendour. 'Hello lady', was Mr Barrett's regular cry, a tireless, eccentric charmer. But in 1988 Mr and Mrs Barrett hung up their overalls and closed the shop. They died within months of each other four years later. Happily, their son David found another shop in Cookridge and Barrett's was back. This isn't the old shop. Hygiene regulations have seen to it that meat cannot be hung outside. But they still sell poultry and game, now safely in the fridge, the full range of top quality vegetables, Jersey potatoes, asparagus, English strawberries and raspberries and double cream.

254a Tinshill Road, Cookridge,
Leeds, W. Yorks
☎ *0113 267 4414*
Open: Tue-Sat 8.30am-6pm

LEYBURN

Carrick's

See Bedale entry.

Leyburn Market, Fri

NORTHALLERTON

Carrick's

See Bedale entry.

Northallerton Market, Wed, Sat

OTLEY

Quantrill's

Once a pacesetter for all things fresh and green, Quantrill's have faced the incursion of the supermarket with stoicism. Nevertheless, their range is less thrilling than it once was now that aubergines and sweet potatoes are as familiar as carrots and cauliflower. With 23 years of trading behind them they know what their customers want and if Otley is not yet ready for sea kale or samphire then be satisfied with top quality Scottish potatoes, golden delicious apples and prime Scottish haddock fillet. They will, they say, buy unusual ingredients on request.

27 Manor Square,
Otley, W. Yorks
☎ *01943 462701*
Open: Mon-Fri 7am-5.30pm
Sat 7am-5pm

RICHMOND

Carrick's

See Bedale entry.

Richmond Market, Sat

RIPON

Carrick's

See Bedale entry.

Ripon Market, Thur

ROTHERHAM

Brian Berry

Within the arches of Rotherham's fine parish church stands one of the town's all too rare bastions of good food: Brian Berry's greengrocer's. There are no weird roots from the African interior or romantic fruits from South Sea islands but there is still a riot of colour underneath his bright green awning. Salad greens, red apples, oranges, plums, fennel, avocados and green chillies are all piled high. Tubs of flowers spilling onto the square enhance the fresh and 'feelgood factor'.

All Saints Square,
Rotherham, S. Yorks
☎ *01709 365780*
Open: Mon-Sat 9am-5pm

SETTLE

Hodgson's

Mind your head as you step down into this shop from Cheapside. Inside there's barely space to swing a string of onions but the one cramped room of Hodgson's of Settle stocks a veritable treasury of fruit and vegetables. In autumn there are 15 varieties of English apple to try and in summer fresh bilberries or the rare and succulent marsh samphire. The shop has been around since the 1860s when Margaret Hodgson's grandfather travelled to Bradford by train to do his buying and made deliveries around Settle by horse and cart. David Hodgson studied agriculture in the 1950s and developed a commitment to home-grown produce that long pre-dates modern organics: 'We just put on plenty of muck and let the birds and the bees do the rest.' Each year his muck produces 160 different pot grown herbs for sale and a range of produce that invariably ends up in the shop. While the shop has everything from lemons to rambutans, the Hodgson have made a speciality of English produce. Apple and pear tasting days feature a mouth-watering selection of fruits with different varieties baked into pies. They make forays into deepest Lancashire for succulent tomatoes and tasty and unusual salad crops. They are constantly on the lookout for growers who are doing something special. Fresh bilberries, those tiny purple/blue berries that were once part of every summer pilgrimage to the North York Moors, are rarely, if ever, seen in the shops today. Hodgson's import their's from Poland to fulfil an annual 20 lb order for one fastidious customer. Rarer still is wild marsh samphire, still found on Britain's remote salt marshes. In the freemasonry of specialist foodism, a list of impatient customers wait for the late summer telephone call to hear: 'The marsh samphire is in.' Can anyone else but Hodgson's make that call?

Cheapside, Settle, N. Yorks
☎ *01729 823772*
Open: Mon 9am-12.30pm &
1.30pm-5pm
Tue-Fri 9am-5.30pm
Wed 9am-12.30pm Sat 9am-5pm

WETHERBY

Johnson's

A wide range of produce that takes in celeriac, red onions, sweet potatoes and Jerusalem artichokes along with the basics. Game in season.

59 Market Place,
Wetherby, N. Yorks
☎ *01937 582070*
Open: Mon-Fri 8.30am-5.30pm
Wed 8am-5pm Sat 8am-5.30pm

THE RHUBARB PATCH

A hundred and fifty years ago, miners from the West Riding pit villages grew their own food. As well as potatoes and sprouts, every allotment and back yard would sport a few sticks of 'tusky', rhubarb grown under an old bucket to keep it pink and tender. From these small beginnings developed Europe's biggest forced rhubarb industry. The miners began by splitting a few roots, acquiring some land and building a forcing shed. Surprisingly, the unpromising setting of industrial West Yorkshire proved to be ideal rhubarb country. The night soil from thousands of privies and the waste from local shoddy mills fertilised the soil. The long low forcing sheds could be kept at the required 60°F with the cheap fuel the former miners had once dug from the ground. By the 1920s there were over 200 rhubarb growers in the 'pink patch', an eight mile stretch between Leeds and Wakefield. A farm might grow up to 90 tons a year and a rhubarb train ran regularly from Leeds to King's Cross. But the popularity of rhubarb has declined. Devastated by cheap imports from Holland and usurped by fashionable fruits from across the world, the number of growers is down to 20. The last rhubarb train left Leeds in 1962. Yet the country's only rhubarb show is still held at Crigglestone, near Wakefield, where sticks of Prince Albert compete with Victoria and Stockbridge Arrow. Chutney's, wines, trifles and pies display rhubarb's versatility and quietly safeguarding rhubarb's survival is the Royal Horticultural Society's northern base at Harlow Carr. It is the home of the 150 varieties of the National Rhubarb Collection.

4

Cheese & Dairy

In 1957 the Milk Marketing Board formally recorded the extinction of the last authentic Yorkshire farmhouse dairy. Their obituary was premature as 'underground' cheesemaking never quite died but it was still an astonishing state of affairs considering that such a famous cheese as Wensleydale was once the staple of every coal miner's lunch and an indispensable ingredient of a Yorkshire Christmas. Yorkshire, so self-conscious of its traditions, had become strangely negligent of nearly 1,000 years of making, serving and, above all, enjoying its own splendid cheeses. Today, however, there is a happy revival with prize-winning small cheesemakers back in the Dales, on the North York Moors and even on the metropolitan fringes. The region's cheeseboards and counters are more adventurously stocked than ever before and if it is still beyond the wit of the average pub, canteen or corner shop to offer the cheese made on its own doorstep then at least the pendulum is swinging. It is also increasingly possible to find the best national and international cheeses in Yorkshire. There is Scottish 'Roquefort' in a Polish delicatessen in Brighouse and a Spanish mountain blue Cabrales in a York off-licence. Real cheese is back. And if the Dales tradition of farmhouse butter-making has long gone, then there is modern compensation in the high quality of yoghurt and ice cream made in the region.

CHEESEMAKERS

ASKWITH

Ashdale Cheese

One hundred goats graze on Town Head's 20 acres of spray-free pasture. The herd provides over 400 gallons of milk a week in summer which is made into Ashdale Cheese. Val Morris has been keeping goats here for eleven years, initially selling the milk to local dairies and allergy sufferers who found relief in goat's milk. In 1991 she began sending her milk to Judy Bell of **Shepherd's Purse**, to be made into two delicate, unpasteurised cheeses: the mild Thistledown and the firmer, more mature Ashdale. In it's first year Ashdale took second prize at the Nantwich cheese show. Now a nine month matured Ashdale is also available in limited quantities. Val began by marketing the cheese herself: 'If a shopkeeper phoned up for one cheese I'd jump in the van and do a 50 mile round trip to make sure they got it.' Such commitment has paid off and her cheese now appears on the menus of smart restaurants and is distributed throughout Yorkshire including her local pub, the Black Horse at Askwith.

Town Head Farm,
Askwith, W. Yorks
☎ *01943 463504*
Open: by appointment

COTHERSTONE

Cotherstone Cheese

No, Cotherstone is not in Yorkshire but it is in the Dales and the soft, crumbly, sweet cheese of Cotherstone that has been made on farms in Teesdale for well over a century is a true Dales cheese. By tradition, the cheeses were made in June, when the milk was strong and rich. They would be left to 'blue' naturally and sold as an alternative to Stilton at Christmas. Today, only white is produced by the country's sole surviving producer of Cotherstone, Joan Cross. After the war cheesemaking in Cotherstone, as elsewhere in the Dales, virtually died out but in the severe snows of 1947 the milk tankers were unable to get through to remote hill farms. Joan Cross remembers: 'Our farm was snowed up for six weeks. We couldn't get the milk away so my mother was forced back to cheesemaking. She continued to make it on a small scale right up to her death.' Joan Cross took her mother's 'basic, simple recipe' and for more than 20 years now she has been quietly producing a superb, unpasteurised cow's milk cheese from Quarry House Farm, 1,000 feet above the River Tees. Cotherstone cheese is available from Cother-

stone Post Office and good cheese counters in Yorkshire and Humberside. It is also stocked by Neal's Yard Dairy in London.

Quarry House Farm,
Cotherstone, Nr. Barnard Castle,
Co Durham
☎ *01833 650351*
Not open to the public

DANBY

Botton Cheese

Botton Village, spreading over 600 acres of the North York Moors, is a unique community living out an ideal. As part of the Camphill movement, it brings together mentally handicapped adults and able people to live and work together without wages for the benefit of all. Botton's five farms are run on bio-dynamic principles, a 'super-organic' system developed by Rudolph Steiner, the Austrian philosopher and guiding light of Botton. Bio-dynamics involve basic organics with the use of homeopathic preparations which, it is claimed, are in harmony with the wider environment and the cosmos. Back on earth, the resulting produce is invariably outstanding. Botton creamery produces two first-rate cow's milk cheeses: Botton Cheddar is a hard, full-cream, unpasteurised, clothbound cheese made with vegetarian rennet and Danbydale is a semi-soft cheese. They also produce cheese spread, curd cheese, yoghurt, butter, cream and ice-cream. They supply to shops in York, Helmsley, Whitby and Middlesbrough but with only 1,200 cheeses made in a year, Botton cheese is harder to find further afield. Botton's village store sells home produced jam, chutneys and peanut butter. There are dried herbs and an excellent range of juices from

---

┌ THE SPECIALIST CHEESEMAKERS ASSOCIATION ┐

The Specialist Cheesemakers Association represents traditional cheese producers who make farm produced, character cheeses on a small scale, often from unpasteurised milk. They welcome associate membership from retailers, restaurateurs and lovers of good cheese. They hold an annual cheese show and publish an invaluable guide to the specialist cheeses of Britain and Ireland.

The Specialist Cheesemakers Association, PO Box 256a, Thames Ditton, Surrey ☎ *0181 398 4101*

YORKSHIRE CHEESES

COW'S MILK

Ashes Farm Wensleydale
Traditional farmhouse. Also garlic or smoked. *Pasteurised/Animal rennet/Waxed*

Botton Hard Cheese
Organic, hard, cheddar-type. *Unpasteurised/Vegetarian rennet/Clothbound*

Cotherstone
Trad. recipe. Mild, soft,nutty with crumbly texture. *Unpast./Animal/Waxed*

Coverdale
Fountains Dairy. Trad.Dales recipe. Crumbly, nutty. Also with chives. *Past./Veg./Waxed*

Danbydale
Botton Creamery. Organic, full-fat, semi-soft. *Unpast./Veg./Clothbound*

Dan Dairies
Soft. Low, medium and full-fat. With garlic, chives or smoked salmon. *Past./Veg./Carton*

Fountains Gold
Fountains Dairy. New recipe. Jersey and Guernsey milk. Smooth and creamy. *Past./Veg./Toasted wheat flour*

Jervaulx
Fortmayne Dairy. Delicate, young semi-soft. *Unpast./Veg./Waxed*

King Richard III Wensleydale
Fortmayne Dairy. Moist, soft but crumbly. Eaten young. *Unpast./Veg./Clothbound*

Longley Farm
Cottage, curd and cream cheese. Also with pineapple or chives. *Past./Veg./Carton*

Ribblesdale Farmhouse
Ashes Farm. Firm, moist, creamy. Also with garlic or smoked. *Past./Veg./Waxed*

Richmond Smoked
Swaledale Cheese Co. Trad. recipe. Smoked over oak or apple wood. *Past./Veg./Waxed*

Swaledale
Creamy, mild.With mint; chives and garlic; and Old Peculier. *Past./Veg./Waxed or Rinded*

Wensleydale
Fountains Dairy. Close textured, smooth. Also a blue Wensleydale *Past./Veg./Waxed*

Wensleydale
Wensleydale Creamery. Firm,crumbly, moist. Available matured. *Past./Veg./Clothbound*

Yorvik
Fortmayne Dairy. Soft, tangy, distinctive orange layer. *Unpast./Veg./Waxed*

EWE'S MILK

Ashes Farm Ewe's Milk Wensleydale
Dry but creamy, crumbly. *Past./Animal/Waxed*

Farmhouse Wensleydale
Shepherd's Purse. Semi-hard, firm, matured. *Past./Veg./Clothbound*

Herriot Farmhouse
Shepherd's Purse. Unpressed, three month matured. *Unpast./Veg./Clothbound*

Olde York
Shepherd's Purse.Delicate, soft. Also with chives, peppercorn, garlic or mint. *Unpast./Veg./Waxed*

Ribblesdale Ewe
Ashes Farm. Firm, nutty. Also garlic or smoked. *Past./Veg./Waxed*

Swaledale Ewe
Swaledale Cheese Co. Soft, light and creamy. *Past./Veg/Waxed or rinded*

Yorkshire Blue
Shepherd's Purse. Mature, full-fat, soft with mellow, blue flavour. Also with cow's milk. *Past./Veg./Clothbound*

Yorkshire Lowlands
Shepherd's Purse. Mature, pressed, nutty flavour. *Unpast./Veg./Waxed*

Yorkshire Feta
Shepherd's Purse. Soft, slightly salty. *Unpast./Veg./Waxed*

GOAT'S MILK

Ashdale
Town Head Farm. Lightly pressed, dry, crumbly Also matured. *Unpast./Veg./Waxed*

Farndale Dairy Goats
Soft, mild. Also unwaxed in olive oil; mint/calvados; whisky/oatmeal; garlic; fresh herbs. *Unpast./Veg./Waxed*

Grosmont
Dog Tree Bank Farm. Small, unpressed, delicate. *Unpast./Naturally soured/Clothbound*

Intake Lane Goat Herd
Soft, mild also a mature pressed. *Past./Veg./Carton*

Ribblesdale Original
Ashes Farm. Fresh, delicate. Also garlic or smoked. *Past./Veg./Waxed*

Thistledown
Town Head Farm. Lightly pressed, delicate, mild and soft. *Unpast./Veg./Waxed*

organic fruit. The bakery grinds its own organic flour to produce nine different types of bread and numerous cakes and biscuits from a wood fired oven. The gift shop, bookshop and tearoom make this a rewarding place to visit.

Camphill Village Trust, Botton Village, Danby, Whitby, N. Yorks
☎ *01287 660871*
Open: Mon, Tue 9am-12.15pm & 2pm-5.30pm
Wed, Thur , Fri 2pm-5.30pm
Sat 9am-12 noon
closed Bank Holidays

GROSMONT

Grosmont Goat's Cheese
Elizabeth Newton's tiny output of excellent goat's milk cheese was inspired by the peasant cheeses on sale in French country markets and her desire to make a proper local cheese and sell it locally even though, as she cheerfully acknowledges, it is hopelessly uncommercial. Her passion for goats came from Turkey where she lived in the 1960s. When she returned to England, Elizabeth bought two pedigree British Toggenbergs and began milking. The kitchen of the lovely Dog Tree Bank Farm serves as the dairy and on the hillside 30 goats now graze on a chemical-free pasture of speedwell, meadowsweet, sorrel, yarrow, cocksfoot, primrose, knapweed, mint and clover. The result is one of the most delicate and distinctive handmade cheeses of the region. Grosmont is a soft, medium-fat goat's milk cheese, soured naturally without rennet. Only sea salt is added before being wrapped in muslin. Elizabeth Newton calls it 'a primitive goat's cheese that worked.' With no more than 60 cheeses made a week, Grosmont is sold only locally, the regular outlets being the **Shepherd's Purse** emporium in Whitby and the **Mallyan**

Hotel in Goathland who are wholehearted supporters of local produce. Farmgate sales are possible with 24 hours telephone notice preferred.

Dog Tree Bank Farm, Grosmont, Whitby, N. Yorks
☎ *01947 895306*
Open: by appointment

HAWES

Wensleydale Creamery
Hawes has been the spiritual home of Wensleydale cheese since time immemorial so when in 1992 Dairy Crest had the bright idea of closing down the creamery, making the town's biggest workforce redundant and sacrilegiously transferring production to Lancashire, it first turned the dairy into a *cause célèbre* and then gave Wensleydale cheese an enormous publicity boost. Six months of rows and failed rescue bids passed before a secret management buy-out prevailed and 20 of the 59 jobs were thankfully saved. Hawes went back into production with the famous lamb's head label updated and a portrait of Kit Calvert on the one pound cheeses. It was Kit Calvert who had been the saviour of Hawes Creamery in 1933 and subsequently ran it for 34 years. The dairy moved from the town centre to its present location on the outskirts in 1957 and features a cheese store set into the hillside in imitation of the caves in France where Roquefort is matured. It was Kit Calvert's doomed hope that the cold, damp conditions would be suitable for blueing Wensleydale. He retired in 1967 the year after the Milk Marketing Board took over. The latest relaunch with production at 10 tons a week is a fraction of former output but it quickly won a place on the Sainsbury and Safeway shelves and the future looks secure, not least because today's cheese tastes better. In all

the furore over the closure it would have been unkind to point out that the Dairy Crest Wensleydale from Hawes was not much to write home about. But in the first year under new management the creamery swept the board at the cheese shows, taking first prizes at the International Food Exhibition at Earls Court for Wensleydale; at Nantwich for smoked Wensleydale; and Supreme Champion at the Bakewell Cheese Show for a three month matured Wensleydale (available from Marks & Spencer, Paris or Madrid or good cheese counters in Yorkshire). All are deserved tributes to the hectic hard work that went into the rescue. The new operation is 'very much in the spirit of Kit Calvert', says Technical Director Michael Webster. 'It's not just a matter of jobs. This area is also our home. We know everyone here and usually their parents and their grandparents too.' Wensleydale cheese from Hawes is available widely throughout the county and beyond or direct from the creamery. A newly opened visitors' centre now runs daily cheesemaking demonstrations.

Gayle Lane, Hawes, N. Yorks
☎ *01969 667664*
Open: Mon-Fri 10am-5pm

HIGH FARNDALE

Farndale Dairy Goats
Milking 60 recalcitrant goats twice daily in one of the most remote dales in Yorkshire could hardly be more different from Peter Wright's former life as a medic on a North Sea oil rig but five years ago redundancy forced Peter and his wife Kath to start a new life at Oak House Farm in High Farndale. On 50 acres of land untouched by pesticides or artificial fertilisers they care for a herd of British Toggenberg goats and convert 20 gallons of milk a day into 200 delicate little cheeses. Self-taught, Kath Wright read

WENSLEYDALE CHEESE

'We stand in reverence and awe as we gaze at the ruins of Fountains or Jervaulx, but the true and lasting memorial is not in the stately ruins but in the miles and miles of limestone walls and that peacetime delicacy, a ripe blue-veined Wensleydale cheese.'

Kit Calvert, Wensleydale Cheese, 1946

A curd strainer dug up at the Roman fort above Bainbridge is the earliest evidence of cheese-making in Wensleydale and by extension the starting point of all Yorkshire cheese. Whatever the distinctions in ingredient, recipe, technique and taste of its neighbours, Wensleydale remains the source. It defines, as it always has done, the rest of the world's estimation of a Yorkshire cheese.

Trust, then, the French to invent it. Their Benedictine and Cistercian monks, sent over in the wake of the Norman conquest, apparently couldn't stand the local food and sent for reinforcement cheese recipes from Burgundy and Roquefort. The monks set up the long lost Fors Abbey, near Bainbridge, lasting only 15 years until they saw sense and rebuilt downstream at the more comfortable setting of Jervaulx. But monastic records of 1150 establish ewe's milk cheese at Fors so it is the true birthplace of blue Wensleydale. The limestone pastures of the monastic granges delivered superb milk; dank cellars and storage vaults coupled with natural moulds that flourished in the stone created the blue veins and hard selling kept the monks in the abbeys to which they were becoming accustomed.

Tastes change and so does the definition of a true Wensleydale. The milk of shorthorn cows gradually replaced ewe's milk through the Middle Ages to the 17th century. The basic Wensleydale techniques spread to Coverdale, Swaledale and Cotherstone. Cheese fairs sprang up across North Yorkshire in the 19th century; Yarm Fair lasting three days with up to 1,000 cheeses on sale. Substantial dairies were built at Hawes, Coverham, Askrigg, Leyburn and Dent.

At the outbreak of the second World War there were still 433 Dales farmhouses making cheese but within 20 years there was none: the creation of the Milk Marketing Board in l933 was the salvation of dairy farmers in the Depression but their dependable market for milk eroded the necessity for cheesemaking. The Dales dairies and cheese factories first merged then closed until only the Wensleydale Creamery at Hawes survived through the inspiration of Kit Calvert, quintessential Dalesman and guardian of the Wensleydale legacy.

Nationalisation, pasteurisation and milk mixed from different herds conspired to bequeathe a bland white Wensleydale that was hardly worth saving on its own account when Dairy Crest announced in l992 that it was closing down the Wensleydale Creamery despite its profitability and coolly relocating Yorkshire Wensleydale in Lancashire. In the ensuing furore a management buy-out saved Hawes and it is already flourishing with better made and marketed cheeses than Dairy Crest could manage. But the real renaissance has come from the independent sector: David Reed's reborn Swaledale; Joan Cross's Cotherstone; Suzanne Stirke's Richard III Wensleydale and Shepherd's Purse ewe's milk Yorkshire Blue are cheeses which have gone almost full circle back to the creation of the monks of the Abbot of Savigny and their forlorn dairy.

books, experimented in the kitchen and spent two weeks visiting French cheesemakers before she was happy with her individual unpasteurised waxed cheeses which can now be found in specialist shops throughout Yorkshire. Her range of fresh, flavoured two ounce cheeses including garlic, applemint and calvados, whisky and oatmeal and a herb coated cheese in cold pressed olive oil are available at **Hunters** of Helmsley; the **Cheese Board**, Scarborough; the **Gillygate Bakery** in York and the **Delicatessen** in Stokesley. In the summer Kath makes a fromage frais with her neighbour's organic fresh fruit in strawberry, raspberry, blackcurrant and blackberry. Tastings are organised on Thursday afternoons in summer with a farm shop selling their own produce of pork, kid meat, quails' eggs, free range hens' eggs and, naturally their own cheese.

Oak House Farm,
High Farndale,
Kirbymoorside, N. Yorks
☎ *01751 33053*
Open: April-December
Wed-Sun 2.30pm-4.30pm

HOLMFIRTH

Longley Farm Dairy
Probably Yorkshire's most familiar dairy brand, Longley Farm cottage cheese, cream and yoghurt can be found on every supermarket shelf as well as the QE2, the French Riviera and Saudi Arabia. Their curd cheese goes into **Betty's** famous Yorkshire curd tarts. One of the largest independent dairies in the country yet despite its size and success it is still run by the same partnership that began the business 45 years ago. Joseph and Edgar Dickinson inherited the 20 acre Pennine farm at Holmfirth from their great-uncle, together with ten cows, a horse and debts greater than the value of the farm itself. They started with a milk round and have now expanded to four farms, including Tyas Hall, Barnsley which is home to a Jersey herd, the source of their popular Longley Farm extra-thick double cream. Despite expansion, an enduring feature of all the farms is a commitment to conservation and the environment. Miles of hedges and trees have been planted and waste products from cheese production at Holmfirth are fed to the pigs. The waste from the pigs feeds the land which supports the cows. A wind generator on the hill above Longley provides ten per cent of their energy. A natural spring running through Longley Farm and a man-made dam collects water from the hillside and is used in the cooling system. Waste heat is recovered and re-used. At the 1994 Nantwich Cheese Show, Longley Farm won prizes for single cream, whipping cream and yoghurt and the trophy for best overall creamery cheese. Longley Farm products are available from shops throughout the county and country. Factory tours can be arranged.

Holmfirth, W. Yorks
☎ *01484 684151*
Open: Mon-Fri 8am-4.30pm
Sat 9am-11am

HORTON-IN-RIBBLESDALE

Ribblesdale Cheese
Iain and Chris Hill of Ashes Farm are the only cheesemakers in Ribblesdale but they are a significant presence with a range of high quality handmade goat, sheep and cow's milk cheeses, widely available despite their remote origins high up in the dale near Ribblehead. The old stone cheese press at the farm bears evidence to earlier generations when a hard dry Craven cheese was made from buttermilk, when every farm had its dairy and it was women's work to churn the butter. The only butter making around now is Associated Dairies Cravendale butter made at their automated plant at Settle. The Ribblesdale cheese revival dates back to 1982 when the Hill's used surplus goat's milk to make their Ribblesdale Original: hard pressed, delicate and mild. They have extended their repertoire to include a traditional ewe's milk Wensleydale and, after year long trials, a cow's milk Wensleydale made since 1987 in the old farmhouse dairy. As they point out, one of the watersheds for Wensleydale is but a short walk away although the milk actually comes from a British Friesian herd rather further away at Austwick. In Ashes Farm Wensleydale the Hill's have produced an excellent cheese: buttery yet still a clean, fresh cheese with a crumbly texture. Ribblesdale (vegetarian rennet) and Ashes Farm (animal

rennet) cheeses are available throughout the region and by mail order.

Ashes Farm,
Horton-in-Ribblesdale,
N. Yorks
☎ 01729 860231
Not open to the public

KIRKBY MALZEARD

Fountains Dairy
Wensleydale is the hallmark cheese here and although a purist may argue that the beautiful village of Kirkby Malzeard is not quite in true Wensleydale, Fountains Dairy is only 800 yards from the river Ure and six miles from Jervaulx, the font of original Blue Wensleydale. The creamery was born out of the closure in the 1980s of Dairy Crest's last two dairies in the district: their run down Kirkby Malzeard operation and Coverham, built around a 17th century pub in Coverdale. Bill Taylor and Les Lambert, the leading Wensleydale cheesemakers of the day, relaunched the dairy as Fountains with 11 staff and now managing director Nick Reaks oversees a team of 40, a £4 million turnover and 1,600 tons of cheese a year, all made from the milk of local herds grazed on limestone fields and pasteurised at the plant. As well as Wensleydale, they produce Leicester (a Nantwich winner), Double Gloucester, Caerphilly, Cheshire, Coverdale – claimed to be the only traditional recipe Coverdale made anywhere – and Fountains Gold, their newest cheese, from Jersey and Guernsey milk. The future of volume Yorkshire cheesemaking at either end of Wensleydale looks secure if the management buy-out of the Hawes creamery flourishes as well as it has at Fountains Dairy. The Fountains range can be bought by callers to the dairy and is stocked by numerous delicatessens across the region and by Harrods of Knightsbridge.

Kirkby Malzeard,
Nr. Ripon, N. Yorks
☎ 01765 658212
Open Mon-Fri 9am-4pm

LEEDS

Dan Dairies
Rafi Bechar learned cheesemaking in Tel Aviv where his father's dairy produced 35 different varieties of cheese and yoghurt. In 1992 Rafi and his Leeds born wife Anne set up a small dairy producing low, medium and full fat soft cheeses, made with vegetarian rennet and accepted by the Beth Din. Dan Dairies cheese is available plain or with garlic, chives or smoked salmon. It is stocked by the **Kosherie** delicatessen in Leeds.

Astley Lane Industrial Estate,
Swillington, Leeds, W. Yorks
☎ 0113 287 7788
Not open to the public

NEWSHAM

Shepherd's Purse
In 1989 when Judy Bell first began milking sheep her farming neighbours thought she was mad. It was an allergy to cow's milk that inspired her interest in making sheep's milk cheese and early experiments soon outgrew the farmhouse kitchen leading to a purpose-built creamery on the farm. Today, Shepherd's Purse is in the top flight of Yorkshire cheesemaking. Les Lambert, lifelong Wensleydale cheesemaker at Coverham and Kirkby Malzeard Dairies, was Judy Bell's guru. He helped her develop Olde Yorke as her first saleable cheese and after only three months in production it took first prize at the prestigious Nantwich International Cheese Show. In the next two years Les Lambert encouraged Judy to produce her Yorkshire Blue but sadly he died before it was in full production. This pasteurised ewe's milk blue, made in traditional open vats, matured for 12 weeks, then muslin wrapped, might well have been recognisable to the original cheesemaking monks of Jervaulx. Now there is constant demand for this wonderfully mellow and creamy cheese. Judy Bell has since gone on to produce an alternative Yorkshire Blue using cow's milk, a welcome addition to her stable of seven distinguished farmhouse cheeses. All Shepherd's Purse cheeses are made with vegetarian rennet and most have wax coatings which Judy acknowledges are not perfect but provide an acceptable compromise giving the cheese a shelf-life of eight weeks. Other distinctive cheeses from Shepherd's Purse include Yorkshire Feta – salty and slightly acid; Yorkshire Lowlands Farmhouse – a hard pressed ewe's milk; Herriot Farmhouse – a mature, semi-hard ewe's milk cheese with a rough, grey rind; Farmhouse Wensleydale – semi-hard ewe's milk, made to a traditional recipe. Mail order available.

Leachfield Grange, Newsham,
Nr. Thirsk, N. Yorks
☎ 01845 587220
Open: Mon-Fri 9am-5pm
Please 'phone ahead at weekends

CHEESEMAKING COURSES

Reaseheath College of Nantwich, Cheshire run a two week cheesemaking course aimed at small-scale producers. They also run short courses on butter, ice cream and yoghurt production.
The Cheese & Dairy Department, Reaseheath College, Reaseheath, Nantwich, Cheshire ☎ 01270 625131

NEWTON-LE-WILLOWS

Fortmayne Dairy

Suzanne Stirke is one of Yorkshire's most distinctive independent cheesemakers boasting a classic farmhouse Wensleydale as well as her own brand Yorvik and Jervaulx cheeses. Her widely acclaimed King Richard III Wensleydale came from the discovery of her grandmother's long lost cheesemaking notes and recipes. From these Suzanne developed a very creamy, soft cheese with unpasteurised milk from a neighbour's herd: 'Older people love it. They tell me it's how their mothers made it before the war.' Muslin wrapped and matured for two to three weeks, it's a moist cheese with an open texture that should be eaten young. The Fortmayne Dairy story is a microcosm of the fall and rise of farmhouse cheese around the Dales. Suzanne's grandmother was a typical small scale cheesemaker of her generation but the family gave up the back-aching seven day a week toil of turning milk into cheese once the Milk Marketing Board guaranteed decent prices for their milk. 'I believe cheesemaking goes hand in hand with poverty', says Suzanne. 'The recession and the difficulties in farming have led people to look for different ways of making a living.' So she turned to cheese in 1987 to supplement the income of the family arable farm. The lost generation has been reclaimed and poverty hopefully averted. Suzanne Stirke's Fortmayne Dairy cheeses are available from numerous shops and delicatessens or direct from the farm. She also gives talks and cheesemaking demonstrations to interested groups.

Newton-le-Willows,
Bedale, N. Yorks
☎ 01677 450660
Open: Mon-Sun all reasonable
hours. Please 'phone ahead

RICHMOND

Swaledale Cheese Co.

Swaledale is another traditional Yorkshire cheese that all but died out after the war only to be saved from extinction by a handful of dedicated cheesemakers. Today's Swaledale is made commercially not on a farm but in the more prosaic setting of a trading estate in Richmond. David and Mandy Reed are the country's sole producer of Swaledale cheese. Their full-fat semi-soft cheese has a waxed or natural rind, a moist creamy texture and an impeccable pedigree, the recipe having been passed to David Reed from Mrs Langstaff at Deer Park above Reeth in the heart of the dale. She is credited as the cheesemaker who kept Swaledale cheese going when it had all but disappeared or gone underground. David Reed, a former chef at the **Black Bull**, Moulton, was sometimes sent to collect the cheeses from Mrs Langstaff's farm and in 1984 he set out to teach himself cheesemaking. 'I read every book I could find and then I went with my notebook to see Mrs Langstaff and took down everything she said.' Back in his kitchen, he experimented with five gallons of milk from a friendly farmer and then organised tastings. 'When we found one that got the thumbs up – that was it, we went into production.' For the first 18 months the Reeds used unpasteurised milk but production problems forced them to pasteurise: 'Unless you have a hun-

dred per cent control over the milk it's the only way.' The Swaledale Cheese Company now produce a ton of cheese per week, distributed throughout Yorkshire, Humberside and most of the UK. They make a cow's milk, a ewe's milk and, as a result of their custodianship of the dairy at Beamish Museum in County Durham, they now make a Beamish cheese. The Reed's demonstrate traditional cheesemaking on four days a week at Beamish, using an 80 gallon vat dating back to 1913.

Mercury Road, Gallowfields,
Richmond, N. Yorks
☎ 01748 824932
Not open to the public

THORNER

Intake Lane Goat Herd

It began with one goat to keep down the grass of a suburban garden and grew into 50 head of Saanen, Alpine and Toggenberg goats, two calves, a large billy goat, a few geese and two decorative peacocks. Cheesemaker Connie Seipp not only cares for her animals single-handed but successfully makes and markets good goat's cheese: a white pasteurised, Coulommiers-style cheese and a mature pressed cheese. Cheese, milk and yoghurt is available direct from the farm and cheese is stocked by **Beano's** and **Grain of Sense** in Leeds.

Intake Farm, Intake Lane,
Thorner, Nr. Leeds, W. Yorks
☎ 0113 289 2483
Open: by appointment

THE BLACK SNAIL

Animal rennet, used to coagulate milk for cheesemaking, comes from enzymes in a calf's stomach. Two centuries ago, Yorkshire cheesemakers would hang the dried and salted stomach on a nail in the kitchen, where a piece could be cut off and boiled with the milk as it was needed. If they ran out of rennet, a black snail submerged in a bowl of milk had the same effect.

CHEESEMONGERS

BINGLEY

Priestley's

A standard market cheese stall which spreads its wings from Heckmondwike to Settle but among its range of 45 cheeses it is well worth discovering four different award-winning Lancashire cheeses: mild, creamy, tasty or strong from Rhodes of Carron Lodge, near Preston.

Bingley Market, Wed & Fri
Hebden Bridge Market, Thur
Heckmondwike Market, Sat
Settle Market, Tue
Skipton Market Mon, Wed, Fri,
Sat

BOROUGHBRIDGE

Cheese & Co

Former estate agent Diana Kidd opened her fresh blue and white delicatessen and wine store in 1992 to plug an obvious gap in Boroughbridge. She stocks local cheeses from **Fountains Dairy**, the **Swaledale Cheese Company** and a good selection from **Shepherd's Purse** including their useful Yorkshire feta. There is also fresh Parmesan and a solid array of French cheeses such as Roquefort, Vignotte, Brie and Camembert. Other lines include fresh oat and grain bread and Belgian chocolates and truffles.

27 High Street,
Boroughbridge, N. Yorks
☎ 01423 323037
Open: Mon-Fri 9am-5pm
Sat 9am-4pm

BRIGHOUSE

Czerwik's

Tom Czerwik's well-stocked store has plenty of delicatessen treats but it's his cheese counter, with 140 different cheeses running the length of the shop, that distinguishes it. There is a credit-able continental choice but the British Isles selection stands out with Mrs Cross's **Cotherstone**, Mrs Appleby's Cheshire, Wensleydale from the Hawes Creamery, Cornish Yarg, Inverloch ewe's milk cheese, Isle of Mull Cheddar and Cooleeney, an Irish Camembert. Note the Lanark Blue, a Scottish version of Roquefort made by the celebrated cheesemaker Humphrey Errington. Don't leave without visiting the dramatic vaulted cellar that is stuffed with fine wine, port, cigars and the fanciest priced malt whiskies this side of the auction room.

82 Commercial Street,
Brighouse, W. Yorks
☎ 01484 720912
Open: Mon 9am-5.30pm
Tue 9am-1pm
Wed-Fri 9am-8pm
Sat 9am-5.30pm

EASINGWOLD

Bates Cheese Stall

The star of the handful of food stalls at the tiny market that huddles every Friday around Easingwold's Buttercross is Sandra Bates' cheese stall. It is popular and deservedly so. Sandra has been standing on Easingwold market for 16 years and she has built up a vast range both here and at Thirsk market, including most of the Yorkshire cheeses and a broad and enterprising selection of continentals like Norwegian Jarlsberg, Mozzarella, Danish Havarti and Esrom, Camembert, Gorgonzola and the mild blue Mycella. The apparent block of brown fudge is the remarkable Norwegian Gjetost, whose natural sweetness comes from the caramelisation of sugars in the milk.

Easingwold Market, Fri
Thirsk Market, Sat

GRIMSBY

The Larder

Side by side in Bethlehem Street can be found the best double act in town: starring The Larder and **Pettit's**, Grimsby's top butcher. The Larder's counter displays 50 different English and continental cheeses. They keep Blue Stilton from Long Clawson's dairy and two quality Cheddars: Horlick's extra mature and Quicke's farmhouse. There is a creditable delicatessen counter, quality tea and a popular coffee they roast themselves. In a sensible *quid pro quo* Pettit's prize-winning sausages are served in The Larder's coffee shop and customers at the butcher's are sent next door for their cheese.

39 Bethlehem Street,
Grimsby, S. Humbs
☎ 01472 361867
Open: Mon-Sat 9am-5pm

GUISBOROUGH

The Cheeseman

With his straw boater and a caravan replete with Georgian bow window, The Cheeseman is an unmistakeable stalwart of the North Yorkshire markets at Guisborough, Leyburn and Northallerton. He is Don Morrison from Coverdale, a cheese vendor for 22 years, whose stall now stocks around 150 different cheeses. Continentals include Pecorino, Parmesan, Gruyere, Vignotte and St. Agur. Closer to home are North Yorkshire's own cheeses: Ribblesdale, Swaledale, Cotherstone, various Wensleydales and Don also stocks a good Lancashire from the Trough of Bowland.

Guisborough Market, Thur
Leyburn Market, Fri
Northallerton Market,
Wed & Sat

HARROGATE

The Cheeseboard

Under the Corp family, this pocket-sized store had queues spilling into Commercial Street and a deserved reputation as the best cheese shop in Yorkshire. Diana Warneken, who bought the shop in 1992 with no previous experience apart from a love of cheese, has done well to maintain its exacting standards. Cheese-lovers of Yorkshire will be mightily relieved. Start outside (as you may have to) with the shop window for the best view of beautifully laid out and labelled cheeses, if awkward to remember once inside. Air conditioning keeps the shop at a chilly 7° C and the staff deserve medals for putting up with the cold, wrapped in scarves and sweaters, and staying cheerful as they serve. All for the sake of good cheese. But what cheese! Packed into a few square feet are some 120 different cheeses almost certainly in superb condition and of excellent quality and character. The British parade is a well judged cross-section of the modern improvement in regional cheeses from Cornwall, Wales, the Midlands, Lancashire and Yorkshire; from goat's, sheep and cow's milk; from dedicated herds, pasteurised and unpasteurised. The best of the Dales farmhouse cheeses are all here. There's the creamy Colston Bassett and Long Clawson Stiltons, the wonderfully soft Pencarreg Welsh Brie, Derby, Leicester and Gloucester. Internationally,

there's Brie de Meaux, Milleens from County Cork, authentic Parmigiano-Reggiano and aged Pecorino Sarda. Other treats include quail's eggs, dried porcini, Serrano ham and Spanish chorizo but the cheese is and should continue to be the magnet.

1 Commercial Street,
Harrogate, N. Yorks
☎ *01423 508837*
Open: Mon-Fri 9am-5.30pm
Sat 9am-5pm

HEBDEN BRIDGE

Priestley's

See Bingley entry.

Hebden Bridge Market, Thur

HECKMONDWIKE

Priestley's

See Bingley entry.

Heckmondwike Market, Sat

ILKLEY

Burrell's

Andrew Leggott keeps a good range of English and continental cheese, including David Reed's plain and smoked Swaledale and **Shepherd's Purse** Yorkshire Blue. Although this old fashioned little shop is known principally for its cheese, it also stocks select groceries and wholefoods. Hunza apricots and Lexia raisins are sold from attractive wooden boxes. Nuts, pumpkin seeds and pine kernels are stored in baskets.

37 Brook Street, Ilkley, W. Yorks
☎ *01943 608769*
Open: Mon-Sat 9am-5.30pm

KNARESBOROUGH

Farm Dairy

This 17th century shop on the Market Square is a powerful contender for Yorkshire's best cheeseboard. There's an outstanding British selection, lovingly kept. The labelling is genuinely informative. The shop is always alive with competitions and cheese tastings. The owners really know their stuff. Lisa and Mark Wilson hold the advanced level diploma of the U.K. Cheese Guild, along with only 50 others. They are expert enough to be maturing cheeses themselves (in the cellar of a nearby gents' outfitters). 'There was red cheese and there was white cheese when we took over the shop', says Lisa Wilson. Eight years on, Farm Dairy goes from strength to strength with English farmhouse cheeses their speciality. The Wilson's search out small-scale cheesemakers who produce character cheeses by traditional methods. Their range is fascinating: there's a nettle wrapped Cornish Yarg, Devon Oke from Curworthy, Irish Cashel Blue from Fethard in County Tipperary and Gubbeen from County Cork. They keep at least three or four different Cheddars but Mrs Keen's from Somerset excels, a traditional unpasteurised cheese with a smooth, clean, grassy flavour. Lancashire cheese produced anywhere outside the large scale creameries is rare but the Wilsons buy Mrs Kirkham's farmhouse Lancashire, still made by traditional methods to produce a superb, crumbly, moist cheese. French cheeses are selected from a group of handmade, farmhouse cheeses stocked usually in the summer months when, according to Lisa Wilson, the cows have been fed on sweet green grass and the milk is of superior quality. For matchless flavour there is an unpasteurised Brie de Meaux which took first

---

BUYING CHEESE

*Only a handful of shops and market stalls in this chapter are exclusively devoted to cheese. The majority also stock a wide and interesting range of delicatessen. They are included here because they have particularly good cheese counters, some of them outstanding. Similarly, the **Delicatessen & Grocers** chapter includes many shops with expertly kept cheese counters.*

prize at London's International Cheese Show. The Farm Dairy is a strong supporter, too, of Yorkshire's best cheesemakers. The delicatessen counter shows imagination with their own roast beef, smoked salmon paté and salads. Fresh olives come with lemon and garlic or Provençal herbs.

3 Market Square,
Knaresborough, N. Yorks
☎ *01423 865027.*
Open: Mon-Fri 9am-5pm
Sat 8.30am-5pm

LEYBURN

The Cheeseman
See Guisborough entry.

Leyburn Market, Fri

NORTHALLERTON

The Cheeseman
See Guisborough entry.

Northallerton Market,
Wed & Sat

OTLEY

Baines Cheese Van
Soft oatcakes – lovely, floppy and slipper-shaped – used to be such a commonplace accompaniment to Yorkshire cheese that they were completely unremarkable, other than as a constant refrain in the history of plain Yorkshire food. Today, they still go beautifully with all sorts of cheeses but are a surprisingly rare find. Baines Cheese Van is the source, plying at Wetherby

and Otley markets. Apart from the precious soft oatcakes Baines keeps a standard range of cheeses and **Ashdale** goat's cheese from Val Morris whose goats are reared at nearby Askwith. It is appropriate that her cheese is sold here as Otley market, dating back to 1222, surrounds the Buttercross where local dairy farmers used to sell their produce. Today it survives as a shelter for weary shoppers.

Otley Market, Fri & Sat
Wetherby Market, Thur

RIPON

Ian Holmes Cheese Van
Ian Holmes sells straightforward local and continental cheeses from a caravan on Ripon market.

Market Square, Ripon, N. Yorks
Thur & Sat

SCARBOROUGH

The Cheese Board
Over six years, Kevin Patton and Ray Birch have brought to Scarborough a delightful and discriminating range of cheese, wine and tip-top delicatessen. The wealth of character cheeses is clearly informed by Kevin Patton's career in the food trade, latterly with the grandee of London cheesemongers, Paxton & Whitfield. Spanish Manchego and Picos Blue are rare finds. There is a matured Old Amsterdam, which Kevin describes as 'a bit like Parmesan.' From elsewhere in

Europe come Norwegian Jarlsberg and Swiss Tilsiter. Their best Brie and Camembert is unpasteurised and sold in peak condition. 'Whenever we get unpasteurised cheeses', says Kevin, 'they go immediately.' His enthusiasm for good food came from watching his grandmother cook back home in Armagh and a broad Irish influence is apparent: Milleens, Irish Cheddar and Cashel Blue are all here. English territorial cheeses are represented by Quickes' 12 month and 18 month unpasteurised Cheddars from Devon, Long Clawson's Blue Stilton, an unpasteurised Red Leicester, and the Coverdale, Cotherstone and Wensleydale cheeses of Yorkshire. The delicatessen counter has good smoked Westphalia ham, Parma ham, authentic Spanish chorizo and saucisson d'Arles. Cervalat, Milano, Danish, herb or pepper are just a few of the salamis. A blue and white pottery urn on the counter hides Italian wild cherries in syrup. Ray Birch, a former full-time wine buyer, continues to expand the wine department.

21 Victoria Road,
Scarborough, N. Yorks
☎ *01723 374527*
Open: Mon-Sat 8.30am-6pm
Wed 8.30am-1pm

SETTLE

Market Pantry
A tourist front could put off the serious cheese hunter from finding this intelligent counter and its knowledgeable proprietors. Elsa and Richard Pollard sold the Market Pantry in Skipton to concentrate their energies in this Settle shop of the same name where they are quietly building a reputable range. Least familiar of the north country cheeses will probably be the Northumberland, a rich cow's milk cheese made approximately to a Gouda recipe, and Redesdale, a full fat pasteurised sheep's milk, both from

---

CHATSWORTH FARM SHOP

The Farm Shop at Chatsworth (entry p120) run by the Duchess of Devonshire has one of the best cheese counters in the region. There are 70 different Irish and English cheeses, many farm-produced and unpasteurised. The estate farms also supply milk for cream, yoghurt and ice cream from the Duchess' prize Jacob sheep.
Stud Farm, Pilsley, Nr. Bakewell, Derbyshire
☎ **01246 583392 Open: April-October Mon-Sat 9am-5.30pm. November-March 9am-5pm Sun 11am-5pm Every Tues opens 9.30am**

Mark Robertson's Redesdale Dairy at Otterburn. All the main Yorkshire cheeses are here, with pride of place for the local cheesemaker, Iain Hill, whose excellent cow and ewe's milk farmhouse cheeses are made just a few miles up Ribblesdale at Ashes Farm. All the cheeses in the shop are available by mail order.

Market Square,
Settle, N. Yorks
☎ *01729 823355*
Open: Mon-Sat 9am-5.30pm
Sun in summer

Priestley's
See Bingley entry.

Settle Market, Tue

SHEFFIELD

Silver Hill Dairy
Silver Hill Dairy was once a delicatessen with a strong hand in cheese. Now, through popular demand, it is dominated by cheese and the counter runs the length of the shop, air conditioned courtesy of the prize money earned by its award winning window display. You won't find a much better stronghold of cheese in the region: Silver Hill is in the very top drawer and Suzanne Hill is a profoundly learned owner, a member of the Specialist Cheesemakers Association, a cheese show judge, a repository of knowledge for food writers but best of all generous with friendly and enthusiastic

advice to her customers (and with well informed staff, too). Her cool, fresh shop attracts pilgrimages from far afield to its exhaustive selection of cheeses featuring 150 British, Irish and continental varieties. A few are mass-produced but Silver Hill's heart lies unmistakeably with its artisan cheeses, many of them exquisite, traditional and unpasteurised, including most of the Yorkshire classics. One visit might see a promotion of Swiss cheeses, another might unearth an acid and crumbly Lancashire from across the border. The place is alive. There is always a reduced price 'cheese of the week' and Suzanne boasts at least one new cheese to taste every week. 'If it sells, we keep it. If not, we don't order it again for a while but then we will usually try again after a few months to see if tastes have changed.' Despite the multiple temptations, Cheddar remains enduringly the best seller. In response, Suzanne offers six different varieties and, if asked, will direct customers towards Quickes mature unpasteurised from Devon.

105 Ecclesall Road South,
Sheffield, S. Yorks
☎ *0114 236 3628*
Open: Mon-Fri 9am-5.30pm
Sat 8.30am-5.30pm

Top Farm Cheese Shop
A big cheese counter with a fast turnover in Meadowhall's massive shopping arena. It has a fair-

ly standard range of English and continentals and a range of salami and pastrami.

Meadowhall Shopping Centre,
Sheffield, S. Yorks
☎ *0114 256 8548*
Open: Mon-Thur 9am-8pm
Fri 9am-9pm Sat 8am-7pm
Sun 9am-4pm

SKIPTON

The Cheese Stall
It's well worth venturing among the cheap vests and plastic flower stalls of Skipton's Black Horse Market to find Janice Edmundson's well stocked cheese stall. Yorkshire cheeses sell well and sales of Wensleydale have picked up since the **Wensleydale Creamery** debacle was settled. 'People refused to buy Wensleydale cheese made in Lancashire', says Janice. Ironically, her best selling cheese is a strong Lancashire from Singleton's Dairy at Longridge, near Preston, but now this, too, is due for closure. Unfortunately, the latest hygiene regulations mean that she can no longer sell soft cheeses such as Brie and Vignotte which have to be refrigerated. As no such facilities exist in this little market, which is refrigeratingly cold in winter and only marginally warmer in summer, it is a sad loss to the cheese lovers of Skipton. Her own home-made cakes, jams and pickles may well serve as compensation.

Black Horse Market,
High Street, Skipton, N. Yorks
Open: Mon, Wed, Thur, Fri
9am-4pm Sat 9am-4.30pm

Priestley's
See Bingley entry.

Skipton Market , Mon, Wed, Fri,
Sat

THIRSK

Bates Cheese Stall
See Easingwold entry.

Thirsk Market, Sat

CHEESE LOVERS CLUB

*Lovers of good cheese in South Yorkshire can indulge their passion and learn about cheese at the same time by joining the Cheese Lovers Club run by **Silver Hill Dairy** (see above). It is organised by cheese expert and owner of the Dairy, Suzanne Hill. The annual subscription of £18 is, she reckons, soon recovered through discounts on cheese from the shop. Members and their guests meet twice a year for talks from visiting cheese experts, tastings, fondues, and visits to local dairies to watch cheesemakers at work.*

TODMORDEN

The Crumbly Cheese

This otherwise unprepossessing
cheese stall in Todmorden's Victorian Market Hall sells a stunning Lancashire. Moist and buttery, it is an assured best seller,
worthy of praise and promotion.
But this is a knotty problem because nobody at The Crumbly
Cheese will divulge the source
its name or particulars. Pasteurised or unpasteurised? From a
farm or a creamery? From the
milk of one herd or many? The
secrecy is imposed from on high.
The owner, Mr Hodson, flatly
refuses to name his supplier for
fear of competition. So, the mystery of a fine Lancashire cheese
goes unresolved. An added treat
are traditional soft oatcakes, a
fitting accompaniment to a fine
but never-to-be-famous cheese.

*Market Hall, Todmorden, Lancs
Open: Wed-Sat 9am-5pm*

WETHERBY

Baines Cheese Van

See Otley entry.

Wetherby Market, Thurs

YORK

The Food Emporium

Brother David is a unique cheese
that begins life as a crumbly
Kirkham's Lancashire and is
then matured and rind washed in
Kentish cider by cheese *affineur*
James Aldridge. The result – an
unusual and distinctive piquant
character cheese. Supplies are
irregular but it can be found,

along with all the Dales cheeses,
in the Food Emporium, a small
shop in an attractive Georgian
terrace.

*25a Front Street, Acomb, York
☎ 01904 781993
Open: Mon-Sat 8.30am-5.30pm*

York Beer Shop

Yes, this is a beer shop in a dairy
chapter and an excellent one to
boot, where Jim Helsby and Eric
Boyd stock 250 different bottled
beers, but they have a second
specialism in a small but exquisite range of well kept farmhouse
cheeses, many unpasteurised and
none of them block. Jim is a
knowledgeable and entertaining
guide of his counter: Mrs Keen's
unpasteurised farmhouse cheddar
from Wincanton in Somerset;
Mrs Appleby's Cheshire, actually made in Shropshire but to an
original recipe, clothbound, with
a crumbly but moist texture.
There is an unpasteurised Red
Leicester, a farmhouse Caerphilly, a ewe's milk Berkswell and a
mature Old Amsterdam. But the
prize find is the strong, creamy
Cabrales Queso Azul, a blue
veined cheese made with a blend
of cow, goat and ewe's milk
which Jim found on holiday in
the Picos de Europa mountains in
Northern Spain and which he
rates higher than Gorgonzola,
going to inordinate lengths to
locate a supply. Cabrales is made
to a centuries old recipe in the
Asturias and Santander mountains in the Cantabria region, matured in the caves that litter the
hillsides and then wrapped in
sycamore or maple leaves. True

believers will leave it for six
months until it is 'con gusanos'
(running with maggots). Northern cheeses are well represented
by Cotherstone, Coverdale,
Swaledale, smoked Wensleydale
and many more. Wash them
down with beer from every continent; wild yeast beers; smoked
German beers, Belgian monastery beers; stone-brewed beers;
Black Sheep, brewed by Paul
Theakston in Masham and
Hunslet's Old Fart, doubtless
your man for maggot flushing.
There are artisan ciders and English and organic wines. A splendid shop.

*28 Sandringham Street,
Fishergate, York
☎ 01904 647136
Open: Mon 4.15pm-10pm
Tue-Fri 11am-10pm
Sat 10am-10pm
Sun 12 noon-2pm & 7pm-10pm*

--- WHANGBY ---

*'The best produce was excellent, but the worst was poor.
Much butter, rancid and uneatable, went for salving
sheep, and old or skim milk cheese made in Wensleydale,
where it was called old peg cheese, or Whangby cheese
made in Wharfedale, was hard and tough – tough enough
to make whangs (thongs) of it'.*

Marie Hartley and Joan Ingilby
Life and Tradition in the Yorkshire Dales, 1968

ICE CREAM

CONONLEY

Yorkshire Dales Creamery

Tim Wilson's grandmother used to have a little shop in Keighley where she made 'proper' ice cream with butter, sugar, milk, eggs and cream. That was before ice cream began sounding and tasting like paint with its emulsified and stabilised concoctions, before the laboratory replaced the dairy. Grandmother Wilson's traditional version, however, was the idea behind Tim's thriving modern operation set up in 1984 at Cononley, two miles outside Skipton. Yorkshire Dales' increasingly familiar tubs and cartons are found widely in shops and delicatessens through–out the region and further afield, including Harrods and Selfridge's. The dairy ice cream comes with the promise of no artificial colouring, preservative or flavouring. Here, ice lollies boast no artificial sweeteners but take their flavours solely from natural fruit juices. They come in three flavours: orange and passion fruit, blackcurrant and apple, lemon and lime. There are also old fashioned milk lollies, dark continental chocolate coated ices on sticks and fruit sorbets. The flagship dairy ice cream comes in various quantities and varieties: natural, vanilla, strawberry, chocolate, hazelnut, black cherry, coffee and orange and passion fruit. Also sold at the cremery counter.

Aireside Mills, Cononley,
Keighley, W. Yorks
☎ *01535 636644*
Open: Mon-Fri 9am-4pm

HIBALDSTOW

Sargent's Dairy Ice Cream

This is windmill and Roman Road country in the furthest reaches of South Humberside, where the Sargent family have been making their full cream milk ice cream to the same recipe since 1922. Apart from their local fleet of ice-cream vans, the family sell it from a modern ice cream parlour at their home in Hibaldstow. The slide and trampoline in the garden constitute somewhat of a tourist attraction in these quiet parts.

Hibaldstow, S. Humbs
☎ *01652 654339*
Open: Mon-Sun 10am-6pm

ALTERNATIVE ICE CREAMS

*Vegans and children with allergies to dairy produce frequently miss out on all the fun of ice cream. They can snap back at **Alligator**, Fishergate, York ☎ 01904 654525, York's oldest wholefood shop, with its supply of soya based non-dairy ice cream and choc ices. Sheep and goat's milk is often tolerated when cow's milk is not. A wonderfully creamy sheep's milk ice cream is available from Judy Bell who makes **Shepherd's Purse** cheeses at Leachfield Grange, Newsham, near Thirsk ☎ 01845 587220 and from Carol and David Clark who run The Big Sheep and Little Cow Museum at Aiskew Watermill, near Bedale ☎ 01677 422125. To make your own, fresh goat's milk is available from **Ashdale Cheeses** at Town Head Farm, Askwith ☎ 01943 469504 and from **Intake Lane Goat Herd**, Thorner ☎ 0113 289 2483*

MASHAM

Brymor Ice Cream Parlour

The story of Brian Moore's struggle to make and sell real dairy ice cream from his farm in Weeton is a bloody-minded Yorkshire classic. Six years of increasingly publicised conflict with his neighbours went to the heart of what a village in the country is supposed to be. It all began in 1984 when there was virtually no real ice cream on the market. Brian Moore's ice cream, made with the rich creamy milk from his Guernsey herd, was an instant success. The pleasant drive out to Weeton, situated between Leeds and Harrogate, for a tub of Brymor became a popular Sunday outing. Brian Moore had found a use for his surplus milk and his customers were enjoying the first decent ice cream they'd tasted in years. Everyone should have been happy. Not, however, his neighbours in Weeton. Weeton might be a village and it might be in the country but nobody could mistake its commuter elite for working farmers. They complained about the cars blocking the road, so Moore built a car park. They complained next about the noise and the litter as Moore continued to defend his right to make and sell ice cream. Finally, in 1990, the High Court ruled that while Brian Moore could continue to make his ice cream at the farm he could no longer sell it direct to the public. After six long years of hassle Brian Moore had won a battle but the ruling meant he would lose the Weeton war. He struggled on for two more years, selling to wholesalers and retailers, but by now there were more ice creams on the market. He needed to run an ice cream parlour again. In 1992, he gave up the unequal contest at Weeton and bought High Jervaulx Farm, near Masham, so that h2e could once again manufacture and sell direct from his farm. It was an expensive but successful move. The ice cream parlour is in full swing; there are farm tours, factory visits and the full range of 30 Brymor flavours on sale. Vanilla, hazelnut and dark chocolate are the best sellers. There's no substitute for putting your own fresh fruit into your own home-made ice cream but this is as good as commercial ice cream tastes in Yorkshire. Brymor at Jervaulx has a smaller catchment population than Weeton but, along with **Yorkshire Dales Creamery**, it is the most reliable independent brand to search out in shop, delicatessen and selected supermarkets. Always in search of new flavours, Brian Moore recently went on an ice cream study tour of the United States, visiting eleven scooping parlours

from Boston to Buffalo. Back at Jervaulx he went on to develop the 'Big Country Range'. Super Gold takes the top prize for its heady mixture of honey, brittle-toffee and peanuts. Not all Brian Moore's flavours have been a success, however: 'We made a popcorn ice cream one summer. It was awful. We had to throw it all away.' For anyone willing to pay for a full batch (20 litres), Brian Moore will make up any flavours on request. He's made sorbets of jasmine tea, apple and cinnamon, lemon and ginger, and champagne and only drew the line at a Bloody Mary sorbet when the customer refused to take a whole batch. Visitors are always welcome at High Jervaulx. Brian Moore is such an irrepressible salesman he'd probably even embrace a coach load from Weeton.

High Jervaulx Farm,
Masham, N. Yorks
☎ *01677 460377*
Open: Mon-Sun 10am-6pm

SNEATON

Beacon Farm Ice Cream Parlour & Tea Rooms

If a day out in Whitby doesn't deliver an ice-cream overdose, stop on the way home for a Beacon Farm ice cream, a cut above the seaside average. The Shardlow family diversified into ice cream and yoghurt production after 35 years of conventional dairy farming. They use milk and cream from their own herd to make 30 different flavours of dairy ice cream: flavours include coconut, toffee, forest fruit or honey and nut. There's a tea room in an old cow-byre and cartons to take away, Pick Your Own soft fruit in summer and a Beacon Farm ice-cream van sits on the beach with the donkeys at Robin Hood's Bay.

Sneaton, Whitby, N. Yorks
☎ *01947 605212*
Open: summer Mon-Sun
10am-6pm winter 10pm-5pm
Pick-Your-Own 10am-8pm

YOGHURT

*Low-fat, luxury, Greek style, Swiss style, even toffee. There is a plethora of yoghurts in the supermarket cabinets and it remains the fastest growing sector of the dairy industry. Despite the addition of emulsifiers, stabilisers, fruit pulp and sugar, yoghurt has managed to hang on to its healthy image. It's a reputation that dates back to 1908 when a Russian scientist Ilya Metchnikoff published 'The Prolongation of Life', in which he attributed the good health and longevity of Bulgarian peasants to the large amount of yoghurt in their diet. Yoghurt is the curdled milk produced by the addition of two bacilli, lactobacillus bulgaricus and streptococcus thermophilis which ferment the lactic acid in milk making it thick and slightly acid. There are claims that the bio-yoghurts help to balance the flora in the digestive system. They are made with different bacilli bifidobacterium and lactobacillus acidophilus. Both types of yoghurt are known as 'live' in that they contain bacteria but the addition of emulsifiers and stabilisers, low temperature storage and sometimes a second pasteurisation all for the benefit of a longer shelf life, has emasculated most of them, Locally produced yoghurt has proved uneconomic for most dairy farmers and cheesemakers faced with competition from giants like St Ivel and Eden Vale. Notable exceptions are **Botton Village Creamery** at Danby who make organic full and low-fat yoghurt from the milk of their own dairy shorthorn herd, **Beacon Farm** at Sneaton who make a plain yoghurt and **Longley Farm Dairy**, Holmfirth whose award-winning yoghurt is available across the region. Yoghurt has been an integral part of the Indian, near and middle eastern diets for centuries, used as a marinade, in soups, as a drink and to soothe the fieriness of a curry. Excellent live yoghurt is available from many of the Asian shops in the region. One of the biggest producers is **Aire Valley Yoghurt** ☎ 01274 731433 of Bradford whose creamy, fresh and sharp yoghurt is also one of the best.*

EGGS

In the last century, eggs from guillemots, razorbills, fulmars and kittiwakes were all collected from the cliffs at Flamborough and Bempton. It was a precarious and nerve-racking operation involving a system of ropes and pulleys and an egg collector who, secured by a rope, stepped backwards over the cliff to the nesting sites. Some discarded gull eggs for their bitterness but the rest were sold to markets in Bridlington and Leeds where guillemot and razorbill eggs were baked into a custard known as sea-bird pie. Sea bird eggs are not to our taste today but duck, goose and hen eggs are widely available on Yorkshire and Humberside markets. Quail's eggs are an increasingly common find in the delicatessen, courtesy of battery production.

Free range hens do not always, as we may fondly imagine, spend their day pecking around the farmyard but are reared in large flocks of 1,000 birds per hectare. The only requirement is that the flock has *access* to vegetation. In a large flock this can mean that different groups may be outside at different times and inevitably some never get out at all. Free range eggs can cost up to twice as much battery eggs. They are liable to be much cheaper from the region's markets but are more likely to come from large flocks.

Barn and deep litter eggs are a halfway house between battery and free-range. The hens are not caged but remain indoors and flock density is still high. Deep litter hens are able to roam the hen house on a suitable base of straw or wood shavings at a rate of seven birds per square metre. Barn hens are kept at a higher density, 25 birds per square metre, but they are provided with perches for greater freedom of movement.

Vegetarian eggs were marketed in response to the salmonella scare of 1989, when the public became aware that some chickens were fed the recycled remains of other animals. The vegetarian egg is produced by barn-reared hens fed on a diet of wheat, barley, maize and oats. They were stocked by the major supermarkets but as the salmonella scare diminishes they are increasingly hard to find.

A bright yellow yolk is no indication of a good egg. In days when hens were genuinely free-range, the colour of the egg yolk would vary with the seasons. Today, feed merchants offer the farmer the poultry equivalent of a paint chart from which they can select the exact shade of yellow they require.

While egg production still has a long way to go, vegetarian, deep litter, barn, and free range eggs are still a better alternative to battery eggs for anyone concerned about animal husbandry. Genuinely free range eggs are available from farms and wholefood shops throughout the region. Peter Cochrane at **Dunnington Lodge,** Elvington Lane, Dunnington near York ☎ **01904 608702** (open: Mon-Sun 9am-5pm. Please 'phone ahead) sells what he describes as: 'Proper free range eggs from hens that do actually roam about.' Peter Cochrane is a member of the Association of Organic Farmers and Growers.

Mrs Husband at **Lodge Farm**, High Catton, York ☎ **01759 371246** (open: Mon-Fri 9am-5pm) sells genuine free-range eggs direct from the farm or from her Saturday stall on York's Jubbergate Market. She has the full range from the largest (size 1) to the smallest (size 7). She also uses her eggs in the cakes she bakes for the stall – sponges, fruit cake, carrot cake, date and walnut loaf, Dundee cake, buns and pastries. She also supplies old hens that have stopped laying for soups and stews.

5

Baking

Yorkshire baking has its roots in the oatcake, the staple of the labourer's diet, baked on a simple bakestone over a basket of hot coals. But it was the arrival of the Yorkshire range in the early 19th century that transformed domestic baking. The cooks and kitchen maids of the wealthy households could now reproduce in their own kitchens the recipes and skills they had learned. This led in turn to the Yorkshire high tea. Originally intended as a light meal to fill the long gap between lunch and dinner, it developed into an ostentatious display of home baking where sandwiches, tarts, custards, sponge cakes, biscuits and tea breads became a source of great pride. Up until the last war, it was not unusual for a day a week to be set aside for baking. Anything bought in was a sure sign of a lazy and slovenly housewife, except perhaps pikelets, muffins and oatcakes from the oatcake man. Thankfully, the tyranny of the baking day has long gone. Now, in-store bakeries offer a vast range of bread and cakes. But the smell of freshly baked bread is largely an illusion. The reality is likely to be factory-made frozen dough baked off in the supermarket. By using the same flour and the same production methods, even the small bakeries produce much the same loaf as the commercial giants. But pockets of excellence do exist. Independent enterprises are producing bread that owes nothing to high-speed baking processes or flour improvers. Traditional oatcakes can still be found on West Riding markets and home-made cakes are regularly snapped up at ever thriving Women's Institute stalls. Whether you crave sour dough Ukrainian rye bread, Jewish matzos, French patisserie, a midnight bagel or organic wholemeal stone-ground flour for home baking, it's all here.

FLOUR & FLOUR MILLS

BARNSLEY

Worsbrough Mill Museum

Barnsley Metropolitan Borough Council might not be the first name that comes to mind when thinking of organic wholemeal stoneground flour but no-one's likely to come across a more politically or environmentally correct flour than that ground at Worsbrough Mill. This 17th century flour mill had been neglected and abandoned until a far sighted council restored it to working order in 1976. Today, it runs as a working industrial museum where visitors can sit by the mill race, watch the seven ton water wheel turning the French burr grindstones and emptying into the river Dove. Worsbrough grinds best West Yorkshire wheat and rye from Fox Farm, Shafton and Wigfield Farm, located on the edge of the park. Both are council owned organic farms. The result is a range of flours from soft white to organic wholemeal, organic bran, semolina and rye. Worsbrough supplies local bakeries large and small. Visitors can buy by the bag or sack from the mill shop. The millers are Garry

Richardson and Andrew Sykes and no mill could be run with more pride and joy than their's. Garry is an ex-teacher who has an infectious enthusiasm and intricate knowledge of milling. Andrew Sykes was a redundant miner. They promise not to introduce the regime of an earlier miller, John Watson, who, in the 1920s, used to fire hard wheat grains from a shotgun at children scrumping fruit. Today, children can safely enjoy a visit to the mill, learn about Barnsley's industrial heritage and at Wigfield Farm, next door, see rare breeds of pig, sheep, cattle and goats and an observation hive of Italian bees. Festivals held throughout the year often include bread-making demonstrations.

Worsbrough Bridge,
Barnsley, S. Yorks
☎ 01226 774527
Open: Wed-Sun 10am to dusk

BEDALE

Crakehall Water Mill

There has been a mill at Crakehall Beck for over 900 years and although nothing remains of the mill mentioned in the Domesday

survey of 1086, the present buildings date from the 17th century. The water wheel was cast at nearby Leeming Bar and it is timelessly impressive to see it in action, the elm blades churning the beck water and turning the millstones gently down the centuries. It was this sense of history that appealed to Peter Townsend who gave up the life of an oil executive to become the miller at Little Crakehall. He uses a mixture of high gluten Canadian wheat and soft English wheat. Ground slowly on French burr stones, it makes good strong wholemeal flour.

Little Crakehall, Nr. Bedale,
N. Yorks
☎ 01677 423240
Open: flour all year round. Mill
visits: Easter-Sep Tue, Wed,
Thur, Sat & Sun 10am-5pm &
Bank Holidays

GREWELTHORPE

Village Craft Flours

There's a green and a duck pond, and a tiny and traditional family flour mill on the main street. It's quaint but it's seriously successful. Joan and Graham Roberts' sales of organic flour went 'off the graph' last year. Top of the range is their wholewheat stoneground flour made from organic English wheat which now proudly displays a Soil Association symbol. 'Flour with nothing added and nothing taken away', says Graham Roberts. However, the government's set-aside scheme means that organic wheat is becoming worryingly scarce. 'Demand is outstripping supply. There are good pockets of English wheat but it is a very variable commodity. All the time you are searching for a high protein, rounded wheat, but it can change from year to year, from

---

FLOUR MILLING

A commercial flour mill can produce hundreds of tons of flour per hour, but the size and the speed of the steel rollers of commercial milling have a different action to the slow turning of traditional millstones. The massive steel rollers, turning at speed, heat up and destroy delicate enzymes in the wheat. The rolling action, too, shears open the wheat berry so that it becomes separated from the bran. In white flour, the bran and wheatgerm is removed and sold off separately and in wholemeal is put back in again. Compare that to the slow turning of two millstones where the wheat is gently crushed and the enzymes are retained. The resulting flour produces bread with a deep, satisfying, full flavour.

farmer to farmer and from crop to crop. Once you've had the best you continue to search for it. Very soon,' he says, tapping a bag of organic flour, 'this will be a rare commodity.' Not all their flour is organic. Village Craft Flours produce 18 different types, using a blend of English and Canadian wheat. It is ground slowly and evenly on Derbyshire peat stones and can be varied between fine, medium and coarse. When his stones became worn, Graham Roberts appealed successfully through the pages of The Dalesman to bring a suitably skilled stone dresser temporarily out of retirement. Despite full order-books and a busy schedule, the Roberts' do take time out to show school children how wheat is turned into flour. Village Craft Flours are available throughout Yorkshire or direct from Thorpe Mill in Grewelthorpe. They also mill flour under the 'Woods' label. Bulk orders of special flours can be discussed with them directly.

Thorpe Mill, Grewelthorpe,
Ripon, N. Yorks
☎ 01765 658534
Open: Mon-Wed 9am-4.30pm
Thur & Fri 9am-12 noon

KIRTON IN LINDSEY

Mount Pleasant Windmill
There were once 700 windmills in Lincolnshire. Now in what became South Humberside there are just three. So there can hardly be a more evocative sight than when the 33 foot sails of the Mount Pleasant Windmill begin to turn, using nothing more than the wind that crosses Lincoln Cliff. Inside, English wheat is gently ground on Derbyshire Grey and French Burr stones. Pat and Jane White found the mill sunk into dereliction after a century of working life. There was an invasion of damp and wood-worm, no cap or sails. With help from English Heritage and

Glanford District Council and the surviving expertise of local mill-wrights, restoration was com-pleted in 1991. Mount Pleasant was again milling stoneground organic English wheat. The flour is fresh and nutty and ideal for breadmaking. Wholemeal and untreated white flour, bran, cracked wheat, wholewheat semolina and rye are all available with the Soil Association symbol in the shop and increasingly through outlets across Yorkshire and Humberside. To further illustrate the versatility of their flour, the White's now have a tea shop serving Jane's delightful cakes: chocolate, date, apricot and walnut, a light wholemeal sponge with raspberry filling, carrot cake, and coffee and walnut. The cakes and tea breads, flapjack, shortbread and scones are all served in a pleasant room opposite the mill.

Kirton in Lindsey, S. Humbs
☎ 01652 640177
Open: Fri 1pm-4pm
Sat, Sun & Bank Holidays
10am-5pm

SHEFFIELD

The Flour Bin
The Flour Bin specialises, natur-ally enough, in flour. What makes it unique in Yorkshire, if not in Britain, is that it brings such dedication and diversity to its specialism. Jim Marsden makes prosaic flour appear posit-ively exotic. Organic wholemeal, strong white and self-raising are familiar to home bakers but what about Cobber, Robema and Grist? There's French flour for bread and brioche, maize, rye and soya flour. In all 24 different flours appear on the Flour Bin roster. Biscuit flour, golden pastry, chapati flour, Hovis and Turog are accompanied by written explanations, behavioural hints and downright orders: 'Do not put any salt into Hovis. It's already in', exclaims one.

'Stoneground needs a touch more water', advises another. What is heartening about the Flour Bin is that such an unlikely shop is thriving, as is the sister stall on Moor Market. All day a stream of customers pass through, confirmation that home breadmaking is flourishing in South Yorkshire. Regulars come every week for a three pound bag of flour and an ounce of barm as yeast is still called in this part of Yorkshire. Jim Marsden sells 120 kilos of yeast a week and his quick turnover ensures that this really is the freshest, sweetest yeast you are likely to find. For tentative newcomers attempting breadmaking for the first time, Jim recommends strong white Canadian flour and gives a recipe for a basic white loaf. The flour for the Flour Bin comes direct from the millers and is weighed into tough brown paper bags then simply stacked on to functional grey metal shelving. 'It is all pro-fessional quality flour used by master bakers', says Jim Marsden, 'and of infinitely better quality than supermarket grades.' An attempt to update with electronic cash tills ended in disaster after flour dust gradually penetrated the delicate workings and they blew up one busy Sat-urday morning. Mechanical scales and cash registers returned to do the job admirably. Besides flour there are grains, pulses, nuts, seeds, dried fruit and what Jim Marsden describes as odds and ends: bicarbonate of soda, oatmeal, rice, semolina, sea salt, cornflour and custard powder. The Flour Bin provides Sheffield's bakers with a privileged and unique service. Long may its star continue to rise.

36 Exchange Street,
Sheffield, S. Yorks
☎ 0114 272 4842
Mon-Sat 8.30am-5pm
Closed Thur
Moor Market: Tue, Fri, Sat

OATCAKES

'A ladleful of batter, first transferred into the basin, was poured on the bakstone and the scraper run over it to spread and control the size and thickness of the cake. Great pride in the shape and size of cake was shown. Very thin and soft after baking, it is rough on one side and smooth on the other. As the steam and roasting smell rose and as one by one the cakes were laid on a white cloth, we felt we were sharing in an age old ritual'.

Marie Hartley & Joan Ingilby, Life & Tradition in the Yorkshire Dales, 1968

Nothing typifies Yorkshire baking more than the humble oatcake. The oats grown on cultivated terraces of the Yorkshire Dales provided the grain staple for peasants of the Middle Ages. While the rich ate meat, the Yorkshire labourer lived on a diet of stiff oatmeal porridge supplemented by eggs, cheese and a few root vegetables. In times of hardship this porridge might be eaten twice a day. Oats continued to be the predominant crop in all three Ridings of Yorkshire well into the 19th century.

Oatcakes, also known variously as havercake, haverbread, riddlebread and clapbread, were of two basic types: a stiff dough rolled out and baked on a bakstone or bakestone until crisp or a batter which was poured or thrown on to the bakestone. The thrown oatcake was the most difficult to make but housewives took great pride in the thinness and the shape of their oatcakes claiming that 'you weren't fit to get married until you could turn a havercake'.

The skill came in handling the soft batter which was transferred from a floured board into a cloth. This had to be lifted and thrown in one deft movement onto the hotplate. After half a minute it could be laid on the bread flake or creel that hung from the rafters, as described by Emily Brontë in *Wuthering Heights*. The warm oatcakes could be eaten with butter and cheese or treacle while still soft or dipped in soup when they had become crisp and dry.

In rural areas 15 dozen oatcakes might be made at haymaking time and barrels of oatcakes accompanied emigrants of the Californian gold rush. The oatcake even became the rallying sign of the 33rd Foot Regiment of Halifax during the American War of Independence when, somewhat bizarrely, an oatcake was impaled on the swords of the recruiting sergeants and they became known as the 'Havercake Lads.

By the mid 19th century home baking had been replaced by public bakers. There were said to be 40 oatcake bakers in Bradford alone. The oatcake man went on his rounds with an oval basket over each arm or balanced on his head, each one covered in a fresh white cloth. Sometimes, mis-shapen oatcakes would be given away to poor children.

Today, Stanley's of Barnoldswick are one of the last remaining oatcake bakers in the country. Betty Wordsworth lived next door to the bakery where, as a child, she learned to throw traditional oatcakes. Now, she owns the company. Distribution is mainly confined to Lancashire, including **The Crumbly Cheese** in Todmorden market hall. **Baines Cheese Van** on Otley and Wetherby markets serves Yorkshire. Personal callers to Stanley's are welcome and so are visits by schoolchildren and W.I. members. All are put to work. Betty warns: 'Everyone gets a pinny when they come here.' A small price to pay for these soft, nutty oatcakes that come, still warm, from Betty Wordsworth's bakery.

Stanley's, Unit 5, Cunliffe House, Manchester Road, Barnoldswick, Lancs. ☎ 01282 816792 Open: Tue-Thur 9am-3pm

CAKE SHOPS & BAKERIES

BARNSLEY

Kelly's Bakery

After years of baking with his father in Bradford, David Kelly bought his own shop and bakehouse on the outskirts of Barnsley five years ago. When he began baking organic bread with flour from Worsbrough Mill in 1992 he doubled his sales almost overnight. A traditional baker, he makes everything himself on the premises. These are not designer breads just good quality, honest baking. Kelly's supply Barnsley's **Le Croque Café** with mini-plaits and sell a solid range of freshly made quiches, pies, pastries from their Carlton Road base.

94/96 Carlton Road, Smithies, Carlton, Nr Barnsley, S. Yorks
☎ *01226 203882*
Open: Mon-Fri 8am-5pm
Sat 7am-2pm

Le Croque Café

A stylish café at the back of Barnsley's most elegant dress shop, Pollyanna's, Le Croque (main entry p136) also operates as a shop and take-away with deep filled quiches; salmon, prawn and spinach plaits; irresistible cakes and pastries, all produced by chef Alison Younis. Be tempted by her wonderful bread and butter pudding, laden with fresh fruit or choose from truffle cakes, frangipanes and other seductive confections. Good bread comes from various sources, including **Kelly's Bakery**.

Pollyanna's, George Arcade. Market Hill, Barnsley, S. Yorks
☎ *01226 733674*
Open: Mon & Sat 9am-5.30pm
Tue, Wed, Fri 9am-6.30pm
Thur 9am-7.30pm

BOROUGHBRIDGE

Bowley's Home Baking

Every Monday former school cook Angela Bowley arrives at Boroughbridge's tiny market with a week's home baking: scones, Eccles cakes, cream buns, ginger snaps, fruit cakes, Yorkshire fat rascals, nig-nags, tea bread and Ripon Yule Bread. Angela is particularly fond of baking to traditional Yorkshire recipes. Her stall also offers her home made jams, marmalades, jellies, pickled onions, pickled eggs and mushroom ketchup.

Boroughbridge Market, Mon Masham: Town Hall, Wed

Sheila's Bakery

If the Yorkshire curd tarts and fat rascals in this smart shop and bakery look familiar it could be because Sheila Gossfield spent 35 years working for **Betty's** of Harrogate before launching her own stylish business. Within a year the river Ure burst its banks and put her High Street premises under five feet of flood water but with remarkable resilience she re-equipped and began all over again. Everything is baked on site. Sheila and her two bakers start the bread at 5am and continue with a flow of delicious cakes and flans: gooseberry and almond, rhubarb and orange, apricot frangipane. Fresh sandwiches are made to order and for instant gratification from Sheila's reckless cream cakes there's a tiny tea shop attached.

13 High Street, Boroughbridge, N. Yorks
☎ *01423 324246*
Open: Mon-Fri 8.30am-5pm
Thur & Sat 8.30am-2.30pm

BRADFORD

Kolos Bakery

Kolos means 'Ear of Wheat' and it represents a heartwarming success story for the Prytulak family whose Ukrainian bakery has become something of a shrine for Britain's eastern European community. Their Ukrainian rye bread, described in The Independent as 'the best rye bread this side of Warsaw', is made with a sour dough starter which is begun 48 hours in advance and delivers a wonderful 'sour' flavour. Kolos bread also has good keeping qualities which enables a mail order service, a select national distribution to Polish delicatessens and a twice weekly delivery to Selfridges. In Yorkshire, we are more regularly blessed. Kolos bread can be bought at continental delicatessens across the county. Better still, visit the bakery itself and see the brown, crusty loaves coming out of the oven and placed on well worn wooden trolleys to cool. Ten employees bake 2,000 loaves a day to Ivan Prytulak's original pre-war recipe. Every one has a tiny Kolos label glued on to the bread itself to confirm its authenticity.

BAKE ME A CAKE

*For every kind of cake-making accessory go to **Lewis & Cooper** of Northallerton. Alternatively, Judith Meek of **Simply Cakes** in Leeds ☎ **0113 269 2238** will design anything from a black Jurassic Park cake to a silver space ship. **Betty's** excellent cakes can be iced with a personal message. **Patisserie Viennoise** of Otley push the boat right out with a bespoke croquembouche, a mountain of filled choux buns decorated with caramel.*

As well as the fabled Ukrainian rye, Kolos bake the German Bauernbrot rye, a dark Bavarian 100% rye, white Italian bread with olive oil, organic wholewheat and good old fashioned large white and brown loaves. The founder and sage of Kolos is Ivan Prytulak, 76, bronzed, hearty and still in daily attendance when he's not in his Spanish retirement home. It's a far cry from his arrival in Britain as a refugee survivor of the concentration camps. He and his wife Olga were Lancashire mill workers until 1961 when Ivan could finally afford to invest in a small Bradford bakery and return to his pre-war family calling in the Ukraine. To his obvious pride the three Prytulak sons, Jaroslaw, Taras and Dmytro have maintained the business in Ivan's cherished 'old fashioned way'.

128-132 Parkside Road,
Bradford, W. Yorks
☎ 01274 729958
Open: Mon & Wed 7am-6pm
Tue, Thur, Fri 8am-6pm
Sat 7am-1pm

DANBY

Botton Village
The Camphill Village Trust community at Botton village near Whitby (main entry p56) strives wherever possible for self-sufficiency. The villagers grind their own bio-dynamic wheat which is converted into nine different types of bread and numerous cakes and biscuits, all baked in a wood fired oven. Their flour, their nutty wholemeal bread and a range of biscuits are available from the Botton shop.

Camphill Village Trust, Botton
Village, Danby, Whitby, N. Yorks
☎ 01287 660871
Open: Mon & Tue
9am-12.15pm & 2pm-5.30pm
Wed, Thur & Fri 2pm-5.30pm
Sat 9am-12 noon
Closed Bank Holidays

DRIFFIELD

The Cake Box
Shortbread, florentines, fruit cakes, almond tarts and decent bread are all made in the bakery behind this little shop. Ken and June Thorley took over the ownership of this shop in 1992 after 35 years in the business. It is the best for miles around.

99 Middle Street South,
Driffield, N. Humbs
☎ 01377 253383
Open: Mon-Fri 8am-4.45pm
Sat 8am-4pm

GRASSINGTON

Harker's Bakery
When Jeremy and Carole Harker took over this immaculate Grassington bakery, neither of them had ever baked a biscuit in their lives. Turning their backs on successful London careers, they settled by the strangest coincidence on a bakery that had once been the rambling Victorian home of Jeremy Harker's great grandfather. They've made it the best in the Dales. Get to the shop early for still warm bread. Next, wonderful smells waft in from the bakery as trays of biscuits are hauled from the big ovens. Tall glass jars are filled with oat bars, Shrewsbury biscuits, shortbread, chocolate crispies, all weighed out and sold loose the old fashioned way. A mixed bag will allow a sample of them all. Then come the cakes: date and walnut, ginger cake, Bakewell tart, carrot cake, blackcurrant and coconut tart and, of course, classic Yorkshire curd tart, bought by so many of Grassington's visitors to take back to the curdless parts. Bread comes in various shapes and sizes: Granary, wholemeal, white farmhouse or crusty rolls. You can have them filled for sandwiches or take out a pie or a hot pizza. The Harker's acknowledge the education received from the previous owners and the

good staff they inherited. Now during school holidays, the next generation of Harker's are in hats and gowns, learning to bake and weighing out the gingerbread men.

1-3 Main Street,
Grassington, N. Yorks
☎ 01756 752483
Open: Mon-Sat 9am-5pm

GUISBOROUGH

Uppercrust
Uppercrust features good cakes, some of them made on the premises, pastries and cooked meats.

15 Challoner Street,
Guisborough, N. Yorks
☎ 01287 636356
Open: Mon-Sat 8.30am-5pm

HARROGATE

Betty's
Back in 1919 Betty's began producing what in those days were called 'fine and dainty pastries', and while there is still much that is fine and dainty in Betty's today, they are not stuck in the past. While retaining the best of traditional Yorkshire baking – tea breads, parkin, curd tarts and fat rascals – they also offer their increasingly cosmopolitan customers the likes of olive bread, sun-dried tomato bread, ciabatta, panforte di Sienna and Swiss Lebkuchen. Each year their Starbeck bakery develops something new to add to Betty's 400 existing lines. Easter and Christmas are celebrated with magical window displays of marzipan animals and foil wrapped mice. Inside, children and the childlike will still fall for golden guineas and silver hearts. There are boozy fruit cakes to send to a maiden aunt, fancy gateaux and tortes to finish off a dinner party and, for final individuality, a bespoke cake decorating service. Betty's speciality coffee and tea, supplied by their once rival and now partner **Taylor's of**

Harrogate, are outstanding. There is top drawer Kenyan Peaberry and an organic Yemeni Mocha; Ceylon's finest Broken Orange Pekoe and the hallmark Yorkshire tea which Taylor's swear really is blended to suit the local water. When the weekend queues for the tea room (see entry p140) are too long, buy a quarter of Darjeeling and a couple of fat rascals. Take them home. Warm, split and butter. Let melting begin and devour for the ultimate tea-time treat. Other branches at Ilkley, Northallerton and York.

1 Parliament Street,
Harrogate, N. Yorks
☎ *01423 502746*
Open: Mon-Sun 9am-9pm

HEBDEN BRIDGE

Waite's

Waite's shop window in Hebden Bridge on any morning of the week is a tribute to British baking. Battenburgs, golden Eccles cakes, chocolate shortbread, almond slice, currant slice, rum truffles, chocolate brownies and, at Easter, spicy hot cross buns. There are soft grained malted cobs, wholemeal and Yorkshire teacakes to be carried home while still warm. Pork pies are topped with apple. Like everything else across a daunting range of 140 varieties of bread, cakes, pastries and pies, each one is made by hand with infinite care and attention to detail. It comprises the achievement of master baker Kenneth Tetlow and his wife Janet, who together run two unassuming little shops in Hebden Bridge and Mytholmroyd that leave standing many of the region's grander baking establishments. This is traditional Calder Valley territory and the work is divided down strictly sexist lines. Friendly overalled women serve behind the counter while the bakery behind the Mytholmroyd shop is a male pre-

serve, dominated by a big old fashioned baker's oven which is never empty. Paper-light pastries come out as trays of onion bread go in, sliding expertly from a long handled wooden bread peel. Through the oven window the unpromising dough can be seen swelling into a golden, onion-flecked cob. The bread prover owes nothing to new technology either. It is a simple wooden cupboard where trays of dough are slotted onto runners and left to rise. Beneath the trays a pan of water simmers on a gas ring creating the ideal warm, steamy conditions. 'It's worked well enough for the last 40 years', says Ken. The shops make no claim to be continental patisseries but there is the occasional touch of Paris in the Pennines. Ken Tetlow's garlic bread, florentines and fresh cream chocolate roulade all developed from trips to the French capital. The Euro-influence could have run deeper. As a 19 year old apprentice attending day-release classes at Huddersfield Tech., Ken won a scholarship to the elite Richemont School of Patisserie in Switzerland but the Huddersfield and District Master Bakers Society knew better. Because his employer was not a member of this august body, Ken was barred from taking up his place. It was a bitter disappointment that still rankles 35 years later. It was some compensation that in 1991 Waite's were awarded the Challenge Cup as the best bakery in Yorkshire. It's unlikely that the Swiss could better these cherry

slices, Yorkshire curd tarts and the best-selling crusty white loaves that need no ascorbic acid to hurry their rise.

Crown Street,
Hebden Bridge, W. Yorks
☎ *01422 842481*
Open: Mon-Fri 8.30am-5.15pm
Tue 8.30am-4pm
Sat 8.30am-3.30pm

HOVINGHAM

The Bakery

This picture-book village embraces the heavyweight Hovingham Hall, family home of the Duchess of Kent, and a nimble all-round village bakery, with an honesty box no urban enterprise could contemplate. Penny Jones' business grew from simple beginnings. She did home breadmaking for the local Post Office when her children were small –w dough preparation at night, baking in the morning. As demand increased, she outgrew her kitchen and now operates The Bakery next to the ford and the footbridge. The ungodly early mornings remain, leavened by help on three days a week. There are four basic choices for the Royal slice of bread: white, wholemeal, nutty brown and a dark brown seed loaf with treacle. The seeds, she reassures those with wartime memories, are not caraway. Then there are milk baps, poppy seed plaits, a lovely fat cottage loaf and a variety of cakes, pies and scones. Flour comes stoneground from **Village Craft Flours** of Grewelthorpe, free of

---

FUNERAL BISCUITS

Up until the beginning of the last war it was a tradition at north country funerals to offer funeral biscuits. In the Yorkshire Dales these were round shortbreads stamped with a heart to symbolise the departed soul. Biscuits were offered to the mourners as they arrived or they were wrapped in paper printed with a suitably solemn verse, sealed with black wax and distributed afterwards.

preservatives or improvers. All fats are suitable for vegetarians. To keep up with Penny Jones' bread and cakes, also visit the **Wine & Deli** shop in Malton or **Nicholson's** of Helmsley.

Hovingham, N. Yorks
☎ *01653 628898*
Open: Tue-Fri 9.30am-6pm
Sat 9.30am-5pm

ILKLEY

Betty's

The same high standards of baking prevail at this branch of the Betty's chain. For details see Harrogate entry.

32-34 The Grove,
Ilkley, W. Yorks
☎ *01943 608029*
Open: Mon-Sun 9am-6pm

LEEDS

Bagel Nash

Bagel Nash describes itself as the 'Famous New York Deli'. Well, Moortown isn't yet Manhattan's lower East side but that is the inspiration for Uri Mizrahi's Jewish take-away, which opened in 1987. Bagels come with poppy seeds, garlic and cheese or herbs. Pastrami makes its natural home on rye. There is good smoked salmon, smoked turkey and salt beef to lead off 50 different sandwiches – just the sort of fillings ordered by TV cops in their Brooklyn precincts. Alternatively, there are tasty

falafels, tortilla chips with melted cheese, potato latkes, stuffed vine leaves and pickled cucumber. The orange juice here comes freshly squeezed. It's a tiny shop with a constant stream of customers and only a couple of seats so it's not an easy place to lounge around and watch the Chinese gamblers arrive rich and leave poor at the casino on the corner. It is essentially a take-away and definitely worth remembering as somewhere that stays open until 1am on Saturday nights, Leeds still being some way off the 24 hour city dreamed of by its political masters. Fax ordering, delivery service and outside catering are all available.

3 The Corner House,
Moortown, Leeds, W. Yorks
☎ *0113 269 7227*
Fax: 0113 237 0607
Open: Mon-Fri 10am-3pm
Sat 7pm-1am Sun 10am-9pm

Chalutz Bakery

Late Saturday night revellers craving a classisc smoked salmon and cream cheese bagel can satisfy their hunger at Chalutz Jewish Bakery in Moortown where bread and bagels are baked behind the shop from sunset, through the night and well into Sunday afternoon and sold over the counter throughout. During more regular weekday hours they sell organic wholemeal, soda bread, granary, an enriched egg bread, Armenian

loaves and a variety of rolls and cakes.

378 Harrogate Road, Moortown,
Leeds, W. Yorks
☎ *0113 269 1350*
Open: Mon-Thur 7am-6pm
Fri 6am-2.30pm Sat one hour
after sunset until 2pm on Sun

Le Croque Monsieur

Briefly, every weekday lunchtime during term-time, Le Croque Monsieur is a place to be avoided as an irresistible mass of hungry pupils from nearby Lawnswood High invade this normally calm, uncluttered patisserie. They come for *pain au beurre* and for their 50p piece they get a third of a baguette, spread with butter, warmed in the oven until the bread is crisp and the butter has melted. When the daily dust has settled, around 200 of these deliciously simple offerings have changed hands. For something more substantial than bread and butter, there are allegedly 7,000 possible sandwich permutations to be had from Le Croque Monsieur. Baguettes, onion bread, herb and spice bread, croissant or spicy pitta are just a few of the breads. Fillings range from guacamole and garlic sausage to cheese, celery and banana or prosciutto ham with avocado. The list goes on. They will make any combination of ingredients and, if required, deliver to your office by refrigerated van. Fiona James, the owner,

---

RAKUSEN'S

Matzo, matzah, matzi, motza – the names given to Jewish unleavened bread vary from place to place but Rakusen's of Leeds don't mind what people call them since they are happily baking 250,000 crackers a week, rising spectacularly to 20 million at Passover. They are firmly established as Britain's oldest manufacturer of kosher foods, including Tomor, a non-dairy margarine suitable for both Muslims and vegans and a range of biscuits, bagels and non dairy ice cream. But traditional matzos made Rakusen's world famous and are still their mainstay, a significant export earner in the United States and as popular, they claim, with Gentiles as with Jews.

Passover, a key event in the Jewish religious calendar, lasts for eight days during March or April and commemorates the liberation of the Jews from slavery in Egypt. The story goes that the Jews were forced to flee so quickly that there was not even time for the bread to rise so they made it unleavened – without yeast – and called it matzah. It was the matzah that sustained them on their journey through the desert and the parting of the Red Sea to freedom.

Each Passover, families hold a special ceremonial meal called a Seder to celebrate their freedom from the Pharaohs. Bitter herbs signify the hardships of captivity; salt water recalls the tears of the slaves; haroset, a mixture of apples, nuts, wine and cinnamon, matches the colour of the clay the Jews used to make bricks; and matzah is eaten in memory of the flat bread they made during their escape. Children search for a hidden piece of matzah called afikomen and the meal ends after everyone has been offered a taste.

The Rakusen company was founded in the wake of the 1880s pogroms of eastern European Jews and the subsequent waves of Jewish migration ending in Leeds. Lloyd Rakusen was a jeweller and his pocket watch still stands today as the company logo. At Passover, he would bake matzos in his back kitchen. By the 1930s, his cottage industry had grown into a thriving business and, with his two sons, he opened a factory in North Street. For the next 60 years the Rakusen's factory was a familiar city landmark until it was compulsorily purchased to make way for new roads and the company moved to a trading estate in the suburbs. In the 1970s Rakusen's were taken over by the mighty United Biscuits but the specialist nature of kosher production was not easily compatible with the aims of a multi-national and in 1983 three of the company's executives succeeded in a management buy-out.

All Rakusen's foods are made under the strictest religious quality control, the kashrut food laws, and sanctioned by the London Beth Din, the recognised Rabbinical Council for the supervision of kosher production. Rakusen's employ two full-time Rabbis and two juniors, or Shomrim, and work will not begin untilthey are in attendance. Even the non-dampened matzo flour milled at Whitley Bridge, near Selby, is supervised by two Shomrim and stored in its own silo before it is transported to Leeds. A strict '18 minute rule' is observed in the preparation of the matzo dough. Flour mixed with water begins to ferment after 18 minutes so any slow down in production means the dough must be destroyed. Nor can any left-over dough be allowed to stand around to contaminate the next batch. The staff operating these kosher regulations are mostly Gentiles, blithely unversed in the religious history behind their labour.

Rakusen's Ltd, Clayton Wood Rise, West Park, Leeds, W. Yorks ☎ 0113 278 4821

trained in patisserie under John Huber, a doyen of the art, who himself baked for all the right people from J. Lyons to King Gustav of Sweden. Fiona worked among other places at London Zoo before setting up in Far Headingley. All the cakes are made on the premises by French patissier and chocolatier Christophe Eytier from Brantôme in the Dordogne. Elaborate 12″ triple chocolate truffle cakes are piled high with delicate chocolate curls, at up to £32 safely out of the average pupil's lunch allowance. Glossy fruit tarts and frangipanes come down to earth at £1.25. Hopefully, Le Croque Monsieur will sustain the fresh, clean style with which it began.

251 Otley Road, West Park,
Leeds, W. Yorks
☎ *0113 278 7353*
Open: Mon-Fri 9am-5pm
Sat 8.30am-4pm
Sun 8am-1pm

Floyd's Creative Cuisine

There can be few chefs with more demonic enthusiasm than Wayne Newsome. Formerly head chef at the Leeds bistro, **Sous Le Nez**, he worked through the night in the restaurant's kitchen producing fresh olive breads, almond croissants, rustic lemon tarts and chocolate truffle cakes for his fledgling business, selling French patisserie on a stall at Granary Wharf. These superhuman efforts paid off and in early 1994 he gave up his day job at the bistro to run his own business from an industrial estate in Holbeck. He supplies cakes and savouries to local cafés and delicatessens, makes ice-cream for the Japanese **Teppanyaki** restaurant and does any outside catering jobs that come his way, to which he brings credentials buried under the rosettes of the Waterside Inn, Bray; London's Le Gavroche and the Box Tree of happier

days. This is a man in a hurry, unashamedly 'working my arse off to get what I want.' What Wayne wants in this world is his own restaurant which will be 'wild and energetic'. What else? Catch his baking now so you can claim you knew him when he had his stall under the Dark Arches.

Granary Wharf, Dark Arches,
Leeds, W. Yorks
☎ *0113 242 8333*
Open: Sat & Sun 10am-5pm

French Revolution

Richard Sutton produces his own handmade versions of the normally mass-produced favourites of carrot cake and Mississippi mud pie along with mouth-watering chocolate tortes, mille-feuille, fruit flans and almond slices. Richard Sutton is, on his own admission, a food obsessive. His wife used to complain of a rare male Yorkshire condition: he spent all his time in the kitchen. Then, totally self-taught, he reached the semi-finals of the TV cookery competition Masterchef and was sufficiently heartened to give up his job at Leeds Infirmary to start his own business. His attractive premises in Leeds' restored Victoria Quarter show every sign of being a success. Apart from well executed patisserie, there are some really imaginative sandwiches. Good bread, bagels and croissants are filled with lentil and hazelnut paté. Are you ready for pork rillettes with onion marmalade? Italian ciabatta takes Parma ham and melon. There is rare roast beef with a coarse grain mustard, mixed charcuterie with black olives or Bayonne ham with gherkins. Savoury tarts are filled with crab and asparagus or there are surprising salads of apple, pecan and celery or potato, chorizo and chive. There's a home-made soup every day. He keeps some good farmhouse cheeses and can supply, on request, fresh truffles, wild mushrooms, foie gras, French puff pas-

try and French butter from the celebrated Rungis market in Paris. Despite these welcome French connections, Richard Sutton's local roots are certainly not forgotten with exemplary Yorkshire curd tart and slices of thickly buttered tea bread, loaded with fruit and nuts.

9 County Arcade, Victoria
Quarter, Leeds, W. Yorks
☎ *0113 234 2290*
Open: Mon-Sat 7.30am-5pm

MASHAM

Bowley's Home Baking
See Boroughbridge entry.

Masham Town Hall, Wed

MYTHOLMROYD

Waite's
See Hebden Bridge entry.

9 Burnley Road,
Mytholmroyd, W. Yorks
☎ *01422 883262*
Open: Mon-Fri 8.30am-5.15pm
Tue 8.30am-1pm
Sat 8.30am-12 noon

NORTHALLERTON

Betty's
The smallest of the Betty's family of cake shops but small can still be beautiful, with all the same good baking as the rest of the chain. See Harrogate entry.

188 High Street,
Northallerton, N. Yorks
☎ *01609 775154*
Open: Mon-Sat 9am-5.30pm
Sun 10am-5.30pm

NORTON

The Bakery
A small bakery but with everything baked on the premises. Good rustic wholemeal loaves.

17 Church Street, Norton,
Malton, N. Yorks
☎ *01653 693343.*
Open: Mon-Fri 8.30am-5pm
Thur 8.30am-2pm
Sat 8.30am-3pm

YORKSHIRE BAKING

Traditions in Yorkshire baking stem largely from economy where home baking was the cheapest way to fill a hungry family. **Sad Cakes, Fatty Cakes, Suet Cakes, Turf Cakes, Gayle Bannock** and **Nodden Cakes** are all variations of flour, lard and water and, if the budget ran to it, sugar and a few currants. They were simple and filling and conveniently used up all the bits of leftover dough on baking day. Doubtless, they tasted good when fresh and warm but there is a monotony about them. Certainly, **Water Cake** made of flour, water and a pinch of salt has had its day. Nevertheless, Yorkshire bread cakes and oven bottoms are enduringly popular and tea shops and bakeries are still serving fat rascals and curd tarts.

Bread Cake: a soft round of bread about 4" across, as appealing today as when it was filled with mucky fat for a weaver's snap. In Yorkshire, the addition of currants turns them into teacakes.

Oven Bottoms: a large bread cake baked on the floor of the oven. Known as Stotty Cake in the north east.

Curd Tart: curd cheese, sugar and currants in a pastry case. Still as popular as ever.

Fat Rascal: another term for a Turf Cake. More sophisticated versions are made with milk and eggs. Usually rolled out into squares or cut into rounds or unformed rather like a rock bun. Served warm with butter.

Gingerbread: a spiced biscuit for which Whitby became famous. Bakers pressed it into specially carved moulds. Brandy snaps and ginger pigs were often sold at the fair.

Muffin: small round breadcakes made on the bakestone over a basket of coals but taken over by commercial bakers who sold them in the streets.

Oatcake: there were two types of this Yorkshire staple: the soft batter that was thrown onto the bakestone to form a soft dough rather like a face flannel or a stiff dough that was rolled out into a biscuit.

Parkin: a heavy cake, sometimes called tharf cake, made of oatmeal, treacle and ginger and traditionally served around the bonfire on November 5.

Pepper Cake: a yeast cake that included flour, butter, treacle and allspice or Jamaica pepper from which it takes its name

Pikelet: a thin crumpet cooked on a bakestone. Like muffins they were later made commercially and sold by the muffin man.

Wilfra Cake: a pastry case filled with butter, ground almonds, lemon zest and breadcrumbs, baked with an egg and milk custard. Made to mark St. Wilfrid's Feast, the patron saint of Ripon Cathedral. Tradition requires that Wilfra Cakes are placed outside the houses for passers-by to help themselves during the week long festivities. Apple and cheese baked together in a pie was another Wilfra week tradition. Yorkshire people still serve apple pie with cheese.

Yorkshire Plum Bread, Ripon Spice Bread, Yule Loaf: there is an endless variety of names to describe the mixed fruit and spiced loaves and buns traditionally popular at Sunday School teas after Whit walks.

Yule Cake: a rich cake of dried fruit, candied peel, spices and sometimes brandy. Still eaten with Wensleydale cheese. Served at Christmas and at funeral teas.

OTLEY

Bondgate Bakery

Here's justification for the Government Enterprise Allowance scheme which helped to bring biochemistry drop-out Stephen Taylor from a squat in Brixton to this tiny but brilliant bakery in Bondgate. He set up shop with no experience or training, bought catering ovens instead of baking ovens and began sweating it out: 'It was literally like hell in here. It got so hot that I began to get cramps in my legs.' With the correct ovens installed, instruction from Connie Woodcock, an old baker from Gomersal, and working all hours to a rigorous philosophy of proper bread without additives or improvers, business gradually flourished. Now nine years on and with the help of his partner Sally Hinchcliffe and baker Stuart Murrie, the output has grown remarkably. There is organic wholemeal bread, unbleached white loaves, sour dough, Granary style, rye bread, oat bread, French sticks, seed bread, tomato bread, olive oil bread, a fragrant herb bread with oregano, a rosemary and sage loaf with a dash of turmeric. . . and so on ad almost infinitum. French sticks are filled with fresh garlic butter ready to pop in the oven. Cakes, tea breads, flapjacks and four varieties of scone – cheese; apple and sunflower seed; sultana; date and walnut – all compete for shelf space. Upstairs, Sally prepares good, mainly vegetarian food to take away: 'shepherdless' pie, mushroom and lentil patés, vegetarian lasagne, pizza, vegetable samosa and a different home made soup every day. Bondgate bread is also available from **Le Croque Monsieur** patisserie in Leeds.

30 Bondgate, Otley, W. Yorks
☎ 01943 467516
Open: Mon-Fri 9am-5.30pm
Sat 9am-5pm

SETTLE

Dales Pantry

For all its popularity, Settle market has little to offer the food lover except for Dales Pantry, a small cake stall run by young, self-taught cook, Rachel Anderson. She has been baking like mad for the last two years to finance her real love in life, horses. Pensioners who fancy a bit of home baking for tea make a beeline for wholemeal honey and date loaves, chocolate cake, shortbread, flapjack, carrot cake and chewy butterscotch biscuits. She also bakes for Settle's **Market Pantry**, the Bolton Abbey Pavilion and her local Post Office at Cowling.

Settle Market, Tue

Glynn's Bakery

Andrew and Gerard Glynn have been baking in Settle for the last 16 years. As trays of sugary doughnuts are swiftly replenished throughout the day, it's easy to understand that more than half of the business comes from tourism: the shop is well sited close to the main car park. Pies, pastries, cream cakes, Sally Lunn's and Yorkshire curd tarts are all well turned out.

1 Church Street,
Settle, N. Yorks
☎ 01729 823218
Open: Mon-Sun 8.15am-5.30pm

SHEFFIELD

La Ceres

Bread, savouries and cakes of the best quality at reasonable prices is the commitment of James Mann and Neil Gibson in the two branches of La Ceres. Bread is made locally without additives or preservatives. Sandwiches include meat but vegan and vegetarian fillings predominate. Try the savoury mushroom paté or a vegetarian burger, bhaji or pasty. Cakes are of the nutty, muesli, oaty kind and there is a popular carrot cake and Danish pastry. A new venture at the Sharrowvale shop only are the classic farmhouse cheeeses that according to Neil Gibson are going like a bomb, notably a selection from his native Ireland, Keen's cheddar, an unpasteurised French brie and Shepherd's Purse ewe's milk cheeses.

398 Sharrowvale Road,
Sheffield, S. Yorks
☎ 0114 266 4423
Open: Mon-Sat 9am-5pm

5 Rustlings Road, Sheffield,
S. Yorks
☎ 0114 261 7541
Open: Mon-Sat 9am-5pm

In a Nutshell

A wholefood and sandwich shop with decent bread made locally by Sheffield's Real Bread Bakehouse: Granary, organic wholemeal, sesame and poppy seed loaves lead the way. Alongside, are sandwiches, vegetarian pastries and pasties, onion bhajis, pakoras, vegetarian Scotch eggs, pizza and good wholemeal cakes.

31 Chesterfield Road, Sheffield
S. Yorks
☎ 0114 250 8555
Open: Mon-Sat 9.30am-5.30pm

Yvonne's

A standard bread and cake shop, open on Sunday for croissants and French bread baked on Friday and Saturday nights.

627 Ecclesall Road,
Sheffield, S. Yorks
☎ 0114 266 2975
Open: Mon-Sat 8am-5pm
Sun 8am-12 noon

SLEIGHTS

Elizabeth Botham & Sons

See Whitby entry.

73 Coach Road, Sleights,
N. Yorks
☎ 01947 810243
Open: Mon-Sat 9am-5pm
Wed 9am-4.30pm
Closed Mon in winter

WETHERBY

Oven Door

Baking bread by the traditional method means using a fermented dough that is given time to rise without the use of flour improvers. That, in turn, means the early morning shift and for Tony Phillips the Saturday morning shift actually starts at 11.30 pm on the Friday for an all night session. His reward is queues stretching up North Street to his tiny shop, patiently waiting for the best bread and cakes in town. Oven Door's pork pies are particularly worth noting, not quite hand raised, but moulded on a small machine and then baked without a tin to give a well glazed, crisp pastry. There are cream cakes, custards, glazed and sugared doughnuts, Danish pastries and sausage rolls. Everything is baked fresh every day and anything left over at closing time is thrown out. There is nothing sophisticated here, just well crafted, fresh baking by tried and trusted methods.

12 North Street,
Wetherby, N. Yorks
☎ 01937 584839
Mon-Fri 9am-5.30pm
Wed until 4pm Sat 9am-5pm

WHITBY

Elizabeth Botham & Sons

Traditional and honest, unsophisticated and homely, Elizabeth Botham's bakery and café was established in 1865 and it is still run by members of the Botham family. Their biscuits and spicy plum bread have been well enough marketed to qualify as Yorkshire food icons. Along with the plain white loaves, the hand raised pork pies and the Whitby gingerbread, they have sustained the Botham mark over the years. Despite setbacks they have seen no reason to change. With such a good name in baking who can blame them? Their

Skinner Street café has no surface pretensions to be Betty's-by-the-sea. Botham's remains true to old Whitby tradition. In the last century, frumenty (a kind of spiced porridge), Yule cake and gingerbread were served on Christmas Eve. Frumenty is no longer to be had but Botham's plum bread, a fruit loaf, reminiscent of the original Yule cake, and their firm, spicy, gingerbread are still going strong. So popular was gingerbread in Victorian Whitby that every family who could afford it would have one at Christmas. Some weighed up to eight pounds and they were often stamped with a pattern from moulds cut by the jet workers. Properly served buttered with a slice of Wensleydale, it is a tradition well worth renewing. Botham's tinned plum bread and biscuits are available from bakeries and delicatessens throughout the region as well as their own shops in Whitby and Sleights.

35-39 Skinner Street &
30 Baxtergate,
Whitby, N. Yorks
☎ 01947 602823
Open: Mon-Sat 8.30am-5pm
Wed 8.30am-4.15pm
Baxtergate shop open Sun in
summer

YORK

Betty's

The York branch of Betty's vies with Harrogate for title of biggest and best of this excellent chain. There's hardly a wafer to choose between them. Both stock the full range of bread, cakes and chocolates with attractive seasonal window displays.

6-8 St. Helen's Square, York
☎ 01904 659142
Open: Mon-Sun 9am-9pm

Tea Time Bakery

There are few job vacancy signs in this stalwart bakery. Vin Clark has been making feather light sponges for 56 years. Freda has

worked the shop for a mere 34 years. Proprietor John Sims is continuing the business begun by his grandfather in 1935, a no frills outfit turning out bread and pastries the old fashioned way. They make a wide range including organic and wholemeal stoneground bread for local wholefood shops. On Thursdays there is a Tea Time Extra, a loaf with added bran, sunflower seeds, cracked wheat and malted wheat flakes. On Wednesdays and Fridays there's a bright, even bold, selection of regional breads: Bara Brith of Welsh origin, cheese and garlic, herb soda bread, sunflower pumpernickel, mustard and cheese. Trade has been badly affected by the arrival of yellow lines outside the shop but a loyal local following has sustained this worthy family enterprise.

4 Mill Lane, Heworth,
York
☎ 01904 424730
Open: Mon 10am-4pm
Tue-Fri 8.45am-5.30pm
Sat 8.30am-5.30pm

Via Vecchia

A tiny shop in the Shambles is where Alistair Lawton has finally docked after cooking for Claridges, the Ritz and the QE2. Via Vecchia has grown from a shoestring start into a successful retail and wholesale business based on the 90s most *de rigueur* food: olive oil bread. Back in 1992, in little more than a domestic kitchen above the shop, Alistair began kneading 60 lbs of dough by hand and had the bruises on his knuckles to prove it. He now has a machine to do the mixing and successfully bakes for half a dozen delicatessens besides his own. He also sells well filled rolls and a different hearty soup every day.

6 Shambles, York
☎ 01904 627701
Open: Mon-Sat 9am-5pm

WOMEN'S INSTITUTE MARKETS

The Women's Institute may have spent many years trying to rid themselves of their 'Jam and Jerusalem' image but if the W.I. markets are anything to go by then they've happily failed on the jam side. Every week, parish rooms and church halls across the region stage whirlwind sales of the most dependable fruit jams, savouries, cakes, tea breads, biscuits and freshly picked garden produce. Standards of production are high. All members are required to pass the Basic Food Hygiene examination of the Department of the Environment. Food is cellophane packed, weighed and labelled in accordance with strict W.I. guidelines.

It is not necessary to be a W.I. member to join the market. All it requires is a shareholding of 5p and some produce to sell. The W.I. takes 10% to cover administration costs and hire of the venue and prices are calculated at roughly double the cost of the raw materials. No one makes their fortune from baking for the W.I. markets but with some 500 markets across the country turning over £10.5 million, the system is thriving.

The markets are seriously organised and administered as only the W.I. know how. Everything is checked in, priced, recorded and accounted for. No Shrewsbury biscuit or ginger nut is missed out. Although this is predominantly female territory, there are exceptions. Beverley's market has a lively male membership which has evolved from helping their wives to arrange the furniture in the village hall. Although few admit to baking themselves, they are keen to remind visitors that the markets were originally set up in 1919 not just for W.I. members but also as an outlet for surplus garden produce grown by ex-servicemen on their allotments after the war. In time, members began baking specially for the markets. Today, fresh produce has given way to a wide range of cakes and savouries, jams and honeys.

The W.I. routine is unchanging from week to week and is replicated in 17 markets across the region. Fifteen minutes before opening time the queues begin to form outside. Inside, white coated women brace themselves for the stampede. It is quite a scrum as dozens of determined shoppers head for the cherry cakes and the curd tarts. Fifteen minutes of frenetic buying and selling and the tables are almost bare. Then it's time for a sit down with tea and biscuits, home made if you're lucky. Regulars who know the score will have avoided the rush by placing orders in advance, often with a particular baker for a favourite tea bread or shortbread biscuit.

Most markets run a parcel delivery service, a sort of Interflora of W.I. produce. The contents of the parcel can be discussed with the regional market organiser. She will then pass on the order to whichever part of the country the parcel is to be delivered. Cakes will be specially baked and the hamper delivered to the recipient's doorstep in any part of the country. It's a scheme perennially popular with housebound relatives and starving students.

There might be a passing nod to food fashion at some W.I. markets with onion bread or home smoked salmon but they remain predominantly the home of Bakewell tarts, tea breads, Victoria sponges, cornflake crisps and butterfly buns; solidly traditional and enduringly popular. The advice is equally unchanging: get there early.

Markets Department, National Federation of Women's Institutes,
104 New Kings Road, London SW6 4LY ☎ 0171 371 9300

TICKHILL

W.I. Market

The urn is on the boil well before 9 o'clock for the first snatched cups of tea in the kitchen of Tickhill's half-timbered Old Parish Rooms. Fran Wright, the market organiser and her team are already preparing the stalls. Flowered cloths cover trestle tables as trays of cakes, garden produce and bedding plants arrive. Someone staggers in under a pile of hollyhocks. Bunches of parsley and chives are laid out. Pre-ordered cakes are sorted, labels hastily written and details entered into a fat ledger. Fran Wright deals with queries covering the price of lemon curd and how much tea to put in the pot. When a dozen jars of honey turn up unexpectedly there is just a faint frisson of panic – will the stall holders be ready in time? Opening time is 9.55am sharp. They are, of course, ready and waiting in crisp white overalls, their six tables groaning with produce. The bolts of the ancient doors are pulled back to reveal a restless queue. A September visit found savoury quiches, individual beef and tomato pies, peach and orange fruit cakes, lemon meringue pies, coffee sponge cakes, packs of almond tarts, date and walnut loaf, cheese and onion bread, chocolate fudge shortbread, flapjack and fruit cakes made with butter and sherry. There's that famous W.I. jam thick with raspberries, strawberries or blackberry and apple. From the garden come leeks, beetroot, baby cauliflowers, savoy cabbage, sprays of cut flowers and free range eggs. Savouries arrive in cool boxes and are placed on frozen plates (secured from a redundant milk float) to keep them chilled. There is a brisk trade in the run-up to Christmas in cakes and puddings and Fran Wright alone makes 2,000 mince pies each year. Tickhill is a well stocked market. Despite the initial rush there was still plenty left for late comers.

SOUTH YORKSHIRE

Doncaster
YWCA Hall, Cleveland Street
☎ *01302 771327*
Fri 10am-12.30am

Penistone
St. John's Community Centre, Church Street
☎ *01302 771327*
Thur 10am-12 noon

Sheffield
Scout HQ, Spooner Road, Broomhill
☎ *01302 771327*
Sat 9am-1200 noon

Thorne
Old People's Centre, Church Street
☎ *01302 771327*
Fri 9.30am-11.30am

Tickhill
See above
Old Parish Rooms, Northgate
☎ *01602 855379*
Fri 10am-11.45am except Christmas week
Closed Good Fri, held Thur instead

NORTH YORKSHIRE

Easingwold
Parish Room, Tanpit Lane
☎ *01751 473526*
Fri 9.30am-11.30am
(Closed Jan)

Guisborough
Sunnyfield House, Westgate
☎ *01642 781889*
Thur 1pm-3pm

Leyburn
St. Matthews Church Hall, Main Street
☎ *01748 850208*
Thur 10am-11.30am

Northallerton
United Reformed Church Hall, High Street
☎ *01751 473526*
Fri 1.30pm-3.15pm

Pickering
Memorial Hall, Potter Hill
☎ *01751 473526*
Thur 9.45am-11.45am

Scalby
Scalby District Council Offices, Scalby Road
☎ *01751 473526*
Fri 9.45am -11.15am

Selby
Hawden Institute, Church Lane
☎ *01751 473526*
Thur 10am-12 noon

Skipton
Black Horse Market, High Street
☎ *01748 850208*
Wed 9 am-12.45pm
(Apr-Dec)

Stokesley
Methodist Church Hall, High Street
☎ *01751 473526*
Fri 9.30am-3.30pm
(fortnightly)

Yarm
Methodist Church Hall, Chapel Wynd
☎ *01642 781889*
Fri 1.30am-3pm

WEST YORKSHIRE

Otley
Community Centre, Cross Green
☎ *0113 265 6353*
Fri 10am-11.45am
(Closed Jan & Aug)

HUMBERSIDE

Beverley
Memorial Hall, Lairgate
☎ *01482 631323*
Fri 10am-11.30am

HISTORIC KITCHENS

Nowhere in Yorkshire or Humberside are there magnificent old kitchens as complete and accessible as those at Calke Abbey in Derbyshire. Nevertheless, there are a number of museums and houses open to the public that paint a fascinating picture of kitchen regimes of the past, for both upstairs and downstairs.

Shibden Hall: the 15th century hall at Halifax has two kitchens with a wide range of 17th, 18th and 19th century utensils. There is a fine collection of brown and yellow local earthenware, a jack driven spit and earthenware ham baths. Curator Ros Westwood has a special interest in food, kitchens, cooking and gardening. There are occasional workshops on domestic life of the past.
Shibden Park, Halifax, W. Yorks ☎ 01422 352246 Open: Mar-Nov Mon-Sat 10am-5pm Sun 12 noon-5pm

Oakwell Hall Country Park: a Tudor mansion in Birstall showing how life was lived in the 1690s. History re-enactments are arranged for local school children who help to prepare an authentic 17th century meal on the kitchen range and eat it, in period costume, in the oak panelled dining room.
Nutter Lane, Birstall, W. Yorks ☎ 01924 474926 Open: Mon-Sun 12 noon-5pm

The Red House: a red brick Georgian house that was the home of prosperous wool merchant Joshua Taylor who wove the scarlet for army uniforms. His daughter Mary was a friend of Charlotte Brontë, who often stayed here. It's believed that Hiram Yorke in Charlotte's novel *Shirley* was based on Taylor. The kitchen has an interesting collection of 19th century utensils and there are intermittent food related workshops.
Gomersal, W. Yorks ☎ 01274 872165 Open: Mon-Sun 12 noon-5pm

Fairfax House: a classic Georgian house in the centre of York completed in 1762 and recently restored by York Civic Trust. The dining room recreates the elegant atmosphere of the day while the kitchen contains models of a meal given by Viscount Fairfax in 1763. There is a bread oven, a spit and all the accompanying trivets and hooks, a bread peel, an oatcake spreader, sugar scissors and Scotch hands for butter.
Castlegate, York ☎ 01904 655543 Open: Mon-Thur & Sat 11am-4.30pm Sun 1.30pm-4.30pm

Castle Museum: the Hearth Gallery of York's Castle Museum contains not only the black-leaded ranges that were once the heart of a Yorkshire kitchen but all the knives, graters, mills and moulds that accumulated in a typical 18th century pantry. The Castle Museum also contains one of the finest collections of traditional dairy equipment in the country. Sadly, much of it is in permanent store because of lack of exhibition space.
Tower Street, York ☎ 01904 653611 Open: Apr-Oct Mon-Sat 9.30am-5.30pm Sun 10am-5.30pm Nov-Mar Mon-Sat 9.30am-4pm Sun 10am-4pm

Merchant Adventurers Hall: not a kitchen but the superb 14th century hall was the home of York's craft guilds including the company of Grocers whose coat arms can still be seen depicting nine spice cloves. Great feasts were held by the Merchants, a tradition that continues today with an annual venison feast held in November.
Piccadilly, York ☎ 01904 654818 Open: Apr-Oct Mon-Sun 8.30am-5pm Nov-Mar Mon-Sat 8.30am-3pm

6

Pickles & Preserves

The Yorkshire fancy for something sweet or spicy to pep up dour and basic foodstuffs has a long history and an active present. Forms of Yorkshire relish date back to the reign of Richard II; Charles I reputedly planted the mulberry tree at Womersley Hall, near Doncaster from which a boutique vinegar is now made; and just as the pre-dissolution monasteries kept bees and sold honey by the comb so, too, do the monks of Ampleforth today. The vast tracts of heather on the North York Moors remain an incomparable source of single flower honey. The odd jar found at the farm gate now is a far cry from when it was sold by the bucketful to factors who bottled it off to Harrods and Fortnum & Mason. Rare, too, was the meat served in Yorkshire without an appropriate sauce or a pickle. Smokestack industries grew up in the West Riding making robust relish and piccalilli – and survived. The best of the new generation of W.I. and cottage industry preserve-makers in the region turn first to local fruits. Their jams and jellies are palpably thick with fruit. Their vinegars are infused with aromatic herbs. Their curd actually tastes of lemon. But whoever the manufacturer, there's no escaping sugar. It has been at the heart of fruit preserving since the slave trade led to the first West Indian cane sugar imports in the 17th century. Imports to ethnic food shops continue to enrich our choice with Polish jams, sweet Chinese plum sauces and the hot stuff: fiery Thai sambals, Jamaican pepper sauces, macho Tabasco, hot sauces from Mexico and Louisiana and the Indian favourite Patak and Rajah brands for pickles, chutneys and mustard oils to fire a home made curry.

PICKLES & PRESERVES

BEDALE

Cunningham's

There are 60 different items on Gordon and Norma Cunningham's product list: apricot and chilli chutney, hot chilli pickle, minted cauliflower, lemon and mustard seed pickle, banana, plum, peach, orange, apple, rhubarb or pineapple chutney and more. The sauces include apricot, orange and tarragon; gooseberry and egg and anchovy. Two new additions are Yorkshire Plum Pudding and Bible cake – all the ingredients are to be found in the Bible, so if you want to know what's in it you need to know your Samuel, Chronicles and Kings. Everything from this admirable little enterprise is made by the Cunningham's themselves, free of additives, preservatives and colouring. They have a growing distribution network across North Yorkshire, from **Reah's** in Masham to the excellent **Farm Dairy** in Knaresborough.

Enterprise House, Bridge Street, Bedale, N. Yorks
☎ *01677 426326*
Open: Mon-Fri 9am-4pm

DARLEY

Farmhouse Preserves

Spend any time in Yorkshire and you are certain to come across those reassuring 'Hand Made' labels with the pretend naive handwriting that proliferate on souvenir jars of jam, marmalade and honey. So prolific are they that the fond starting notion of 'Farmhouse Preserves' being made to a hand-me-down recipe in granny's country cottage is soon overtaken by more industrial imaginings. Sure enough, the 'farmhouse' at Darley turns out to be more of a small factory.

But never mind. It is in the countryside and Andrew Wild's 'Hand Made Preserves' use nothing more elaborate than six preserving pans bubbling away on a gas hob. The only concession to technology is a small automatic bottling machine, which completes up to 100 jars per day. His best selling Lemon Curd devours 3,000 eggs per week. Fruit is bought locally where possible but is also imported blast-frozen from abroad. Producing truly distinctive preserves is a hard trick. There's only so much that can be done with a Seville orange and a heap of sugar whether its mother, master chef or a multinational wielding the wooden spoon. But Andrew Wild achieves both quality and range: 22 jams, 12 marmalades, nine mustards, eight chutneys and four honeys, involving all the familiar variants and liquor additions. Each year, Farmhouse Preserves add something new to their repertoire and the latest plans involve a range of flavoured oils and experiments with various chillies, herbs and spices.

Stumps Lane, Darley,
Nr. Harrogate, N. Yorks
☎ *01423 780996*
Open: please 'phone ahead

HEALEY

Rosebud Preserves

Rosebud Preserves in picturesque Healey make jams brimming with fruit and their chutneys are positively crammed with nuts and spices. Yorkshire born Elspeth Biltoft and her Australian husband Philip reckon that only by using the best ingredients and loading in the same unstinting proportion found in domestic recipes do they achieve equivalent boldness of flavour. The result is that the two of them have expanded to seven and they've decamped from the kitchen to a converted barn next door. It's been a fast commercial success story since their 1989 launch. Classic jams apart, their Indian and Far East range includes such fiery specimens as Bengal Chutney, Hot Lime Pickle and Aubergine and Chilli Pickle. Then, there are gentler sage jellies, apricot chutneys and an old fashioned, buttery lemon curd. The quality of Rosebud Preserves has seen them picked up by London's blue chip food halls at Harvey Nichols, Neal's Yard Dairy, Conran's and even by New York's flagship food emporium, Dean & DeLuca.

— YORKSHIRE RELISH —

It was a Leeds chemist Robert Goodall who in 1837 set up in business to bottle his wife's recipe of Yorkshire Relish. The success of this and other relishes and ketchups developed into the Hammond Sauce Works, based today at Apperley Bridge. Yorkshire Relish had been known for generations. The earliest references to it come in the Yorkshire Archaeological Pipe Roll of Richard II in the 14th century. The thin spicy sauce of vinegar, molasses, sugar, onion, tamarind and spices remains essentially unchanged today. Sadly, the famous Hammond Sauce Works Band was considered too expensive and was sold to the Yorkshire Building Society two years ago.

More accessibly, they appear throughout the year in many good Yorkshire delicatessens and in the summer months at Middleham and Masham markets and the region's agriculture and flower shows. The Biltoft's operate a mail order service and are happy to serve callers at the farm with the caveat that they are often out walking on Sundays. As the New Yorkers at Dean & DeLuca would doubtless say – enjoy!

Rosebud Farm, Healey,
Ripon, N. Yorks
☎ *01765 689174*
Open: Mon-Fri 9am-5.30pm
May-Oct Masham Market: Wed
& Sat Reeth Market Fri
Phone ahead at weekend

HUDDERSFIELD

Shaw's of Huddersfield
Yorkshire's definitive food historian Peter Brears tells us that whenever meat was served in 19th century Yorkshire it was always accompanied by the appropriate sauce or pickle. If it was beef then it would be pickled red cabbage. So, in 1889, when George Shaw and his two sons, Vincent and Walter, set up a stall in Huddersfield's covered market selling relish, vinegar and pickles (alongside ink, patent medicines and bleach) they could hardly

fail. Shaw's grew to supply wholesalers and other pickle manufacturers and their delivery team of heavy horses and covered wagons became known in Huddersfield as 'Shaw's Circus'. Then, in the depression of the 1930s, son Walter developed a best-selling, cheap and easy pickle that would make Shaw's an indelible household name in Yorkshire food. No Yorkshire Sunday tea was complete without pickled beetroot. Shaw's sold it on their own market stalls across the north of England and when the war brought shortages of most other fruit and vegetables, home grown beetroot reigned supreme. Today's business is run by Martin Shaw, the great grandson of founder George. You won't find Shaw's pickles on the trendier delicatessen shelves but after 100 years their pickled red cabbage, the all conquering pickled beetroot and their vivid yellow piccalilli, another brand leader, are all still turning up on Sunday tea tables across Yorkshire and countless ploughmen still crunch into a Shaw's pickled onion in a thousand Yorkshire pubs.

Ivy Street East, Aspley,
Huddersfield, W. Yorks
☎ *01484 539999*
Not open to the public

LEEDS

Granny's Kitchen
Granny's Kitchen did indeed begin life as a kitchen table enterprise back in 1986 when David and Meg Cooper started selling their jams, chutneys and marmalades at flea markets and craft fairs. Now they have moved out of the kitchen and into a converted mill in Bramley as they have expanded their sales to grocers and gift shops throughout Yorkshire. Their preserves remain low-tech, made in small batches and with local and regional fruit whenever possible.

St. Catherine's Mill, Broad Lane,
Bramley, Leeds, W. Yorks
☎ *0113 255 3884*
Open: please 'phone ahead

OSMOTHERLEY

Trevor Swales Honey
Trevor Swales at Osmotherley is perfectly situated on the edge of the North York Moors. Like generations of bee-keepers before him, he takes his hives to the moors as soon as the heather begins to bloom: 'It should be early August but I always get jumpy and take them up in the last week of July.' Trevor is a milkman who developed his enthusiasm for bee-keeping after taking over

---

YORKSHIRE HONEY

*The North York Moors have been bee country for hundreds of years. Records going back to the middle ages establish honey being collected from wild bees in the Forest of Pickering, a tradition sustained by the monks of **Ampleforth**. In the last century honey still provided a valuable income for rural families. Hundreds of hives could be seen in the shelter of the dry stone walls on Egton, Goathland and Wheeldale moors. Although there has been a decline in bee-keeping, a visit to the honey tent at the Great Yorkshire Show reveals its enduring popularity and a visit to the honey bee exhibition at **Betton Farm** at East Ayton will explain what it's all about. For real honey, search out the shows, serious food shops and country markets. A great deal of cheap supermarket honey is blended Australian and Mexican honey which is little more than a sugary preserve whereas real honey has a definite flowery taste. Honey enthusiasts regard single-flower honey as the best. In Britain, there are few large areas that contain only a single flower but the North York Moors are exceptional. Acre upon acre of purple heather make it the largest expanse of heather in Europe and the envy of the honey world.*

his father's hives in 1977, building them up from 20 hives to the 70 he keeps today. His mixed flower honey comes from oil seed rape, bean and lime tree flowers. It is a delicate, mild honey, available set or clear: there's no difference in the flavour. But Trevor's real passion is reserved for ling or heather honey. Extracting the honey is normally done in special presses but for heather honey Trevor still uses the traditional method of squeezing the honey through a straining bag. The result is a natural jellied texture, full of minute air bubbles. It has a strong and distinctive aromatic flavour. 'Whenever people taste it', says Trevor, 'they say it's the honey they remember from childhood.' Honey is seasonal. A cold, wet summer can mean a disastrous yield and it requires a tolerant retailer to put up with an erratic supply. Tony Howard of **Lewis & Cooper** in Northallerton, a notable supporter of local food producers, stocks the flower and heather honey made by Trevor Swales. It's the real thing.

32 South End, Osmotherley, Northallerton, N. Yorks
☎ *01609 883320*
Open: any reasonable hour

WOMERSLEY

Womersley Hall Preserves

Hyssop and rosemary, fragrant lavender and Friar's Balsam

were the smells of Martin Parson's childhood. Home was Nymans House, near Haywards Heath, in Sussex, where Martin's parents, the Count and Countess of Rosse, created one of the country's great gardens. During the war the family moved north to Womersley Hall, a beautiful Queen Anne house, where Martin grew up sharing it with the British Army who were billeted there. Nymans House has since been passed to the National Trust. Those evocative smells of childhood, along with an affinity with gardens, must have left their mark because since 1979 Aline and Martin Parsons have successfully grown herbs, soft fruits and 14 varieties of peppers which they make into an original range of preserves, oils and vinegars. In their clever hands, what might be pretentious actually tastes superb. Their bottles and jars are in a fair range of the region's delicatessens but it's worth calling in to sense something of a unique operation and buy the produce at its starting price: some retailers have managed olympic mark ups. Martin does the growing in a magical picture-book walled garden. Great drifts of flowers and herbs compete for space: santolina, pennyroyal, lady's mantle, curry plant, sage, oregano, tansy and golden rod. Herbs are made into jellies and vinegars. Flowers and seed heads hang in a distant dry-

ing room to be used for decoration or pot pourri. In her enormous kitchen, Aline prepares jellies from a base of apple infused with the flavours of geranium, lavender, tarragon and oregano. They all have a pure but delicate intensity. Apache jelly, made from a surplus of chillies, has a good hot kick that goes best with smoked meats or cold roast beef. Their unusual vinegars include golden raspberry, dark opal basil and mulberry from a tree reputed to have been planted by Charles I. There are flavoured oils, chutneys, strawberry jam, honey from their own hives, creamed horseradish and pickled walnuts from a walnut tree in the garden. They have a wide range of fresh cut, dried or pot grown herbs, including 16 varieties of basil and unusual ones that include bergamot, borage, chervil, costmary, curry plant, bronze and green fennel, a fabulously scented lemon verbena, mugwort, Greek oregano, pennyroyal, rosemary, rue, pineapple sage, salad burnet, French tarragon and lemon thyme. The list goes seductively on.

Womersley, Nr. Darrington, Doncaster, S. Yorks
☎ *01977 620294*
Open: summer Sat & Bank Holidays 10.30am-6pm Sun 12 noon-6pm Dec-mid March Sun 2pm-5pm Hours variable, please 'phone ahead

---

THE JAM FACTORIES

Before the Second World War fruit growing was a significant part of the rural economy in the Vale of Pickering and the villages of North Yorkshire. Teams of women and girls were recruited to pick fruit for the big jam factories: Hartley's of Liverpool or Moorhouse's of Leeds. Apples were picked by the barrel load and sent to Rowntrees of York to be made into their famous jelly. Everyone from cottage gardeners to commercial fruit growers was involved in fruit picking during the summer months. Women sometimes earned pin money by collecting crab apples for the jam factories. Sacks of gooseberries, baskets of plums, redcurrants, blackcurrants, raspberries and pears left Kirkbymoorside station every day between July and September, bound for the conurbations. The best quality went to shops in Whitby and Scarborough or on to wholesalers for the markets of the West Riding. Everything else went to the jam factories. Fruit growing declined in North Yorkshire after the war.

7

Sweets & Chocolates

Yorkshire has always had an exceedingly sweet tooth. The love affair probably dates from when sugar stopped being an expensive luxury reserved for the gentry; probably from 1660 when John Taylor set up his sugar refinery in Skeldergate, York and dentists started rubbing their hands. When the Victorian Staithes Group painted the fishing villages of the north east Yorkshire coast they found the poorest children sucking home-made dummies made from linen soaked in sugar. In contemporary York, British Sugar turns out 600 tonnes of sugar per day from the beet grown in the Vale of York. Above all, Yorkshire has given Britain an historic conveyor belt of household names in chocolate and confectionery. The likes of Quality Street, Liquorice Allsorts and Kit Kat are all still made in astonishing quantities in Halifax, Sheffield and York despite the multinational upheavals in the trade. Yorkshire manufacturers made world-beating breakthroughs in the development of toffee, chocolates and boiled sweets and in enlightened management before foreign regimes took over. Yorkshire spawned the famous high street chain of Thornton's, too, but if old fashioned sweet shops and tobacconists are on the wane, little Maxon's of Sheffield are still independently making their mint humbugs and Jesmona black bullets for the big screw top jars of the North. At the chic end of the market there is the arrival of the chocolatiers with their truffles and their Belgian fineries. And when, in 1990, the Chocolate Society launched their national campaign for real chocolate, where else could they conceivably have been based but Yorkshire?

MANUFACTURERS

DERBY

Thornton's

They're now based in Derby but the roots of Thornton's chocolate remain resolutely in Sheffield. For a household name, Thornton's are relative newcomers in Yorkshire's chocolate history. They trace their roots to Joseph William Thornton who in 1911 forswore commercial travelling to set up hopefully 'the best sweet shop in town' in Norfolk Street, Sheffield with his 14 year old son Norman installed behind the counter. It worked. Two years later Joseph opened a second Sheffield shop at The Moor. Here, sugar was boiled up in copper pans in the cellar. Violet, rose and fruit creams dipped in chocolate were produced upstairs. Today, Thornton's plc are in every town centre and high street in Britain. There are 232 shops, 221 franchises, two factories (in Derbyshire) and a presence in France and Belgium. More than £5 million is taken in the four days leading up to each Christmas. Their research reveals that the classic Thornton's customer is a middle class woman in her mid 20s buying a gift for her mother. If she lives in the north she will marginally prefer Thornton's Special Toffee over her southern sister's choice of Continental Assortment, which they also make for Marks and Spencer and is their best seller, followed by Thornton's Special Toffee. They have recently added diabetic chocolate, personalised Easter eggs and ice cream to their range. A wide number of shops throughout Yorkshire and Humberside.

Thornton Park,
Somercotes, Derbys
☎ *01773 540550*
Not open to the public

ELLAND

Dobson's of Elland

Huddersfield, Halifax and Sheffield rock, pear drops and herbal lozenges of dubious medicinal benefit are some of the long lost lines produced by sweet makers Dobson's of Elland. The demand for Halifax rock may have dried up but the production of boiled sweets in Elland has continued ever since Joseph Dobson boiled up his first vat of sugar in 1850. It's still a family firm and one story handed down the generations is that Joseph Dobson gave his friend John Mackintosh of Halifax his first recipe on the road to Rolo and Quality Street fame. Modern day Dobson's is run by Joseph's great nephew Tony Chadwick and they still specialise in old fashioned boiled sweets. Their biggest customer is Morrison supermarkets. Groups can tour the factory by arrangement and taste the sweets still warm from the production line. Mrs Chadwick runs Dobson's sweet shop in the centre of Elland, selling Dobson's Herbal Voice Tablets and Yorkshire Mixture.

Factory: Northgate,
Elland, W. Yorks
☎ *01422 372165*
Visits by arrangement
Shop: 70 Southgate,
Elland, W. Yorks
☎ *01422 377365*
Open: Mon-Fri 9am-5.30pm
Sat 9am-4.30pm

HALIFAX

Mackintosh

Halifax's John Mackintosh was responsible for two major developments in British confectionery from his humble beginnings in 1890 as a fledgling toffee maker at the age of 22 in King Cross Lane. First, he blended traditional English butterscotch style toffee with American caramel for the first modern British toffee. Mackintosh's Celebrated Toffee became famously popular with soldiers in the Great War. Then, out of what became his main factory in Queen's Road, he began coating his toffee in chocolate. It was the breakthrough that eventually led to world beaters like Quality Street in 1936 (named after a play by the author of Peter Pan, J. M. Barrie) and Rolo in 1937. Son Harold Mackintosh was successively made knight, peer and finally 1st Viscount of Halifax in 1957, the year that Munchies were invented. Mackintosh's other famous names were Weekend, Caramac and Toffee Crisp. They acquired Fox's Glacier Mints before being swallowed up by Rowntree's in 1988 who in their turn fell to Nestlé. The Halifax factory still employs 2,500 people and churns out Toffo, Walnut Whip, Easter eggs and £80 million worth of Quality Street every year.

Albion Mills, Halifax, W. Yorks
☎ *01422 365761*
Not open to the public

HULL

Needler's

With over 300 staff, Needler's is one of Hull's biggest employers, but it began simply enough when in 1886 Fred Needler took his mother's life savings of £100 and bought a sweet shop in Anne Street. In 1916 he began the present building in Sculcoates Lane, producing toffees, boiled sweets, pastilles, sugared almonds and chocolates. In 1938 Needler's devised a transparent sweet, the glacé, which dominated the fruit drop market for more than a decade. They still have

THE CHOCOLATE SOCIETY

Have you ever tried listenening to your chocolate? Apparently, when tasting real chocolate you should use touch, sight, smell, taste and sound. In the words of the Chocolate Society: 'It is the crystalline structure of cocoa butter which gives real chocolate its distinctive crisp snap with a texture of tree bark in the break.' So asking a member of the Chocolate Society to share your Cadbury's cream egg is like inviting Baron de Rothschild to have a glass of Blue Nun. Even the vocabulary is closer to wine than chocolate. Valrhona's Grand Cru Manjari has, according to the Society, 'a clear and warm robe typical of Criollos. Only moderately bitter, its soft and refreshing taste has light spicy tones, reminiscent of almonds on a background of cherries and strawberries' and a Valrhona Grand Cru Pur Caraibe made from the best Trinitario beans is described as 'a warm feminine chocolate, dark and sultry'.

The Chocolate Society was launched in Yorkshire in 1990 by Chantal Coady, who runs Rococo, a fashionable chocolate shop in Chelsea, and Nicola Porter, wife of chocolate importer Alan Porter. Apart from the obvious aim of drumming up some sales at the rarified end of the business, their mission is to 'encourage an understanding of fine chocolate'. We are talking serious chocolate: rich, dark, bitter and expensive. Fine chocolate is low in sugar and high in cocoa. A 50% cocoa content is considered good. Upwards is better. The flavour comes from the quality and variety of the cocoa bean with Criollo and Trinitario rated two of the best. The level of roasting gives it a 'roundness of flavour'. Real chocolate should contain cocoa butter rather than substitutes; natural rather than synthetic vanilla and sugar should be used sparingly. 'The low grade, cloying confection which the British consume by the ton every week is candy', sniffs the Society. It contains only 20% cocoa and large amounts of sugar, vegetable fat and powdered milk.

The Society blend their own chocolate at Norwood Bottom Farm in a lovely unspoilt fold of the Washburn Valley overlooking Lindley Reservoir. They market the chocolate under their own labels. 'Cocoa Pod' comes in blocks consisting of 64%, 66% and 70% cocoa solids. The 'Classic' range is available in milk (35% cocoa solids) and white chocolate that does not contain any cocoa solids but contains real cocoa butter. It is available from a number of good chocolate shops in the region or through membership of the Society.

Membership of the society costs £30 which includes a lapel badge, a box of Valrhona chocolates, a mail order list of speciality foods and invitations to chocolate functions. A further £25 pays for a subscription to the quarterly newsletter with erudite titles such as 'Tempering Couverture: Part II'. All of which means you have to be a committed chocolate lover (chocaholic is a non-word in these circles). Key words from the real chocolate glossary: couverture (a French word for professional chocolate), ganache (a blend of chocolate and cream used in truffles), amer (bitter), carre (a small square of dark chocolate of 3cm x 3cm). Not least, the Society can tell you how to eat the stuff: 'A small piece of chocolate should be placed on the tongue and allowed to melt of its own accord – no sucking or chewing'. Members and non-members can buy chocolate and speciality food items from the Society's mail order list.

Norwood Bottom Farm, Norwood Bottom, Nr Otley, W. Yorks ☎ 01943 851101 Not open to the public.

Glacé Fruit Drops today as well as Jersey Butter Toffees, Eclairs, Sensations and Thomas the Tank Engine Jelly Shapes. But now the company is owned by Nirdar of Norway, Scandinavia's biggest sweet manufacturer, who every Christmas erect a 60 foot Norwegian spruce in Queen Victoria Square.

Sculcoates Lane, Hull, N. Humbs
☎ *01482 42435*
Not open to the public

PONTEFRACT

Trebor Bassett

The story of Pontefract liquorice and the road to Bertie Bassett is splendidly hoary. The liquorice root has been attributed with curative properties since Cleopatra's reign and when monks settled in England at the time of the Crusades they planted liquorice. But it was only around Pontefract that the soil depth and limestone pastures encouraged the shrublike bushes to flourish. After the dissolution, local growers turned liquorice into a cottage industry, making lozenges for stomach disorders. In 1760 George Dunhill added sugar to the mix, moulded it into a small black medallion, stamped it with the town seal and completed the first Pomfret cake, also known as Yorkshire Pennies. Their popularity may have had something to do with the extract of liquorice which is 50 times sweeter than sugar. At any rate, ten Pontefract companies jumped on the bandwagon of which the most successful was Wilkinson's. But it was the Sheffield firm of Bassett who ultimately dominated the business through a tale that has doubtless improved in a century of telling. In 1899 a Bassett salesman Charlie Thompson dropped all his samples on the floor of a shop. Upon seeing the mixture of buttons, cubes and nuggets of liquorice, the shopkeeper immediately ordered a

similar mixture. Charlie the salesman was charged with naming the new product and Liquorice Allsorts were born, destined to become a world best seller of more than 10 million sweets per day. Bassetts went on to produce liquorice catherine wheels, pipes and bootlaces as well as famous brands of wine gums, dolly mixtures and jelly babies. In 1961 Bassetts took over Wilkinson's of Pontefract and in 1966 Barratt's, makers of the famous sherbet fountain. Then, in 1990 Cadbury Schweppes took over the lot. The liquorice is all imported from the Middle East these days but Bertie Bassett still marches out of the Sheffield works and 20 liquorice bushes still bloom around the flagpole at Ferrybridge Road.

Monkhill Works,
Ferrybridge Road,
Pontefract, W. Yorks
☎ *01977 701431*
Not open to the public

SHEFFIELD

Maxon's

A determinedly northern manufacturer. Not one of their 80 varieties of rock and boiled sweets is sold in the south of England. They also take some tracking down in Yorkshire. **Reah's** of Masham is one dependable source. Their hallmark products are Yorkshire Mixture and 'Jesmona' Black Bullets, strong mint flavoured boiled sugar balls, marketed in an uncompromising black and white tin which could easily double as a paint pot. Black Bullets originated in Jesmond in Northumberland before being transferred to Sheffield in the 1960s. Much sought after as a gift for grandmothers, according to the man at Maxon's.

Bradbury Street,
Sheffield, S. Yorks
☎ *0114 2 554216*
Not open to the public

YORK

Nestlé Rowntree

It remains hard to place the word Nestlé in front of as fine a Yorkshire institution as Rowntree. Unbelievable amounts of chocolate still pour out of the mighty 140 acre Haxby Road complex and the company is Britain's biggest confectionery exporter but the sad truth is that Rowntree is just a name now, albeit with a history worth remembering. The maverick Mary Tuke is the unsung heroine of the Rowntree story. In the 18th century, aged 30 and scandalously unmarried, she ran an illegal grocer's shop in York without a licence from York Merchant Adventurers. She was hauled before the courts before they finally allowed her to trade in 1732. It was her descendants who began manufacturing plain and milk chocolate for the family business and it was not until 1862 that Henry Isaac Rowntree acquired the company. Besides cocoa, the company produced chocolate drops, beans and balls. In the late 19th century they acquired bigger premises from which to produce their famous fruit gums and fruit pastilles. It was brother Joseph who bought the Haxby Road site and whose name is indelibly stamped upon all the great Rowntree enterprises. He introduced various welfare initiatives including a pension scheme on which many of today's systems are based and the first ever works suggestion scheme. He set up cookery training for his full-time women workers but abandoned coach trips after they all got drunk at Whitby on the first outing. He built a model village at New Earswick, a library for his employees and started the famous Rowntree Trusts, one of which grew into the powerful Westminster Press newspaper chain. In 1933 Rowntree developed Black Magic described as 'the first chocolate assortment for the mass market', still the best selling box. There followed Aero and Kit Kat in 1935, the latter today's top U.K. brand and made at a rate of 3,400 bars a minute in York; Dairy Box in 1936 and Smarties in 1937, still the outright children's favourite. War interrupted this astonishing creative run and production was given over to munitions but within two years of the war ending, Rowntree's were once again developing new products and providing mass employment. The idea for Polo, 'the mint with the hole', came from the American G.I.s who sucked a sweet called Lifesavers. Other famous successes for Rowntree's were After Eight mints in 1962 (now made alongside Toffee Crisp in Castleford) and the Yorkie bar in 1976 (disappointingly made outside Yorkshire). Rowntree's had strong roots both in Quakerism and its York identity. When in the mid 1980s the firm was threatened with a hostile takeover by the Swiss multi-national Nestlé, the response was deeply felt. Opponents even travelled to Vevey in Switzerland to protest at Nestlé headquarters. The takeover went ahead despite the public outcry. Although no longer in Quaker hands when Nestlé won, the company was still recognised as a highly ethical firm. Nestlé was and remains the world's biggest and most powerful food

multi-national. It also stands condemned in 14 countries for its marketing of infant formula in the developing world. A British boycott of Nescafé has been in place for several years, supported by bodies from the Catholic Institute of International Relations to the Women's Institute. There can be little doubt where Joseph Rowntree would have stood. The Rowntree Trust, set up by the chocolate company to fund charitable and ethical enterprises, severed its final links with the firm after the Nestlé takeover went through. They've even changed the colours in the Smarties tube.

Haxby Road, York
☎ *01904 653071*
Not open to the public

Terry's Suchard

It still doesn't rate a mention in Pevsner's authoritative Buildings of England although the rest of York's architecture fill 90 pages but Terry's factory, properly The Chocolate Works, is still a magnificent edifice, with its 1,000ft red brick frontage and 135ft high clock tower standing sentinel over the Knavesmire and the Ring Road. Its 170 acre site at Bishopthorpe Road has been visited by kings and queens. Like Rowntree's, it was a pioneering Yorkshire giant whose glories lie in the past. Today it's owned by an American cigarette company. Terry's can trace its roots back

to 1767 when Mr Berry and Mr Bayldon began selling candied citron, jujubes, mint cakes, coltsfoot rock and acid drops from their Bootham works. In 1823 they were joined by an apothecary named Joseph Terry who moved the company to St. Helen's Square, and laid the foundations for the famous company. He was eventually knighted by Queen Victoria for his philanthropic services. Although there were many companies making sweets and candies, chocolate wasn't made into bars until the mid 19th century. The fashion of the day was to drink chocolate in coffee houses not eat it in chunks. It was the second Joseph Terry who saw the solid potential of chocolate. Terry's bought their own cocoa plantation in the Venezuelan Andes and based the elegant company logo on one of the native cocoa palms. Their specialisation in chocolate led to Neapolitans, the famous All Gold assortment and the Chocolate Orange. Terry's were once a paternalistic company who back in the 1930s initiated insurance and pension schemes, holidays with pay and ran convalescent homes and sports clubs. The Second World War halted all chocolate production and Terry's made aeroplane propellers instead. From the 1960s onwards, the story of Terry's is one of take-over and merger, first by Trust House Forte, then Colgate Palmolive, on to United Biscuits and finally in 1993 by Kraft Jacobs Suchard who in turn are owned by Philip Morris, the mega U.S. tobacco conglomerate. The last family chairman was Peter Terry who retired in 1986. The factory tours have finished. The shop in St. Helen's Square is now a gents' outfitters. A replica of a Terry's shop can be found in York's Castle Museum.

Bishopthorpe Road, York
☎ *01904 653090*
Not open to the public

JOSEPH ROWNTREE TRUST

The Joseph Rowntree Trust still exists today to support research into housing, social policy and social research to the tune of £6 million a year. The trust has carried out housing schemes in York and elsewhere in Yorkshire. It is responsible for the Family fund established to support handicapped children in the wake of the Thalidomide tragedy and conducts research through the Policy Studies Institute in London. The Trusts have always worked independently of the Rowntree company and over the years have divested themselves of all Rowntree and subsequently Rowntree Nestlé shares.

SWEET & CHOCOLATE SHOPS

BRADFORD

Ambala Sweet Centre

Invited to an Asian wedding? Then it's good form to take along a box of mithai or Asian sweets. **Mumtaz Paan** have Royal sweets and **Kashmir Crown Bakeries** make their own but recommendations are unanimous for the sweets made by the Pakistani chain of Ambala. There are no spotlights or glitzy displays, just a discreet little shop on Great Horton Road where you can buy a one pound box of mixed sweets and impress the bride, the groom and his mother.

205 Great Horton Road,
Bradford, W. Yorks
☎ 01274 579374
Open: Mon-Sun 11am-midnight

Kashmir Crown Bakeries

A classic corner-shop to chain store success, Mohammed Saleen has taken Kashmir Crown Bakeries from infancy in 1956 to probably Bradford's biggest Asian sweet producer. The glossy shop in Lilycroft Road is one of the smartest sweet counters in town, popular with both Asian and English customers. Kashmir's best seller is barfi, a sort of fudge made from milk, sugar and butter, sold here in five different varieties, including almond and pistachio. There are gulab jaman, the sausage-shaped doughnuts, deep fried and dripping in syrup. The jellied sweets are halwa, flavoured with carrot or pistachio nuts. Patisa is a nut toffee. Butter pinni is a rich mixture of butter, sugar, rice flour, semolina and gram flour. Kashmir Crown also make both English and Asian cakes and biscuits. The fairy cakes, sold under the somewhat spurious Yorkshire Cottage label, are

rather dull but the Asian range is more interesting: caraway biscuits, coconut macaroons and Khasta Khatie, a soft biscuit flavoured with pistachio nuts and cardamom.

81-83 Carrington Street,
Bradford, W. Yorks
☎ 01274 668190
Open: Mon-Sat 9am-6pm

210-212 Lilycroft Road,
Bradford, W. Yorks
☎ 01274 497872
Open: Mon-Sun 9am-6pm

Office & Bakery:
1-2 Worthington Street,
Bradford, W. Yorks
☎ 01274 735967
Open: Mon-Sat 9am-6pm

HARROGATE

Betty's

Champions of the tea room and the fat rascal, Betty's are also up there challenging the chocolatiers. Speckled hens or black and white pandas were part of last year's Easter theme. But there are new lines and stunning window displays every year. Heat means certain death to chocolate so work begins in the cool early hours. Year round, Betty's produce boxes of assorted Belgian chocolates but these can look positively mundane beside the white and milk chocolate saddle-back pig, the chocolate fish or the golden guineas and silver hearts. Available from all four Betty's branches.

1 Parliament Street,
Harrogate, N. Yorks
☎ 01423 565191
Orders by post: 01423 531211
Open: Mon-Sun 9am-9pm

Farrah's Toffee

The familiar old fashioned blue and silver tins of Farrah's Harrogate toffee have remained virtu-

ally unchanged since John Farrah began packaging them in 1840. His mother had already been making and selling the toffee to visitors to Harrogate for ten years before her commercially minded son decided that they could also send souvenir tins of toffee through the mail. The tins are said to have found their way to a Nigerian tribal chief as a purse and to Brezhnev's Kremlin. The toffee is still made in copper kettles and stirred with oak paddles which the owners claim is important to the taste. The recipe is 'a closely guarded secret' but as food regulations insist that all ingredients must be printed on the packaging it can be boldly revealed that Farrah's toffee contains oil of lemon, butter, palm oil and, above all, heaps of sugar. If the toffee has benefited from keeping a steadfast image, the half-hearted shop on Royal Parade could do with a fresh sense of purpose. Also available from sweet shops around the region.

7 Royal Parade,
Harrogate, N. Yorks
☎ 01423 565014
Open: Tue-Sat
winter 11am-4.30pm
summer until 5.30pm

Fine Chocolate Company

Violet and rose creams suggest the delicate tastes of an earlier era. In genteel Harrogate they remain the contemporary best selling chocolates for the Fine Chocolate Company, an exquisite and delightfully dated chocolate shop not a stone's throw from **Betty's** tea rooms. Cream fudge, Harrogate toffee, champagne truffles and white and milk chocolate sea shells are all here. They can be packed, as befits such luxuries, in sumptuous flowery boxes and tied with a big satin bow. The shop stocks the quality chocolate bars made by the **Chocolate Society** in Otley under the brand name Cocoa Pod. It is available with 64%, 66% and 70% cocoa solids. There's milk and white from their 'Classic' range. A simple café at the back of the shop serves tea and cakes.

31 Montpellier Parade,
Harrogate, N. Yorks
☎ *01423 503337*
Open: Mon-Sat 9.30am-5.30pm
Sun 11am-5pm

ILKLEY

Candy Box

Refined tastes and careful purses appear to be the hallmark of the Ilkley shopper at the Candy Box. High percentage Cocoa Pod chocolate from the **Chocolate Society** comes in second place to the German Feodora bar that sells for half the price for the same amount of cocoa solid. Still, the overall winners as everywhere seem to be the truffles, butter creams and liqueur cherries of the loose Belgian chocolates. Rowntree, Terry's and the like can rest in peace; sugar still wins over cocoa solids every time.

15 Grove Promenade,
Ilkley, W. Yorks
☎ *01943 608705*
Open: Mon-Sat 9.30am-5.30pm
Sun 1pm-5.30pm

Humphreys

Being let loose in a chocolate factory should be every child's dream but when your Dad runs one you can afford to be blasé. David Humphreys' children apparently find helping out in the family chocolatiers simply boring. His customers are less indifferent facing a choice of 50 different varieties of handmade chocolate, all produced on the premises. No need to get left with the strawberry creams – choose instead a box of walnut

cups, vanilla creams, soft caramel or pralines or any combination. There are 18 different fresh cream truffle flavours like rum, kirsch, cointreau, chartreuse, vanilla, passion fruit and the best selling champagne. David Humphreys has been making chocolates for 40 years, 12 of them with the old Union Castle line at a time when cruise ships had their own dedicated confectioners. After jobs in Switzerland, France and Belgium he came home to open his own shop in Skipton. The business was a success. But as they obtained ever larger contracts and took on more staff, David Humphreys felt he was losing control. In 1985 he decided to take a step back and revolt against volume in favour of his version of perfectionism. He closed the Skipton shop, found smaller premises in Ilkley and started all over again. The business today is strictly small-scale and the smell of melted chocolate pervades as David can be seen tempering his chocolate at the back of the shop. His wife Jenny looks after the customers and the mail order business. The reluctant children help out in the holidays. Prices range from 40p to £40.

16 Leeds Road, Ilkley, W. Yorks
☎ *01943 609477*
Open: Mon-Sat 9am-5pm

LEEDS

Ambala Sweet Centre

See Bradford entry.

210 Roundhay Road,
Leeds, W. Yorks
☎ *0113 235 0309*
Open: Mon-Sun 11.30am-
midnight

MASHAM

Reah's Gourmet Confectionery

Reah's Gourmet Confectionery in Masham's stately Market Place is a real old fashioned

sweet shop. In fact, much better than that institution of fond memory. It has long and serried rows of sweets and chocolate, a celebration of sugar and stickiness, where children of all ages need to be forcibly restrained. Pick and mix bins may have replaced the traditional jars but the contents reverberate down the years. Remember cherry lips and floral gums? Rhubarbs and custards, acid drops and 'Jesmona' black bullets from Sheffield? There are even aniseed balls with a real aniseed in the middle. John Reah, for 15 years a grocer in Masham, came out of retirement with a memory of his childhood sweet shop in Saltburn to inspire this misty-eyed selection. A jar of giant gob stoppers on the counter makes the point emphatically. It almost goes without saying that it's an adult not a child making the order. With all the jelly babies, sherbet dips and humbugs, the 'Gourmet' of the shop's title might make chocolate purists shudder at first but then there are bars of high cocoa, bitter chocolate here: France's Valrhona and the best of Belgium. Three times a week Reah's turn producer, making a delicious butter fudge in an endless combination of flavours but one way and another containing chocolate, nuts, raisins and coconut. The best seller, appropriately, is 'Old Peculier', doused with Theakston, Masham's most famous brew. Reah's also support their two local cheesemakers with **Fortmayne Dairy**'s Richard III Wensleydale and **Hawes Creamery** mature Wensleydale among a small but respectable cheese selection and a range of preserves from **Cunningham**'s local producers in Bedale.

7 Market Place, Masham,
Nr. Ripon, N. Yorks
☎ *01765 689021*
Open: Mon-Sat 10am-5pm
Sun 12.30pm-5pm closed Thur

NORTHALLERTON

Bellina

The school children of North-allerton have refined tastes. Aniseed balls? No thanks. Unfased by the chandeliers and sumptuous ribboned boxes of Bellina's, they often call in after school for a single champagne truffle or a cherry dipped in kirsch and bitter chocolate, if you please. Owner Paula Rowntree (no relation to the famous chocolate family) has 80 kinds of chocolate on offer. Some of the flavours verge on the bizarre. How about banana, blueberry or pistachio cream? Everything is available by mail order.

4 Market Row,
Northallerton, N. Yorks
☎ *01609 774148*
Open: Mon-Fri 9.30am-5pm
Sat 9.30am-5.30pm

OTLEY

Patisserie Viennoise

Three tons of chocolate pass through the door of 34 Westgate every year to go into Trevor Backhouse's handmade chocolates. Meditate upon it. With 48% to 53% cocoa solids to be fortified by whisky, Grand Marnier, Kirsch and, rather worryingly, Malibu, these are truffles and chocolates for the determinedly sweet toothed. In fact, Patisserie Viennoise chocolate is probably too sweet for the fundamentalists of the **Chocolate Society**, based just outside Otley at Norwood for whom bitterness is the true gospel. Trevor Backhouse began his career working in the village bakery in Gildersome, learning as he puts it 'the old skills' with part-time study at the local catering college. He then spent four years mastering continental skills at Patisserie Viennoise (hence the shop name) at Juan les Pins in the south of France. Back in Westgate you can order an 8" Black Forest ga-teau at £13 or an elaborate three tier wedding cake at £200 and upwards. For something different and almost certainly ceremonial, Trevor Backhouse can construct a croquembouche – choux buns, filled with crème patissiere, dipped in sugar and then piled high into a fantastic pyramid.

34 Westgate,
Otley, W. Yorks
☎ *01943 467927*
Open: Mon-Fri 8.30am-5.30pm
Sat 8.30-5pm

SCARBOROUGH

Bonnet's

Bonnet's are proud of their English traditions: chocolate by Lesme, an old established British firm, tempered and hand-dipped the old fashioned way on a marble slab with traditional fillings of orange, fruit, nuts and ginger. That the original Bonnet was a French Swiss confectioner hardly counts since he arrived back in 1880. It's been run by the Fairbank family since 1959. A café operates behind the shop.

38-40 Huntriss Row,
Scarborough, N. Yorks
☎ *01723 361033*
Open: Mon-Sun 9am-5.30pm

SHEFFIELD

Thornton's

In 1913 Joseph Thornton and his family lived over a shop on the Moor, making chocolates in the basement and began an empire that has become a household name. The original shop failed to survive the Sheffield blitz, but this shop, still on the Moor, is the nearest you'll get to the original Chocolate Kabin selling Thornton's vast range: continental, luxury white, luxury dark, toffees, fudges, personalised Easter eggs, the lot.

129 The Moor,
Sheffield, S. Yorks
☎ *0114 272 5320*
Open: Mon-Sat 9am-5.30pm

SKIPTON

Whitaker's

The anonymous square of mint chocolate that comes with the coffee in hotels and restaurants across the length and breadth of Europe probably began life in Skipton. Whitaker's remains the family firm it has always been since 1889. It started life as a grocer and draper's in Crosshills, near Keighley. Chocolate making was a sideline but it soon took over from everything else. At their height Whitaker's had five shops spanning the Lancashire/Yorkshire border but the concentration on the wholesale and export markets led to the closure of all but the Skipton branch. Here, Whitaker's mis-shapes are so popular that the company has even considered manufacturing them specially, according to Claire Whitaker who runs the retail side. Other best sellers are dipped ginger and dipped brazils but it's their after-dinner mints produced at a rate of 10,000 boxes a day that have quietly conquered Europe.

25 High Street, Skipton, N. Yorks
☎ *01756 700240*
Open: Mon-Sun 9am-5.30pm

WHITBY

The Chocolate Box

If you make it just a little way up the one in three hill on Whitby's north side, you will be rewarded with a sweet shop of the old order. The best seller remains Whitby fudge (inevitably made in Cornwall) but there are boiled sweets and, if you must, Whitby rock. Upmarket brands include Linden Lady, Bendicks chocolates, blocks of Valrhona and the **Chocolate Society's** own brand Cocoa Pod.

3 Golden Lion Bank,
Whitby, N. Yorks
☎ *01947 603255*
Mon-Sat 9am-5pm
summer Sun 1.30pm-5pm

8

Wholefoods

Of all the sectors to face the battering of the superstore explosion, wholefood shops have done better than most, more through homespun instincts than voracious capitalism. Nearly every town in Yorkshire and Humberside has a wholefood store of sorts and the cities support several. Not that they have been untouched by the supermarkets. Brown rice and pulses were once considered to be niche foods, too trivial for the big chains. Then came the bran revolution. Fibre was fashionable, roughage was good for you and F Plan was the diet. Suddenly Tesco and Safeway were filling their shelves with aduki beans and wheatgerm. Inevitably, some wholefood shops went under. Others were seduced by the lucrative market in nutritional supplements and all manner of pills and potions

– anathema to real wholefood shops committed to unadulterated wholesome food with nothing added and nothing taken away. High minded principles, however, never fought off a bank manager and there's little more dispiriting than a struggling, under-stocked wholefood shop. The successful ones know their stock, advise on special diets and search out unusual items like Japanese ume vinegar, ramen noodles, sea vegetables, Guatemalan honey, organic pulses, pure juices, fresh yeast and much more. Happily, our wholefood shops are also repairing their poor reputation for organic vegetables. Limp lettuces and tired cabbages used to be the norm but improved distribution means that shops can buy little and often at prices comparable to those in a conventional greengrocer.

WHOLEFOOD SHOPS

BARNSLEY

Pickering's

Hidden away in the far reaches of a florist's shop is Barnsley's best wholefood outlet. It's attractively laid out with big pine tables piled with produce and baskets of dried fruit. They stock a wide range of wholefoods from **Suma** and other quality suppliers. There are Puy lentils, the lentil connoisseur's lentil from Central France, with the utterly French cachet of its own appellation. There are pine kernels, Yorkshire honey and free range eggs. There's fresh yeast in the fridge and a wide range of flours from chapati to **Rakusen's** potato flour.

*36 Shambles Street,
Barnsley, S. Yorks*
☎ *01226 282862*
*Open: Mon-Fri 9am-5.15pm
Sat 9am-5pm*

BRADFORD

Bradford Wholefoods

Organic fruit and vegetables are few and far between in inner city Bradford so the organics delivered to this wholefood co-operative twice weekly (Tuesday and Thursday) are welcome. They are grown by co-op member Jack First and supplemented by supplies from Mike Sellers' **Stand-**

ford Hall Farm** at Pickering. They stock wholefoods and a limited range of homeopathic remedies.

*78 Morley Street,
Bradford, W. Yorks*
☎ *01274 307539*
*Open: Mon-Fri 9am-5.30pm
Sat 9am-5pm*

CLEETHORPES

Cleethorpes Wholefood Co-op

Part of a three strong chain of wholefood co-ops with sister ventures in Grimsby and Louth. Dependable for the mainstream needs.

*33 Cambridge Street,
Cleethorpes, S. Humbs*
☎ *01472 602880*
Open: Mon-Sat 9am-5pm

DENBY DALE

Your Nuts

How does a rye bread made with a sourdough culture from the town of Kostroma on the river Volga end up in Denby Dale? Well, it's made by Andrew Whitley of the famous Village Bakery in Melmerby, Cumbria. He developed a passion for traditional rye breads while working for the BBC's Russian Service. His bakery supplies Your Nuts with a wonderful range of bread and

cakes of which the Russian rye bread is his pride and joy. There are also Greek olive bread with onions, pumpkin seeds and stuffed olives, peanut butter shortcake, sticky Westmorland parkin, apricot slice and rich fruit cake, all delivered on Tuesday and Saturday to the converted mill in the centre of the village. Martin Fulton's Your Nuts is one of the biggest and most enterprising wholefood shops in the region and is well worth a detour. He also runs a wholesale operation and it's this that provides the vast range of produce for the retail business. Besides organic fruit and vegetables there is a 40 foot avenue of help-yourself dispensers containing sunflower seeds, pine nuts, carlins, green and Puy lentils, sun-dried tomatoes and all the wholefood regulars. They sell four kinds of prunes, Lexia raisins, figs, unsulphured apricots and candied fruit caps. Nuts span the range from macadamia to pecans. Anyone who mourns the loss of sago and tapioca from the national diet will find them here. Next come Indian spices, Chinese noodles, Japanese wholewheat ramen or tamari, teriyaki and shoyu sauces. The staff know their stock and can advise on sugar-free and gluten-free products. Jane Coleman, a tutor with the Vegetarian Society, holds rolling cookery demonstrations on Saturday mornings once a month and some pre-booked evening sessions using Your Nuts ingredients. Whether it's cold-pressed organic olive oil, ground nut oil from Burkino Faso or your favourite seasonal Provençal safflower oil, Your Nuts considers it a point of honour to find it and bring it back to Denby Dale. However, they are still puzzling over a purchase of Pau d'Arco.

THE FOOD COMMISSION

The Food Commission is an increasingly influential consumer watchdog on food. It is independent of industry and government and has run important campaigns through the pages of its quarterly 'Food Magazine', which it publishes with the Soil Association. The Commission relies for its funding on grants, donations and subscriptions. It has produced a number of useful books on food issues

The Food Commission, 3rd Floor, 5-11 Worship Street, London EC2 ☎ *0171 628 7774*

Beyond the fact that it's an organic Brazilian spice, nobody knows what to do with it. Answers to...

Springfield Mill, Norman Road, Denby Dale, W. Yorks
☎ *01484 865979*
Open: Mon-Fri 10am-5pm
Sat 9.30am-5pm
Sun 11am-5pm

DEWSBURY

Evergreen Wholefoods

If you were giving up a steady job with a building society to open a vegan wholefood shop, Dewsbury might be the third last place in Britain you'd choose as it comes third in the national heart attack league table after Glasgow and Wigan. Even climbing Daisy Hill to Evergreen Wholefoods could worsen the statistics but owner Mark Popplewell says he is slowly winning converts. Optimism suggests Dewsbury has plenty of sinners to repent. Customers, he says, usually come with an allergy problem. Once they've been in the shop they often come back. Besides wholefood, gluten-free and sugar-free products, there is fresh organic wholemeal bread on Wednesday. On other days, it is available frozen. There are pot grown herbs in summer.

70 Daisy Hill,
Dewsbury, W. Yorks
☎ *01924 457900*
Open: Mon-Sat 9am-5pm
Tue 9am-2pm

EASINGWOLD

Alternatives

Wholefoods and healthfoods are the basis of this small but well stocked wholefood shop run by Sally Clarke. She also has frozen vegetarian meals, goat's milk, herbal tea and coffee substitutes, a range of nutty breads, quiches and pasties. Eggs come from hens in small flocks which wander outside in daytime but are enclosed at night. Stoneground wholemeal flour comes from **Village Craft** at Grewelthorpe.

Chapel Lane,
Easingwold, N. Yorks
☎ *01347 822215*
Open: Mon-Wed 9.30am-1pm
& 2pm-5pm
Thur-Sat 9.30am-5pm

GRIMSBY

Grimsby Wholefood Co-operative

Grimsby Wholefood Co-op suffers by being down a hard-to-find passage next to the gas showrooms. Once located it has all the required grains, pulses, herbs and spices. They keep a good supply of organic vegetable juices but turnover has proved too slow for fresh fruit and vegetables. Pasties, vegetarian sausage rolls and savoury slices are baked locally by Linda Peterson using organic ingredients wherever possible. It is also a source of free range eggs. The shop is the mother ship of three wholefood co-operatives in Grimsby, Louth and Cleethorpes.

7b East St. Mary's Gate,
Grimsby, S. Humbs
☎ *01472 251112*
Open: Mon-Sat 9am-5.30pm

HALIFAX

Helios Wholefoods

This shop on the outskirts of Halifax is bright, clean and as neat as a pin. Besides the basic

---

YORKSHIRE TOFU

*Tofu can be translated from the Japanese as 'meat without blame' and for millions of vegetarians that's just what it is: a high protein food they can eat with a clear conscience. In restored farm buildings in the lovely village of Buttercrambe, Ron Malarkey produces organic tofu, made from the separated curds and whey of the soya bean. In recent years, tofu has become a heavily promoted vegetarian food, produced commercially on a massive scale. Ron's tofu is made in essentially the same way but he believes that by using Nigari, a Japanese extract of sea salt, to separate the curds and whey instead of the calcium sulphate used commercially, he has a better flavour to compensate for his smaller yield. Ron began making tofu at York's **Gillygate Bakery** during the evenings and weekends when they were closed. He delivered his tofu personally, travelling to Leeds by train while precariously balancing dripping boxes of tofu on his knees. Business has improved in the eight years since. Now he works from a smart self-contained workshop at Buttercrambe. His tofu is vacuum packed and sold under the 'Clear Spot' label and distributed by wholesalers in London and Manchester. It is available from wholefood shops in Leeds, Bradford and York or direct from Buttercrambe. Only **Alligator** of York sell it loose, stored in water. Ron also sells it marinated, smoked or made up into cheesecakes, flans and pasties.*

R & R Tofu, Fold Court, Buttercrambe, York ☎ *01759 72979 Open: Mon-Fri 9am-5pm*

SUMA

S uma Wholefoods was born in the early 1970's when four hippies took a transit van to London to buy muesli in bulk. There's some mystery and sensitivity about these origins but today, with two of the founders still involved, Suma has grown into one of the largest wholefood wholesalers in the country, one of the few surviving large scale workers' co-operatives and it is still run on the same ethical principles that were its inspiration 20 years ago. Anyone in the region with half an interest in wholefoods will know its produce. It is an amazing success story which all began from a terraced house in Headingley when Leeds had next to nothing to offer on the wholefood side. Sacks of brown rice and lentils soon filled the house so they found a cheap and delapidated warehouse at 42 The Calls, now restored as Leeds' most glamorous hotel.

With the Wharf Street café virtually next door, a useful synergy developed. Suma supplied the goods and the café produced well cooked, innovative vegetarian food. Around another corner was Leeds Other Paper but the fledgling alternative community never quite took off. Bigger money was eyeing this corner of Leeds and Wharf Street and L.O.P. eventually bit the dust. Suma, however, had stronger roots, moving to bigger premises at Dean Clough in Halifax in 1986 in the first days of the regeneration of Halifax's mighty carpet mill complex. Today, the co-op is flourishing with 60 members. Everyone, from the commodities buyer to the warehouse person, earns the same wage (around £250 a week). Policy decisions are taken at a monthly meeting and no job is sacrosanct. Marketing manager Peter Caldwell spends two days a week on deliveries driving an HGV. Members take their turn at cooking lunch and the results suggest they would be equally successful at running a vegetarian restaurant.

Suma has 76,000 square feet of warehouse space and stock a staggering 4,000 different lines: grains, beans, dried fruit, nuts, seeds flours, oils, honeys, cereals, pastas, herbs and spices. They have own label margarine, fruit juice and a pear and apple spread made from pure fruit. Their philosophy is that food remains as near to its natural state as possible, with no artifical additives, colouring or preservative. Where anything has to be added to comply with food regulations, it is labelled as such. Where possible, produce is organic and Suma is Soil Association registered. Nor is the stock restricted to food. There are homeopathic remedies for people and pets. They sell beeswax candles, herbal cigarettes and wholefood cook books. Cleaning products are bio-degradable and cosmetics are not tested on animals. Suma seek out agencies who are committed to trade fairly with the Third World, stocking Equal Exchange Nicaraguan peanut butter, Palestinian almond butter, Inca pecans and rainforest Brazil nuts. Suppliers come under constant review. Until recently they refused to buy from South Africa or Israel. Afghan raisins and Turkish apricots were next under scrutiny.

Suma is not open to the public but they supply their quality wholefoods to shops throughout the British Isles from tiny outposts such as **Wheelbarrow Foods**, run from Betty Whitwell's pantry at Barrow on Humber to the country's biggest supermarket chains. Their reputation is solid with their customers. Indeed, Suma's success story is a tribute to an ideal that worked: that wholefoods, principles and a modern, profitable business can co-exist. Strange but true.

Suma Wholefood Co-operative, Dean Clough, Halifax, W. Yorks
☎ 01422 345513 Open: wholesale only Mon-Fri 9am-5pm

wholefood range, he sells packets of Japanese sea vegetables, free range eggs, organic bread and various vegetarian and vegan flans, pasties and pastries.

225 King Cross Road,
Halifax, W. Yorks
☎ *01422 330445*
Open: Mon-Sat 9am-5.30pm

Food Therapy

This healthfood and wholefood shop has its own bakery, takeaway and café and its in-house nutritional adviser. Unfortunately, the adviser, while not denying the benefits of sensible eating, heavily promotes the shop's vast range of vitamins and supplements. Ignore the bizarre body-building pasta at £4 a box and head for the bakery at the back of the shop where there are good breads, savouries and cakes.

11 Northgate,
Halifax, W. Yorks
☎ *01422 350826*
Open: Mon-Sat 9am-5.30pm

HARROGATE

Frazer's Wholefood Emporium

If you've been searching for mango powder or asafoetida, then Dan Frazer's your man. Old wooden spice drawers contain 360 different herbs and spices in this charming basement emporium. There are whole cap candied peels, geranium jellies and corn grits for authentic American cornmeal muffins. Daniel Frazer is an American who gave up a star wars career with Lockheed at Menwith Hill for the love of Mexican food. Everyone has to have priorities. He claims to be the largest Tex Mex stockist in the north of England. He sells corn and flour tortillas, bean dips, guacamole and picante salsa to serve with startling navy blue tortilla chips. There are burritos, enchiladas and sliced green Jalapeño chillies. He's extending the range to take in bar-

becue and Cajun flavourings and Frazer's is a rare outpost of Monterey Jack cheese for an all-American hamburger topping. The delicatessen counter has naturally smoked ham and turkey, patés and excellent samosas, spring rolls and onion bhajis. There's a take-away menu of hot food every day which includes a homemade soup, baked potato with various fillings and vegetable burritos. When she's not running the shop, Lindsay Frazer makes quiches, onion flans, salmon profiteroles and 20 different kinds of dessert. Asafoetida? It's the bitter resin of a plant from Iran or Afghanistan used as a condiment. The Romans used it to counter flatulence. The Germans who are less enthusiastic about its pervasive smell of garlic, call it Devil's Dung.

117 Cold Bath Road,
Harrogate, N. Yorks
☎ *01423 504709*
Open: Mon-Sat 9am-5.30pm

The Green House

From low energy light bulbs to recycled toilet paper, you can get anything green and environmentally friendly at The Green House. There are **Suma** wholefoods, fresh organic produce and Fair Trade tea and coffee. At the back of the shop there's a useful free notice-board and the vegetarian café has a selection of books and pamphlets on health and environmental issues. It also has the appropriate chunky pottery and pine tables. Mushroom pancake or lasagne, served with roast potatoes, salad and a glass of fruit juice typifies a nice and simple menu. It's an easy going place to while away some time and two courses and a drink for a fiver definitely represents fair trade.

5 Station Parade,
Harrogate, N. Yorks
☎ *01423 502580*
Open: Mon-Sat 9am-5.30pm
Café Mon-Sat 10am-3.30pm

HOWDEN

Bridgegate House

A wholefood shop and café attached to the Webb family's lovely Georgian house. Lesley and Jim Webb sell a good range of wholefoods: nuts, grains and pulses, organic free range eggs together with all the ingredients that make up a good wholefood store. Best of all is the café where sandwiches, savouries and cakes are made from ingredients found in the shop. It's all executed with admirable expertise by ex-cookery teacher Lesley. Everything she makes is vegetarian but adds: 'We don't shout about it because some people think that's very odd.' Instead they get on with serving good food in immaculate surroundings. The only disappointing note is that they are planning to sell up, so for anyone with ambitions ...

15 Bridgegate,
Howden, N. Humbs
☎ *01430 431010*
Open: Mon-Sat 9am-5.30pm
Café 9am-4.30pm

HUDDERSFIELD

Wholefood Shop

Judith Beresford has been running this tiny wholefood outpost for eight years. In that time it has developed into a well respected and patronised shop that matches concern for ethical marketing with the selling of good wholesome food. Judith supports the boycott of Nestlé because of their marketing policies of infant formula in the Third World and refuses to stock any of their products. No small gesture when that involves the biggest food company in the world. Instead, bright, fresh organic vegetables turn over quickly. She stocks the excellent Rachel's Dairy organic yoghurt from Dyfed, organic wines, free range eggs and Green and Black's Fair Trade organic chocolate from Belize. It's also rare to find **Botton Village** cheeses this far from their North Yorkshire home.

Half Moon Street, Huddersfield, W. Yorks
☎ *01484 663301*
Open: Mon-Sat 9am-5.30pm

KNARESBOROUGH

Herb of Grace

A well stocked shop with all the wholefoods and a source for awkward to find items like vanilla pods. Anita Dyson keeps a decent range of honey which includes Yorkshire and leatherwood. She has free range eggs but no fresh produce. There is a wide selection of teas: Assam, Darjeeling, Ceylon and more esoteric names such as Bitter Almond, China Rose and Keemun.

11 Castlegate, Knaresborough, N. Yorks
☎ *01423 862351*
Open: Mon-Sat 9.30am-5pm

LEEDS

Beano's Wholefood Workers Co-operative

Beano's co-op have survived successfully for 15 years now, flying in the face of inner city Mammon and sky high rents. Perhaps it's the patronage of Opera North a few doors away –

Beano's claim to be popular with members of the Company. Or maybe it's their wide range of good, fresh stock. Organic fruit and vegetables come from **Standford Hall Farm** in Pickering and tofu cakes, flans and cheesecakes from **R & R Tofu** of Buttercrambe. Beano's use local producers for honey, bread, goat's milk and cheese. Their dried herbs and spices, sold from big toffee jars, benefit from the quick turnover. Customers choose and weigh for themselves. There's also top of the range Japanese organic ingredients. This is a well run wholefood store of the best kind. There's plenty of help if you need it but otherwise the co-op members leave their customers in peace to browse among the shelves.

36 New Briggate, Leeds, W. Yorks
☎ *0113 243 5737*
Open: Mon-Wed 9am-5pm
Thur & Fri 9am-5.30pm
Sat 9am-5pm

Grain of Sense

The archetypal wholefood shop in Leeds archetypal bedsit land. It's a return to the womb for any self-respecting hippy. The window is plastered with posters offering mask workshops, right on house removals and the latest

gen on toxic shock from tampons but the handpainted sign offering hot food, tea and coffee showed little evidence of delivering. Still, the wholefoods are here in abundance: rice, grains and pulses, organic bread and wholemeal pastries, fresh organic fruit and vegetables and local goat's cheese from Connie Seipp who keeps the **Intake Lane Goat Herd**. For all it's wholefood worthiness, Grain of Sense remains one of the few truly community shops left in a city given over to shopping malls and fast food. It is well patronised by students and the service is helpful and friendly to young and ageing hippies alike.

28 Brudenell Road, Hyde Park, Leeds, W. Yorks
☎ *0113 275 7410*
Open: Mon-Fri 9.30am-7pm
Sat & Sun 9.30am-5pm

Natural Food Store

A fresh, clean and well stocked shop that has survived the changing fortunes of food shopping in Headingley. Where high rents have forced out some of the best like Groocock's, a real old fashioned grocer, and **Barrett's**, a classic greengrocer that has moved out to Cookridge, this shop has hung on in. Bread makers can buy Woods or **Village Craft** flour, both ground locally at Thorpe Mill, Grewelthorpe and there is invariably a supply of fresh yeast in the fridge. Reliable organic bread and pastries come ready-made from **Saker Foods** in Todmorden and a small supply of organic vegetables are usually crisp and fresh. Recent developments are the hot croissants and bagels served with coffee either inside or out in the garden on a sunny Sunday morning.

23 North Lane, Headingley, Leeds, W. Yorks
☎ *0113 278 4944*
Open: Mon-Sat 9am-6pm
Sun 8am-2pm

SAKER FOODS

Old veggie hands will know Saker Foods, Todmorden by their more familiar name of Phoenix Bakery, the wholesale co-operative that supplies many of the region's wholefood shops with organic wholemeal bread and pastries. In 1994 they changed their name to Saker Foods, although even long standing customers stick resolutely to Phoenix. Either way, the 10 strong workforce continue to produce 50 different lines – five different organic breads and sweet and savoury pastries. They use only organic flours and grains and the fillings are either vegetarian or vegan, though not necessarily organic.

Canteen Mill, Burnley Road, Todmorden, Lancs
☎ *01706 818189*

MALTON

Realfare

Realfare, a franchised operation, may be the name above the shop but it's known to everyone in Malton as Beecham's after the owner who also owns the chemist shop opposite. It's clean, and well packaged. Dried herbs and spices, both culinary and medicinal, pulses, dried fruit, muesli, herbal teas, soya milk and fruit juices provide the permanent backdrop for the daily deliveries of ready-cooked savouries: tomato bhaji, bean and tomato pasty, cottage pie with cheese and quiche. Wholemeal bread is baked locally in Norton and organic bread comes from **Botton Village** on Thursdays.

16 Yorkersgate,
Malton, N. Yorks
☎ *01653 695145*
Open: Mon-Sat 9am-5.30pm
Thur 9am-5pm

RIPON

Raw Deal Wholefoods

Raw Deal is better named than Nick Thompson imagined when he set up in the 1980s. He's seen the small food shop culture of Ripon squeezed by the proliferation of supermarkets. He's seen the very supermarkets that once turned up their noses at grains and pulses start stocking them to his detriment. He has reluctantly turned to herbal remedies and food supplements as an alternative source of income. But his heart remains resolutely with wholefoods. He tries to keep ahead of the supermarkets by stocking specialist items as well as the staples. His interest in Indian food is reflected in a wide range of sub-continental spices, chutneys and tubs of ghee. There is a choice of flours but Woods and **Village Craft** flour are both milled locally at Grewelthorpe. He keeps **Taylor's** tea and coffee and seasonal vegetables come

from his own organic garden and are sold whenever there is an excess.

7 North Street, Ripon, N. Yorks
☎ *01765 604726*
Open: Tue-Sat 9.30am-5pm
Wed 9.30am-1.30pm

SELBY

The Granary

Selby's wholefood shop, situated behind the Abbey and run in pleasant style by John and Penny McCartney, is a warm friend to local cake makers and bakers. The Granary keeps 10 different kinds of flour, fresh yeast and is a handy source of baking equipment. They have plenty of unusual cake tins for hire, ideal for children's birthday cakes. The McCartney's also make their own cakes, Christmas puddings and frozen vegetarian meals.

13/15 Church Lane,
Selby, N. Yorks
☎ *01757 708516*
Open: Mon-Fri 9am-5pm
Sat 9am-4pm

SHEFFIELD

Crookes Valley Wholefoods

Better known as Beanies, this wholesome workers' co-operative sits happily alongside the 'Green' shop next door but one and the real ale Dram Shop across the road. How green is Crookes Valley. . . Beanies is certainly popular with students, packed full of wholefoods and it sells good fresh brown bread and wholemeal savouries and cakes. They have a choice of organic vegetables often locally grown, all in good condition and at reasonable prices. They keep even more reasonable opening hours.

207 Crookes Valley Road,
Sheffield, S. Yorks
☎ *0114 268 1662*
Open: Mon-Fri 9am-8pm
Sat 9am-7.30pm
Sun 10am-6pm

Down to Earth

Organic oats, muesli, rice and pulses are sold loose from bins in this well stocked shop. There is Clear Spot tofu supplied by **R & R Tofu** and a range of organic and wholemeal bread baked locally. Wholemeal and white flour comes from Caudwell's Mill, a restored water mill at Rowsley near Matlock, Derbyshire.

406 Sharrowvale Road,
Sheffield, S, Yorks
☎ *0114 268 5220*
Mon 1.30am-5.30pm
Tue-Sat 9.30am-5.30pm

In a Nutshell

A standard wholefood shop whose wholefood starting point has been somewhat overtaken by the simple practice of selling proper bread. It comes from a local wholefood bakery, the Real Bread Bakehouse, and is made into satisfying sandwiches. Granary, organic, wholemeal, sesame and poppy seed loaves lead the way in priming an enthusiastic lunchtime sandwich trade which Vicky Boadle and her young staff take in their stride. Alongside the sandwiches are vegetarian pasties and pastries, onion bhajis, pakoras, vegetarian Scotch eggs, pizza and good wholemeal cakes.

31 Chesterfield Road,
Sheffield, S. Yorks
☎ *0114 250 8555*
Open: Mon-Sat 9.30am-5.30pm

SKIPTON

Healthy Life

A health food shop with **Herbs** vegetarian restaurant upstairs. The shop has a wide range of oats, muesli, rice etc., some of it organic. A good dried fruit section includes Hunza apricots, Lexia raisins, Vostizza seedless currants, unsulphured apricots. They stock some interesting olive patés, cashew nut butters and it's the place to find fresh yeast and more unusually, tiny bottles

FAIR TRADE FOODS

S mall producers the world over are at the mercy of global policies and a world market which cares little for their livelihoods and families. Tumbling world commodity prices can overnight make it uneconomic for farmers even to harvest their crops. A pattern of spiralling debt and poverty is repeated throughout the third world fuelled by the policies of bankers and multinational companies.

The answer for many small producers has, with the help of alternative trading organisations, been to gain more control over their own futures by finding fair trade partners. Producers are paid a fair price for their product which means more money to spend on the necessities of life – health, education and housing. And it means that people in developing countries have more influence over the international trade process.

Twin Trading is one of a number of organisations including Oxfam Trading, Traidcraft and Equal Exchange Trading that has sought to provide partnerships with third world producers by opening up markets in the UK. However, fair trade in the 90s has come a long way from the 'buying out of charity' mentality. Lorna Young, Sales Director of Cafédirect coffee, is quick to point out: 'From the beginning Cafédirect was developed as a product that could compete on taste, quality and price alongside top brands, rather than a niche product, sold to people who wanted to be charitable.'

'We're not ramming a message down people's throats – we want people to buy a product because they like it', says Pauline Tiffin of Twin Trading. But the message does get through. By providing information about a product – where it comes from and who produces it – a link develops between consumers and producers.

Fair trade products have traditionally been available through Oxfam shops, church groups and mail order such as Traidcraft. But the newer interest of supermarkets offers real opportunities to expand beyond the 'ethical consumer' market. Major retailers consider it good for their image to be associated with fair trade products and opinion polls show that consumers do feel more positively about stores that embrace the fair trade concept.

Suppliers are assessed on a number of criteria including worker representation, employment conditions, fair contracts, workers' health and safety and welfare. Environmental issues are also important with increasing emphasis on organic production.

Top selling fairly-traded foods are: **Cafédirect** who benefit its growers in Costa Rica, Peru, Mexico and Nicaragua by paying them up to double the market rate for their coffee. **Mascao** chocolate is made in Switzerland from fair traded Bolivian cocoa and muscovado sugar from the island of Negros in the Philippines. **Green and Black's Maya Gold Chocolate** is made with 70% cocoa solids grown to organic standards by the Maya Indians of Belize in Central America. Green and Black's pay about twice the world market price for cocoa beans. Other fair trade products are Peruvian Brazil and pecan nuts, almonds from Hebron in Palestine and **Barrita** sesame snack bars from Nicaragua, Mexican honey, organic forest honey from Zambia and Tanzania and guava and mango jams from Burkino Faso, one of the poorest countries in Africa.

Sue Dibb, The Food Commission, 1994

of vegetarian rennet for cheese-making.

10 High Street, Skipton, N. Yorks
☎ 01756 790619
Open: Mon-Sat 8.30am-5.30pm
Tue 10am-5pm

TODMORDEN

Bear Healthfoods
The sweeping mahogany staircase, the wooden shelves, old mirrors and a black and white tiled floor reflect this shop's previous incarnation as the Co-op gents outfitters. Now it's an all-women co-op who run Bear Healthfoods. They have retained the old features and have an attractive wholefood shop downstairs and a gift shop and café on the first floor. The café is friendly and relaxed with a useful bulletin board but the microwaved flans, onion bhajis and hommity pies were disappointing. Down below are rice, flour, pulses and free range organic eggs. Organic bread is delivered daily and organic vegetables once a week.

29 Rochdale Road,
Todmorden, Lancs
☎ 01706 813737
Open: Mon-Sat 9.30am-5.30pm

WHITBY

The Mustard Seed
'A holistic wholefood shop specialising not just in wholefoods but in wholesome lifestyles' is the slightly unnerving motto of The Mustard Seed. The entrance is punctuated by more messages of green and spiritual worthiness, giving way to a thoroughly relaxed and friendly interior. James and Jackie Fearnley run a super shop. Rice, pulses and the usual wholefood goods are ready weighed and bagged for convenience. The excellent Danbydale cheese comes from the bio-dynamic farm at **Botton Village**, as well as the community's cream, milk, yoghurt and delicious bread. Look out for the pots of

honey from the Scarborough Honey Farm where James Fearnley is a partner. The organic vegetables, laid out in wicker baskets outside, look fresh and wholesome. They also stock breakfast cereals and tins so that shoppers can buy everything they need under one roof. The Fearnley's refuse to stock Nestlé products because of their Third World practices, they support various environmental causes and have a large community notice-board, where customers can place advertisements free of charge. They also plausibly claim to be the only wholefood shop that also offers printing and fax facilities from an office at the back of the shop.

1 Skinner Street,
Whitby, N. Yorks
☎ 01947 820217
Open: Mon-Sat 9am-5.30pm

Shepherd's Purse
Not to be confused with the Thirsk cheesemaker of the same name, especially as the dark interior of this Aladdin's Cave of a shop has amongst all its other merits, a fine cheese counter. The prize find is Elizabeth Newton's fresh **Grosmont Goat's Cheese**. Her delicate little muslin wrapped cheeses are unpasteurised, naturally soured, and made in small batches at nearby Dog Tree Bank farm. Quite definitely

a local speciality, found only here and at the **Mallyan Hotel**. Shepherd's Purse is also a good source of **Botton** produce: Cheddar and Danbydale cheese, organic live Danby yoghurt and loaves of nutty wholemeal bread. At Christmas, mountains of dried fruit are heaped into wooden barrels enticing a try at plum pudding and Christmas cake. Year-round there are slabs of moist, rich Captain Cook fruit cake, with more than a hint of ginger, baked locally at Great Ayton. Shepherd's Purse is also the place for carlings (or carlins), a traditional east coast dish served on Carling Sunday, the fourth Sunday in Lent (see below). There is a gift shop and the vegetarian restaurant at the back of the shop offers a fresh soup every day, bowls of salad and a selection of vegetarian bakes such as pasta and seaweed, cauliflower and broccoli, and mushroom and leek. Cakes and sticky puddings are mostly made on the premises. Banoffee pie, banana and marshmallow pudding and banana and strawberry scrunch all suggest a modern cargo of bananas might have recently run aground off Whitby.

95 Church Street,
Whitby, N. Yorks
☎ 01947 820228
Open: Mon-Sun 9.30am-5pm
Jan & Feb closed Mon & Wed

CARLING SUNDAY

Carlings or carlins are served on the fourth Sunday in Lent in a tradition peculiar to a stretch of the north east coast around Whitby. The brown, nutty, dried peas are soaked overnight, simmered, then fried in lard and eaten with salt and pepper or sugar and vinegar. Carlings are believed to have saved the local populus from starvation after a ship carrying a cargo of carlings ran aground. Legend has it that the peas swelled in the sea water and provided nourishment for the hungry inhabitants of Whitby. Today, they are still served in Whitby pubs on Carling Sunday but rarely anywhere else. Heed the concise Yorkshire wisdom: 'Carling Sunday, farting Monday'.

YORK

Alligator

York, for some reason, has established itself as the wholefood capital of Yorkshire with at least three shops and two restaurants. Alligator can fairly claim to be the first and is undoubtedly still the finest. Their shelves of abundant tins, packets and sacks also make them the biggest with the whole gamut of chick peas, pasta, okra, beans and a wide range of flours. They have **Botton** organic bread, bio-dynamic yoghurts, cream, butter, jams and fruit cordials. Fresh tofu is made locally by Ron Malarkey of **R & R Tofu** at Buttercrambe. They thoughtfully stock supplies of non-dairy ice cream and choc ices especially for children allergic to dairy produce who would otherwise miss out. For fresh organic produce their policy is to buy at realistic prices which generally means seasonal British produce. In winter, there are slim, fresh leeks, celeriac, carrots and swedes. In summer, they buy aubergines, tomatoes and other hothouse produce from Greg Bucknill at **Stark Farm**, Tollerton. Imported organic produce is ridiculously expensive, claim Alligator, and so they sell some conventionally grown imported citrus fruits and continental vegetables. The partnership consists of Woof, Arthur and Kate with no obvious rank or surnames. No one even admits to knowing or remembering exactly when they started. The photographs in the shop show long hair, loons and beards circa 1975. They claim they could be selling bicycles but, however self-effacing they pretend to be, there is real commitment and quality in their work. Wheatfree bread available to order, delivered every Wednesday.

104 Fishergate, York
☎ 01904 654525
Open: Mon 10am-6pm
Tue-Sat 9am-6pm

Gillygate Vegetarian Restaurant & Shop

The Gillygate Bakery, as it has come to be known, is a co-operative founded on the belief that everyone should be given the opportunity to work according to their ability and to this end a proportion of the staff have learning difficulties or psychiatric problems. Everyone earns the same wage. They believe, too, that good nutritious food can be created without the use of meat, with eggs that are free range and without the use of artificial flavourings, preservatives or colourings. For ethical food they don't come more correct than the Gillygate Bakery. The shop stocks all the wholefoods but is best known for its baking: sunflower loaves, rye bread, organic white and brown breads, soda bread, cheese and herb bread, fruit and walnut loaf, bread rolls and teacakes. For savoury snacks there are slices of pizza, tofu burgers or ratatouille pasties. They make a tasty range of cakes including baklava, apple flapjack and slices of bread pudding. The **Gillygate Restaurant** (daytime opening only) serves many of these and imaginative vegetarian dishes of its own.

Gillygate, York
☎ 01904 610676
Open: Mon-Sat 9am-5.30pm
Restaurant 10am-5pm

Tullivers

Hunza apricots, Californian almonds and jumbo pistachios catch the eye in this well stocked, high quality wholefood store which has been run for 10 years in the shadow of York Minster by Helen Spath and David Weston. They also have an extensive range of Japanese, Chinese and Indian produce and 200 different herbs and spices.

29 Goodramgate, York
☎ 01904 636437
Open: Mon-Sat 9.30am-5.30pm

THE VEGETARIAN SOCIETY

The Vegetarian Society supplies advice and information on vegetarianism. They publish The Vegetarian magazine, an excellent book list and provide information sheets on everything from infant feeding to vegetarianism for cats. Their Cordon Vert Diploma is a well respected cookery course aimed at people planning a career in catering. They also run a popular series of residential short courses for the enthusiastic amateur. The aims of the Society: 'To increase the number of vegetarians in the UK in order to save animals, benefit human health and protect the environment and world food resources'. Branches and affiliated groups throughout Yorkshire and Humberside.

Parkdale, Dunham Road, Altrincham, Cheshire
☎ 0161 928 0793

Cafés and restaurants serving predominantly vegetarian food:
Harrogate, The Green House, Tiffins on the Stray
Howden, Bridgegate House
Middlesbrough, Filbert's
Otley, Curlew Café
Skipton, Herbs
Whitby, Shepherd's Purse
York, Blake Head Bookshop & Vegetarian Restaurant, Gillygate Restaurant, Sesame Café

9

Delicatessen & Grocers

The encyclopaedia of food, *Larousse Gastronomique* describes the delicatessen as 'a shop selling high quality groceries and luxury food products'. This chapter broadens the definition to embrace ethnic specialists, selected farm shops and market stalls, the Danish ship's stores in Grimsby and the Japanese mobile van that visits Sheffield and Castleford. The most interesting food is still often found in the hands of the small, independent shopkeeper. The best of the new wave delicatessens are making their own chicken liver parfait, pork rillettes, soups, sausages, fresh pasta and proper bread. They stocked the region's burgeoning cheeses before the supermarkets bothered and will continue to nurture and mature them better. Ask for anything from truffle oil to tuiles and most will make it a point of pride to find it. They

may be better outside caterers than the full time professionals. Bigger Yorkshire markets are rich in traditional European delicatessens set up to serve a post-war immigrant population, where spoken Russian, Polish and German is still commonplace. Bradford has the biggest stores for the spices and herbs of Indian cuisine, live yoghurt and halal meat. Leeds supports two eye-opening Chinese supermarkets and the best Jewish and Polish specialists. A handful of farm shops in the region are committed to supplying quality meat, fish and game but too many fail the starting test of selling their own produce fresh, offering frozen retail lines instead. Taylor's of Tickhill and Lewis & Cooper of Northallerton are still proud to call themselves grocers offering old fashioned service and orders delivered to the door.

DELICATESSEN & GROCERS

BALDERSBY

Smithy Farm Shop

Most farm shops raise the expectation that you're going to find distinctive, wholesome, home grown produce and then almost invariably fail to deliver. Susan Brown's well stocked shop near the A1 is a happy exception. She travelled long and wide to set up her supply lines of high quality, traditional meats and local produce and the journeys were worthwhile. Her best seller is Richard Woodall's dry cured bacon produced on a family pig farm in Cumbria. It doesn't ooze water and scum when you cook it but crisps up beautifully. Woodall's Cumberland rings and honey roast pork sausages are popular too. More highly principled pork comes from Berkshire pigs reared traditionally on Humberside, delivering meat which has more fat but an intense flavour and crisp crackling. Beef comes from Humberside too, from Helena Ellis's prize-winning, pedigree herd of diminutive Dexter cattle reared at **Bursea Farm**. Lamb is from Nidderdale. There is wild boar and wild or farmed venison. Chickens are raised locally in small numbers without the use of growth promoters or antibiotics. There are free range eggs, duck breasts, quail and specialist turkey and geese to order for Christmas. Although there is a small fresh meat counter, the majority of the meat is frozen but it all comes from reputable producers and is labelled as such. Other local produce includes sea trout and salmon from Whitby; **Rosebud Preserves** from Healey, near Masham; **Brymor** ice cream; **Pepper Arden** game pies; local cheeses and Yorkshire fruit wines. There are

home made desserts like sticky toffee pudding and white chocolate torte in Susan Brown's freezer and ready-made vegetarian dishes by local cook Verity Steele. 'Ideal', says Susan, 'for people with teenage vegetarian daughters.' Apparently a booming market.

Baldersby, Nr. Thirsk, N. Yorks
☎ *01765 640676*
Open: Mon-Sat 9.30am-5.30pm

BEVERLEY

Jack & Son

Duncan Jack is the third generation Jack to run this attractive shop in Wednesday Market and he has endeavoured to keep it looking like a traditional grocer's. Stock could be wider but there's still an interesting supply of pickles, patés, jams and honey, backed up by a modest cheese counter, some cooked meats and a supply of the best selling **Botham's** plum bread.

6 Wednesday Market,
Beverley, N. Humbs
☎ *01482 882437*
Open: Tue-Fri 8.30am-5.30pm
Mon & Sat 8.30am-5pm

BINGLEY

The Really Good Food Shop

Anne Preston's small delicatessen in Queen's Court packs in cooked meats and, notably, a wide selection of cheeses including Monterey Jack for an authentic American hamburger and Long Clawson's Blue Stilton. Cakes, puddings and ready meals are available from the freezer.

2 Queen's Court, Main Street,
Bingley, W. Yorks
☎ *01274 567867*
Open: Mon, Wed, Sat 9am-5pm
Tue 9am-1pm Thur, Fri 9am-
5.30pm

BOSTON SPA

Hunter's

From the same stable as Hunter's of Helmsley this tiny branch on the main street compensates for lack of size by packing in delicatessen goodies from floor to ceiling. While cooked meat is their obvious speciality, manager Linda Humphrey also stocks organic bread and runs a quality cheese counter with a strong range of English, regional and continental cheeses.

160a High Street,
Boston Spa, W. Yorks
☎ *01937 844111*
Open: Mon-Fri 8am-5.30pm
Sat 8am-5pm

BRADFORD

Al Halal Supermarket

Al Halal, also known as Panorama Stores, has often been called the biggest Asian supermarket in Britain which is not as awesome as it sounds. It's big, but not for a supermarket. It is, however, a fine place to browse the aisles without interference or pressure to buy and to investigate a wide range of international ingredients. Everything in the store complies with Muslim dietary laws. Non-meat items rigorously exclude animal fats which will suit vegetarians as well as Muslims. A fresh halal butcher is situated next to the main supermarket. The total halal policy dates to the foundation of the store in 1970 when the shareholders, now numbering 130, correctly reckoned that a large co-operative could achieve greater buying power, variety and value than the myriad independent corner shops. Al Halal is now strong enough to import directly and market its own brand Indian and Pakistani spices. Fruit and vege-

NATIONS OF SHOPKEEPERS

The flooding of a valley in Mirpur in Pakistan to make way for a dam in the 1950s was the trigger for the initial wave of immigration from the sub-continent to the West Riding and the Mirpur connection remains at the heart of today's Bradford Punjabi population. Pathans followed from the North West Frontier, Sylhet Bengalis from Bangladesh, Hindus and Sikhs from Gujarat. In Dewsbury is a tight community of Indian Muslims. The immigrants manned the night shifts in Yorkshire's textile mills and cheap curry and chapati stalls sprang up to feed them. When families joined their men through the 1960s, Asian food stores opened in the communities of Bradford's Toller Lane, Leeds Road, Great Horton Road and Bradford Moor, in Leeds, Keighley, Halifax, Huddersfield and the Heavy Woollen district.

Second and third generation Asians still value home cooking over eating out as Indian restaurant food is considered expensive and inferior. Girls learn to cook from watching their mothers, grandmothers or aunts; families invariably sit down together to share the curry or salan, as the gravy of the dish is known, and fresh chapatis are made daily. The infrastructure to provide the raw ingredients for all this home cooking has never stopped growing and there is little doubt that Asian food shops are withstanding the heat of supermarket competition better than their English counterparts. They now provide all of us with a dazzling variety of international ingredients.

Buy gram flour for bhajis; collect fresh ginger, garlic and green chillies for the starting components of a home cooked curry; pick up fat bunches of flat leaved parsley and coriander for under 50 pence. Try mooli (long white radish), doodhi (Indian gourd), tinda (pumpkin) or jelly nut (unripe coconut). Bradford's **Al Halal** is surely the biggest and best of the major grocers. **Haq Halal** in Legrams Lane and **Bradford Superstore** in Gilpin Street sell the freshest of spices: cumin, cloves, cardamom, cinnamon, turmeric and peppercorns – by the sackful if required – and any sizeable Asian food store will almost certainly stock the best live yoghurt going, as well as unusual olive oils and fiery chilli sauces from all over the world. **Baig's** on Dewsbury and Wakefield markets and **Ahmed Foods** in Bradford have exciting and exotic fruit and vegetables. Look out for eddoes, Indian yams, squashes, bitter gourds and mighty melons.

For lurid green, pink and orange sweets, **Bobby's Sweet Centre** on Roundhay Road, Leeds, the **Kashmir Crown Bakery** chain in Bradford and Royal sweets from the **Mumtaz Paan House** all have their champions. But **Ambala's**,with branches in Leeds and Bradford is the prestige sweet to take to an Asian wedding, where food for up to 500 guests might be prepared by the family or by one of the local restaurants: **Moghul** and **Pakeezah** on Leeds Road, Bradford, are currently popular choices for outside catering. In Dewsbury, wedding parties can hire the Town Hall, where the hapless bride and groom will be sat up on stage and fed to the gills with unrelenting tributes of sweets while their guests tuck into dishes of chicken and pilau rice and such labour intensive luxuries as koftas (hand made meat balls) and nargisi (a sort of spicy Scotch egg).

For the best handmade bhajis and samosas anywhere go to **Mariam's** of Dewsbury, also delivered fresh each day to **Maumoniat's** of Leeds, which in turn has a splendid rice selection, including Tilda 'from the fertile plains of the Mississipi basin' or a Basmati 'watered by the snow-fed rivers of the Himalayas'. Match that for romance.

tables are bright and fresh, running from the regular to the exotic. There are piles of okra, sweet potato, root ginger, garlic and less familiar tindoori (mini cucumbers), mooli (Indian radish), Pakistani guava and green mango. Ramadan is the best time for Iranian or Medina dates, eaten when the fast is broken. Al Halal is also a dependable source for sharp, live yoghurt and generous bunches of fresh methi (fenugreek), dhunia (coriander) and flat leaved parsley. The nan breads are baked locally and there's every kind of papadom – plain, chilli, cumin and punjabi masala. Rices and pulses come in half pound bags through to whole sacks. The cosmopolitan range takes in Middle Eastern, Greek and Italian foodstuffs. Al Halal also has an interesting selection of cooking pots, skillets and karahis – the double handled metal bowls for balti cooking.

Woodhead Road,
Bradford, W. Yorks
☎ 01274 736294
Open: Mon-Sat 9am-8pm
Sun 12 noon-6pm
Halal butcher Mon-Sat 9am-7pm
closed Sun

Haq Halal Superstore

The latest addition to the Asian supermarket scene is Haq Halal. While it stocks the supermarket staples of baked beans and breakfast cereals there are also all the spices and condiments for Indian cooking. Most of the meat is frozen. There is a small range of fresh fruit and vegetables but there are plenty of ripe, juicy Pakistani mangoes from Lahore. Haq Halal announce themselves as 'The UK's Number One Multi-Cultural Discounter!' But they can't yet match **Al Halal** for freshness and variety.

16 Legrams Lane,
Bradford, W. Yorks
☎ 01274 743338
Open: Mon-Sat 9.30am-8pm
Sun 9am-6pm

Slavia Stores

From their tiny but classic shop in Rawson Market, Napoleon and Irena Puc will sell you any one of an amazing 300 different cooked meats with all their full blooded Polish charm and good cheer thrown in. There's blutwurst (black pudding) or kabanos (smoked sausage). The rye bread from Bradford's prize **Kolos** Ukrainian bakery should go splendidly with the charcuterie or, even better, the Beluga caviar. One day the shelves really will collapse under the combined weight and calories of Greek olive oil, German cakes, Italian pasta and Polish cream fudge. The Puc's slip seamlessly between English, Russian, Polish, Italian and German. With Bradford's 12,000 expatriate Europeans searching out a little taste of home, they have plenty of opportunities. Napoleon Puc left his native Poland at nine years old, first for Siberia and then for Britain. Since opening Slavia stores 38 years ago, the Puc's have been a magnetic presence on the Bradford food scene, both for produce and personality. There's certainly nowhere more enjoyable to go delicatessen hunting in Bradford than this. Siberia's loss is West Yorkshire's gain.

21 Rawson Place, Rawson
Market, Bradford, W Yorks
☎ 01274 721675
Open: Mon-Sat 8am-5pm
Wed 8am-1pm

CONISTON COLD

Coniston Hall

An easy and popular stop on the Skipton – Settle road, providing a lovely view of the lake and Coniston Hall so briefly seen from the car. The farm shop is as close as the public gets to real stately home living. The emphasis is strongly on fish and game, the best of which have estate connections, so there is pheasant, venison, guinea fowl and quail.

Fresh trout comes from the estate farm. It's also possible to fish for brown and rainbow trout on the 24 acre lake or along a two and a half mile stretch of the River Aire (contact estate manager and owner's son Tom Bannister for details). Parrot fish and other varieties alien to the Aire are found in the freezer. Their own smoke house handles trout, halibut, duck breasts, chicken and ham. The cheese counter has little but an Irish Cashel Blue to write home about. There's a strong if largely predictable array of jams, patés, sauces and chutneys. The adjoining café serves soup and sandwiches, a couple of hot dishes and a tempting display of home made cakes and puddings. It's straightforward food, reasonably priced and prepared by good home cooks.

Coniston Cold,
Nr. Skipton, N. Yorks
☎ 01756 748136
Open: Mon-Sun 10am-6pm

DONCASTER

Scicluna's

A seemingly miniature delicatessen run by husband and wife team Nigel and Josephine Cooke, née Scicluna. Originally from Malta, the Scicluna's have had stalls on Doncaster market for 15 years and this latest one is positively lifting with a cosmopolitan selection of Polish, German and Hungarian meats, Parma ham, unbleached Polish rye bread, poppyseed cakes, fresh Parmesan, different kinds of olives, gherkins, pickled herrings and Californian, Jalapeño and Greek chillies. At Christmas the shop overflows with continental biscuits and German and Italian cakes. The customers reflect the international flavour, Yugoslavs, Spaniards, Italians, Greeks and Poles all zeroing in to this magnetic shop in Doncaster's indoor market. As ever with continental delicatessen, the shopkeepers are absolutely charming. The Cooke's customers really are their friends.

Indoor Market, Market Square, Doncaster, S. Yorks
Open: Tue, Fri, Sat 8am-5pm

EAST AYTON

Betton Farm Shop

Sally and Stuart Hardy run a well stocked shop from their farm at East Ayton. Potted beef, pork pies and cakes are all made on the premises. Much of it goes to supply the tea shop next door. Organic bread is available on Saturdays, non-organic on other days. The meat counter has the usual cuts as well as rabbit, duck, pheasant, woodcock and snipe in season. Around the corner from the shop is Sneaton Dale Honey Farm, a bee exhibition where the story of honey is told and Yorkshire heather honey is produced and bottled.

Racecourse Road, East Ayton, Scarborough, N. Yorks
☎ *01723 863143*
Open: Mon-Sat 9am-5.30pm
Sun 10am-5.30pm

ELLAND

Belicatessen

Not a misprint but the home of some well prepared dishes and a respectable cheese counter – without much local competition.

Tim Ingham prepares savouries of fresh poached salmon, Scotch eggs, haddock fish cakes and chicken liver paté while his wife Jane concentrates on desserts.

The Cross, Westgate, Elland, W. Yorks
☎ *01422 370589*
Open: Mon 10am-2.30pm
Tue-Sat 10am-5.30pm

GRIMSBY

Oriental Spices

Linda Maddison was born in war-torn Saigon to a Vietnamese mother and English father and when Anthony Maddison brought his family safely home to Grimsby there was already a significant Chinese and Vietnamese community in the port. Opening a food store specialising in the tastes and spices of the Orient was a natural. Twelve years on many of the families have dispersed and Linda believes the Maddison's are the only Vietnamese family left in Grimsby. Nevertheless, she continues to run an immaculate and charming shop with her aunt Xuan Dao. They sell sacks of rice to visiting oriental fishing crews who still find their way down the once bustling thoroughfare of Freeman Street. They supply Chinese and Japanese essentials to the local catering college and the additional basics of Indian, Thai,

Mexican and Greek cuisine over the counter. Also pots, pans and chopsticks.

Freeman Street,
Grimsby, S. Humbs
☎ *01472 241130*
Open: Mon-Sat 9.30am-5pm

HALIFAX

Design House Delicatessen

David Watson, former chef of **Pool Court**, moved in late 1994 to launch Dean Clough's stylish new Design House food complex. Naturally, the **Design House Restaurant** and **Café/Bar** are both serving excellent food under his direction. Yet in such a mighty complex as Dean Clough, the delicatessen has been strangely squashed into a narrow alleyway and you could be mistaken for thinking that it is another exhibition gallery with fancy French butter going on £2 for a half pound. Still, there are undeniably some alluring takeaway snacks and quality marque international ingredients. There are Italian, Greek and Spanish olive oils of impeccable pedigree and at fair prices. There are various vinegars, packaged porcini, pasta, Italian meats and a rare Yorkshire visitor in ready-made polenta. **Farmhouse Preserves** from Darley appear to be the only goods produced on the Yorkshire doorstep. They could do better here. The takeaway offers chunky sandwiches with French and Italian breads, generously stuffed with chorizo, avocado and smoked chicken; banana and cream cheese; ham, mozzarella and sun dried tomatoes. Nutty loaves, moist passion cakes, pecan nut brownies and fresh fruit salads further conspire to make this the most tempting deli and takeaway in Halifax.

Dean Clough, Halifax, W. Yorks
☎ *01422 383242*
Open: Mon-Fri 10am-6pm
Sat & Sun 10am-5pm

SHIP'S STORES

*Known locally as George Herd's Ship's Stores, the **Danish Food Centre** is one of the few survivors on Grimsby's ghostly fish docks. George and son Paul supply everything for a voyage from soap to rope. As well as bulk supplies of baked beans, they have marinated and sweet pickled sild (herring) and rye bread for homesick Scandinavian fishermen. There is Danbo, Esrom and Havarti cheese, all with the charisma of Edam, and a freezer full of kødboller (meatball), frikadeller (hamburger) and biksemad (diced meat, potato and onion).*

Auckland Road, Fish Docks, Grimsby, S. Humbs
☎ *01472 342080 Open: Mon-Fri 8am-5.30pm*
Sat 8am-12 noon

HARROGATE

Arcimboldo's

Arcimboldo was a 16th century painter of surreal food collages. His speciality was human heads constructed of miscellaneous fruits and vegetables and this shop goes some way to living up to his vivid imagination. The smell alone is tempting enough, a heady mixture of cheese, herbs, salami and spicy sausage but the food excels. The best is produced on the premises by the three-way partnership of Peter Flavell, Ann Samuel and Rosemary Brassington. Freshly made soups come by the half litre (enough for two) and reflect the seasons. In winter, try carrot and artichoke, fish or curried parsnip. A box of over-ripe Italian plum tomatoes from **Barber's Fruiterers** next door inspires a Spanish gazpacho in early spring. Dishes are always changing. Recent treats were French onion tart and pissal-adière flan. They make their own sausages with pure shoulder or belly pork flavoured with real ingredients rather than a manu-factured 'sausage mix'. They are dense and meaty in a range of flavours: apple with cider; mush-room; peppery Moroccan mergu-ez; South African Boerewors. Two famous English cooks are honoured, with Elizabeth David's Cypriot sausages with cori-ander and Jane Grigson's pork, leek and ginger. A limited selec-tion of fresh meat includes cubed lamb marinated in olive oil, pa-prika, garlic and ginger ready for the stew pot. Chickens are free range and free range ducks and guinea fowl can be ordered. There's smoked trout and chick-en liver paté. The cheese counter shows off British Isles cheeses best. **Suzanne Stirke's** Richard III Wensleydale, **Swaledale, Ribblesdale** and **Ashdale** goat's cheese are the local heroes. From Scotland there is Isle of Mull Cheddar and the soft, bloomy rinded Bonchester that develops a creamy interior rather like Camembert. From County Tip-perary comes a soft Cooleeney. Now, the search is on for some hand made French cheeses to supplement the more familiar St. Agur and Roquefort. Elsewhere in the shop, the shelves are stuffed with Italian pastas, classy olive oils, **Rosebud Preserves, Womersley Hall** flavoured vine-gars and dangerously addictive marinated green olives. Arcim-boldo can go to your head.

*146 Kings Road,
Harrogate, N. Yorks
☎ 01423 508760
Open: Tue-Sat 8.30am-5.30pm*

Herriot's

Tucked away in a side street off James Street, this shop is a win-ner with Harrogate's lunchtime sandwich trade. They keep a trusty cheese counter with a British and continental selection and Herriot's has a good Lanca-shire goat's cheese from Rib-chester as well as most of the Yorkshire cheeses. Continentals include Le Rustique Camembert.

*4 John Street,
Harrogate, N. Yorks
☎ 01423 564252
Open: summer Mon-Sat 9am-5pm winter 8am-5.30pm*

Pasta Romagna

One might expect the son of Gil-dea Porcelli, the ebullient owner of the Leeds **Pasta Romagna,** to be a chip off the old block. Not a bit of it. James Walker is so self-effacing as to be almost diametri-cally opposite of his mother whom he fondly describes as 'mad'. But he has learned well, working quietly away in the basement kitchen of this delica-tessen/bakery/coffee shop where locals drop in for what one de-scribed as 'the best cappuccino in England'. Authentic Italian pizza comes out of the oven in big square tins, topped simply and classically with tomato, mozzarella, parmesan, oregano and olive oil. It's sold Neapolitan style by the slice, hot or cold. There are 20 types of fresh pasta and dozens more dried pastas. Match up sauces from vongole, fungi, Bolognese or Napolitana. Italian cheeses are Caciocavallo, Parmesan grana padana, Mozza-rella, Gorgonzola and Mascar-pone. Saturday morning is the day to visit for home made bread: spinach and garlic, rose-mary and garlic, nuts and cinna-mon, sun dried tomato and basil or black olive.

*53 Cold Bath Road, Harrogate,
N. Yorks
☎ 01423 564160
Open: Mon-Sat 9am-6.30pm*

HEBDEN BRIDGE

Country Stores

There must be a sweet-tooth fac-tion among the diverse tenden-cies of Hebden Bridge because John Harris keeps four varieties of halva. As well as conventional grocery items there's cheese and good cold meats: roast ham, smoked turkey, roast topside and sopocka, a Polish cured pork loin.

*11-13 George's Square,
Hebden Bridge, W. Yorks
☎ 01422 844279
Open: Mon-Sat 8.30am-5.30pm*

Pennine Stores

Old fashioned woody sticks of liquorice root catch the eye on the counter but organic whole-meal bread and Polish rye bread constitute the principal attrac-tions along with 80 regional, British and European cheeses. There's continental smoked ham and salami at the delicatessen section and plenty of reliable **Suma** wholefoods. A selection of herbs and spices are sold loose.

*21 Crown Street,
Hebden Bridge, W. Yorks
☎ 01422 844945
Open: Mon-Sat 9am-5pm*

HELMSLEY

Hunter's

The Hunter's flagship. Cooked meats and sausages, a choice of Yorkshire, English and continental cheeses, cakes and good bread are on the ground floor. Upstairs are 33 different kinds of mustard. Tourists take home **Taylor's** tea, Yorkshire biscuits and **Yorkshire Country Wines**. Regulars top up with dried fruits, dried chestnuts, beans, pulses and sunflower seeds.

13 Market Place,
Helmsley, N. Yorks
☎ *01439 771307*
Open: Mon-Sat 8.30am-5.30pm
Sun 9.30am-5pm

HESSLE

James Patrick

Cheddar with Guinness or fruit cake? Stilton with ginger or peach and pear? Such concoctions may make the purist wince but flavoured cheeses are the best sellers here. Malcolm Crease's customers are clearly an idiosyncratic lot. He claims it is not only impossible to sell Lancashire cheese in Humberside but even pretty tough to shift Yorkshire cheeses too. Without a native Humberside cheese to cater for this baffling sub-regional chauvinism, he offers 70 cheeses from further afield. A mature Cheddar from Chewton Dairy in Somerset sits alongside a mellow Dorset Cheddar from Sturminster Newton. A mature deep orange cheese labelled 'Very old Gouda'

had the strength and flavour of a Parmesan, a great surprise. Malcolm Crease's shop is full of such discoveries. A fine array of olive oils and aged balsamic vinegars come direct from Fratelli Camisa, the Italian delicatessen in London's Berwick Street. There are superb French oils from Nicholas Alziari at £15 a tin and Californian oils flavoured with rosemary, basil or roast garlic from the Oil Merchant. You can put together your own hamper from the shelves: French aperitifs, whole black truffles, dried ceps or own label jams and pickles made for them by Dart Valley preserves. Smoked salmon and oysters come from Loch Fyne Oysterage and can be despatched through the mail. They do a rip roaring lunchtime sandwich trade with such originals as chicken with banana and mango chutney or green pepper salad with sauerkraut and dill cucumber. Malcolm Crease's food credentials come from his days running the Pipe and Glass in South Dalton, taking the food into the dizzy heights of the Good Food Guide. Happily, his food can still be tasted via his outside catering.

11 The Weir, Hessle,
Nr. Hull, N. Humbs
☎ *01482 641053*
Open: Mon-Sat 9am-5pm

HULL

Sui Hing Supermarket

A small supermarket serving Hull's Chinese community. Besides oriental basics in packets

and jars, are Chinese newspapers and videos. Fresh vegetables arrive on Friday and Sunday.

22-23 Story Street,
Hull, N. Humbs
☎ *01482 226387*
Open: Mon-Sat 10am-5.30pm
Sun 12 noon-5pm

ILKLEY

Powell's of Ilkley

Grove Promenade is in good shape for food finders these days with **Longbottom's** and **Asquith's**. Powell's popular delicatessen boasts quiches, game pies, nut loaves and lasagne. Beyond lie potted beef, chicken liver paté and lemon and garlic flavoured olives. Maureen Stansfield and Margaret Preston also keep a worthy two year old Cheddar, a full-flavoured Swiss Appenzell and Raclette for cheese fondue.

19 Grove Promenade,
Ilkley, W. Yorks
☎ *01943 607681*
Open: Mon-Sat 8.30am-5.30pm

INGLETON

Country Harvest

This renovated barn just north of Ingleton on the A65 promises a commitment to fresh local produce but then commits a large proportion of floor space to gifts and kitchenware. Fortunately there is a decent café, a healthy meat counter which includes Woodall's dry cured bacon, a conventional fruit and vegetable display and a cheese counter which genuinely exhibits a full selection of Yorkshire and Lancashire cheeses. There are speciality mustards and pickles and what must be the full range of Cottage Delights: how much black cuttlefish pasta in pricy glass jars does Ingleton need?

Ingleton, N. Yorks
☎ *01524 241655*
Open: Mon-Sun 9am-5.30pm
Café Mon-Sun 10am-5pm

OLIVE OIL

*Yorkshire has no single Italian grocer to compare with Soho for extra virgin Tuscan oils. But apart from delicatessen and Asian stockists, there are some rarified bottles at the smarter wine merchants. **Heber Wines** of Skipton import five litre cans of Umbrian extra virgin. **Martinez** of Ilkley and Harrogate specialise in under-rated Spanish oil and **Great Northern Wine Company** of Leeds and Ripon go French with walnut, hazelnut and pistachio.*

KEIGHLEY

The Delicatessen

Keighley's Italians, Germans and Poles head here. Dried pasta predominates and there is a challenging selection of continental charcuterie. Choose from Polish wiejska smoked ham, sopocka pork loin, Hungarian, Danish and Italian salami, cervelat, bratwurst, pepperoni sausages, mortadella Bologna sausage and pastrami. They keep Parma ham and pancetta, an air dried streaky pork, to eat cooked or raw. **Kolos** Ukrainian bread is the natural partner. Cheeses include Wensleydale from **Hawes Creamery**.

62 North Street,
Keighley, W. Yorks
☎ *01535 669006*
Open: Mon 8am-1pm
Tue-Sat 8am-5pm

LEEDS

Casa Mia

Originally a dedicated Italian delicatessen but while there is still dried pasta, crusty Italian bread, coffee, olive oils, Parma ham and a selection of Italian cheeses, Casa Mia is really now primarily a pizza and pasta takeaway with ice cream in the summer months. Pizza slices and a tasty parmigiana (layers of aubergine, tomato, basil and mozzarella), red pepper salad, artichokes in herbs, garlic and olive oil are all available through the day. From 5pm a takeaway offers 20 different pizza and pasta.

10 Stainbeck Lane, Chapel
Allerton, Leeds, W. Yorks
☎ *0113 266 1269*
Open: Mon-Sat 10.30am-5pm
Tue-Sat 10.30am-10.30pm

Continental Supermarket

Probably the best of the ethnic food stores on Chapeltown Road. It certainly reflects the area's ever potent racial pot. Afro-Caribbean tastes bring yam, breadfruit and sweet potato, peeled sugar cane and ripe mangoes. There are boxes of chillies, okra and limes. Cho-cho is a South American member of the squash family, popular in Australia and Louisiana and used for soup in Nicaragua. Couscous comes from North Africa, olive oil and vine leaves from Greece. Coriander and fenugreek are always a bargain. There's a choice of pourgouri, gram or chickpea flour, Patak's brand chutney's and pickles, and scores of spices. The staff can be sullen but with self service it's easy to root around.

125-7 Chapeltown Road,
Leeds, W. Yorks
☎ *0113 262 1244*
Open: Mon-Sun 9am-7.30pm

Gourmet Foods

A small Jewish grocery and delicatessen with a fresh meat counter as well as smoked salmon, fish balls, chopped herring and bagels from Tobias and **Chalutz** bakeries.

584 Harrogate Road.
Leeds, W. Yorks
☎ *0113 268 2726*
Open: Mon 8.30am-5pm
Tue-Thur 8.30am-5.30pm
Fri 8.30am-1.30pm
Sun 8.30-12 noon

Haley and Clifford

Dishes straight from the award-winning kitchen of Headingley's **Haley's Hotel** top the bill at Leeds' most exciting new delicatessen. Under chef Chris Baxter, Haley's was named as County Restaurant of the Year by the Good Food Guide in 1994. But despite its laurels, the hotel felt the competitive heat from the wave of new restaurants spearheading the Leeds riverside renaissance: 'To be honest, the lunchtime trade in the hotel was falling off', says former manager Stephen Beaumont. 'We had staff and equipment not exactly standing idle but certainly not fully utilised.' So they were put back to work making food for a purpose built deli. It is such a simple and sensible solution that everyone involved can't imagine why they didn't think of it sooner. Or why more restaurants don't follow suit. A former butcher's shop in Roundhay was lined up. They kept the old butcher's block and chrome meat rails but redecorated in stark cream and white. The design is modelled on Carluccio's of Covent Garden and the new Harvey Nichols food hall in Knightsbridge, both of the minimalist tendency. Prices, thankfully, make a nod to the northern realist school. Salami prices match Sainsbury, bread is the best seller and there's a pensioner clientele for well baked ham and cooked meat. They cater for more than just well heeled foodies. But it is the influence of the restaurant that really distinguishes H & C. Patés and terrines, char grilled vegetables, celeriac salads and couscous make the daily three mile trip from the restaurant kitchen to Roundhay. Pickles and jams are prepared when there's a quiet period in the kitchen. A glut of yellow plum tomatoes was converted into chutney and chutneys are now a permanent feature along with pickled vegetables, marmalade and Christmas mincemeat. Potato salad is made with shallots, vinaigrette and waxy French Charlotte potatoes. The tail is beginning to wag the dog. As shop manager Sue Clements saw salmon en croûte and chicken liver going well with her Street Lane faithful so the system adapts. The kitchen notes that their grilled swordfish will sell in Roundhay at the end of the week but not before. The shop's chutney sells at the hotel reception. The synergy is working.

43 Street Lane,
Leeds, W. Yorks
☎ *0113 237 0334*
Open: Mon-Fri 9.30am-5.30pm
Sat 9.30am-5pm

Hing Fat Hong Supermarket

Duck's feet in oyster sauce, cubes of pig's blood in brine, fresh tripe with ginger and spring onions are everyday items at Hing Fat Hong, Leeds' biggest Chinese supermarket. Lumps of what look suspiciously like Coalite turn out to be salted duck eggs encased in black charcoal. Not to be confused with preserved or one hundred year old eggs, which are actually six week old eggs preserved in lime and mud and coated with fine woodchips. Inside, the egg white is transformed into a dark transparent jelly and the yolk is greenish black – an acquired taste. Ting Hing Chan and his son Steven Chan have taken only two years to establish their supremacy since coming to Leeds after running a similar enterprise in Manchester. Yorkshire Chinese restaurant and takeaway owners come on Sunday morning to buy in their weekly supplies from the supermarket. Anyone who has nurtured the dark thought that outside the very best Cantonese restaurants one Yorkshire Chinese is indistinguishable from the next, will have their suspicions further fuelled by the sight of bulk buying of identical catering packs. Certainly, all the starters that ever appeared on a restaurant menu are here en masse:

steamed buns, crab claws, prawns in rice paper, prawn toasts and spring rolls ad infinitum. Hing Fat Hong is nevertheless a revelation for the browser or the amateur Chinese cook. There is a wide range of fresh fruit and vegetables: green radish, arrowroot, lotus root, winter melons, bitter gourds, guavas, loquats, lychees, rambutans, pak choi (Chinese leaves), daikon (white radish), fresh lime leaves, chillies and lemon grass. What look like gladioli bulbs are in fact fresh water chestnuts which are wonderfully sweet and crunchy when peeled, sliced and stir fried or eaten raw in a salad. Shelves overflow with spices, bags of almonds, peanuts and cashews. There are giant bottles of sesame oil and soy sauce and packets of dried seaweed, mushrooms and lotus petals. They have dozens of different fresh and dried noodles and every imaginable kind of rice from fragrant Thai to glutinous Japanese, all piled up in huge sacks. All the utensils required for oriental cooking are here: thick wooden chopping boards, evil looking choppers in numerous sizes, woks, china bowls and, of course the indispensable chopstick.

Templar Place,
Leeds, W. Yorks
☎ *0113 234 8168*
Open: Mon-Sun 10am-6pm

Kendal Moore

A superior hamper for the cricket at nearby Headingley can easily be assembled from this thriving and well established delicatessen. Easy because the best picnic items are tantalisingly shown off in the big showpiece window. It's primed daily with deep filled quiches, chunky game pies and gateaux. Most are made on the premises by the brother and sister team of Frank Collins and Lorraine Tatler and their capable baker Eva Pritchatt. The first room has patés, lasagne, salads, olives, jars of coffee, herbs, a compendium of spices and selected fancy chocolates. Down a step and a second room has oils, vinegars, preserves and a well stocked cheese counter with the main emphasis on continental and English cheeses, with Yorkshire gaining strength. Frank Collins was a prominent supporter from the start of the staff buy out of the Wensleydale creamery. They sell the local Leeds Kroustie bread but far better are their own herb, cheese, wholemeal and white loaves which they bake on Saturday nights for a healthy Sunday morning breakfast trade. A small café at the back serves food from the shop.

74 Otley Road, Leeds, W. Yorks
☎ *0113 278 3439*
Open: Mon 9am-6pm
Tue-Sun 9am-10pm

JAPANESE FOOD

A rare and authentic Japanese experience is supplied by Yoko's, who produce exquisite meals in the unlikely setting of suburban Harrogate. Shopping is harder still but on the last Friday of every month, a mobile shop drives some 200 miles up the M1 from Croydon to the residential driveway of Mr & Mrs Hasegawa in Sheffield and dispenses rice, noodles, shoyu sauce, pickles and frozen meat and fish to South Yorkshire's Japanese community centred round Sheffield University's department of East Asian studies. The numbers are still too small to spawn a Japanese food culture in the city so Miuri Foods who run the mobile shop are a much needed lifeline for Japanese ex-pats. The shop also calls at the Pioneer Electronics factory in Castleford where Japanese executives can stock up with ingredients not otherwise obtainable in Yorkshire. Times and locations of the van may change.

Miuri Foods ☎ *0181 549 8076*
Pioneer Electronics, Whitwood Common Lane, Castleford, W. Yorks 12 noon-1pm
9 Kingfield Road, Sheffield, S. Yorks 2pm-3pm

The Kosherie

Still known by regulars as the Moortown Deli, this delicatessen cum supermarket changed its name to the Kosherie, reflecting its prime service to the 10,000 strong Jewish community of North Leeds. Everything sold here is permissible under the Jewish faith and almost everything carries a supervision label indicating that it has been made in compliance with Jewish dietary laws. It's an attractive shop for Gentiles as well. The delicatessen counter offers pastrami with peppers, pressed beef, the traditional Jewish favourite of chopped liver, latkes (deep fried minced potato and onion), gefilte fish, chopped herring and herrings in sweet or spicy pickles. There is rye bread, black bread, poppy seed rolls, caraway bread, onion cakes and kuchen (an iced fruit loaf) and bagels. Kosherie smoked salmon to go with the bagels may not be cheap but it's top quality and smoked salmon trimmings are a compensating bargain. Cream cheese comes from **Dan Dairies.**

410 Harrogate Road,
Moortown, Leeds, W. Yorks
☎ 0113 268 2943
Open: Mon 9am-5.30pm
Tue-Thur 9am-6pm
Fri 8.30am-2pm Sun 8am-2pm

Maumoniat International Supermarket

There are 7,000 varieties of rice in the world, and while Maumoniat's don't keep them all, they look as if they're trying with Basmati, Indian sweet, Thai fragrant, Carolina from the U.S.A , long grain and easy-cook. All the spices of the Orient seem to pitch up here too. Buy an ounce or a sackful. Go round the world with Bombay duck, West Indian hot pepper sauce, Chinese green tea, Greek feta cheese, olives, vine leaves and baclava. There is a good fresh fruit and vegetable section with okra, bitter melon

and dubi kadu as well as onions, garlic, carrots and potatoes. They stock 12 different kinds of bread from nan, chapati, poppadom, pitta and pizza bases. In the freezer: okra, coconut and melokhia, a middle eastern vegetable similar to spinach. There's pure butter ghee and the best samosas and onion bhajis in town made by Yausaf Maumoniat's sister-in-law at **Mariam's** in Dewsbury. They are delivered fresh each day.

35 Brudenell Grove
Leeds, W. Yorks
☎ 0113 275 1887
Open: Mon-Sun 1pm-10pm

Pasta Romagna

It first hits you from about three streets away. Not the smell but the soprano, probably Puccini, probably full blast. Known locally as the Opera Shop, this priceless Italian deli and café is run with ferocious energy by Gildea Porcelli. A native of Salerno, she came to England at 18 on the unlikely assignment of 'a modelling job in Halifax', met and married an Englishman, had three children, baby sat Leeds-born superstar chef Marco Pierre White and when her children grew up, wondered what to do next. She decided to open the sort of Salerno café where customers could sit all day over a proper cup of coffee and eat a slice of pizza smeared with tomato. Albion Place can't quite hack it as Southern Italy but the café is a popular city centre meeting place whose success has spawned another **Pasta Romagna** in Harrogate, run by Gildea's son James. Gildea and her staff make a dozen types of fresh pasta in a basement kitchen. She stocks countless varieties of dried pasta, makes a crisp olive oil bread and rustic pizza slices topped simply with tomatoes, garlic, olive oil and oregano. There are Italian pastries and cakes, olive oils, balsamic vinegars and every type

of Italian liqueur. Cheeses include Parmesan, Ricotta, Mascarpone, Caciocavallo and Gorgonzola. All the while, Gildea plays merry hell with staff, customers and Madame Butterfly in her charming broad Yorkshire/Italian accent. In her favourite phrase, she is 'never, never, never' downhearted.

26 Albion Place,
Leeds, W. Yorks
☎ 0113 245 1569
Open: Mon-Sat 9am-6pm

Warsaw Stores

Mrs Mirska keeps Leeds' best selection of Polish tinned foods and induces deeper homesickness with golabki or little pigeons – cabbage leaves stuffed with mince, rice, spices and herbs to look like a pigeon breast; rolady which is beef sliced and rolled with smoked bacon and onion; and an array of pastries from babki – grandmother cakes, through fruit loaf mounds, black and white pastry to poppyseed cake on a hard Polish cheesecake base.

151 Chapeltown Road,
Leeds, W. Yorks
☎ 0113 262 8455
Open: Mon-Sat 8am-8pm Sun 9am-6pm

Wing Lee Hong

Until **Hing Fat Hong** arrived in Templar Place, this was Leeds' premier Chinese supermarket. Although it's smaller than its new competitor across the car park, there is still plenty here for the Chinese cook. An added bonus is that all the fresh produce is labelled so the uninitiated can tell choi sum from pak choi and learn that see-gaw and okra are the same thing. A recipe that calls for bitter melons, lotus root or lemon grass can be easily assembled. Although Chinese ingredients naturally predominate, there are rices and spices for Indian, Korean and West Indian cooking. The freezers and fridges are stocked with salted jelly fish, Chinese sausage, chicken feet, beef and fish balls, fried bean curd and fresh noodles. They keep every size of shrimp and prawn and a comprehensive dim sum selection. There are Chinese cookery books and plenty of kitchen equipment from plate-warmers and woks to earthenware cooking pots and Thai pestles and mortars.

6 Edward Street, Leeds,
W. Yorks
☎ 0113 245 7203
Open: Mon-Sun 10am-6pm

MALTON

Delicatessen & Wine Shop
Really an old fashioned grocer's where sacks of dried fruit rub shoulders with ground almonds and ladies in overalls will happily weigh out a quarter of Norwegian goat's cheese, a two year old Gouda or an Irish Cashel Blue. There are tins of smoked oysters and snails in champagne in the black and green livery of the Epicure brand. Gentlemen's relish, bottled fruit and tins of Walker's shortbread echo another age. Local producers are well reflected in the 70 strong cheese counter, and with cream from a Jersey herd at Farlington beneath the Howardian Hills. Bread is baked by Penny Jones at **Hovingham**

Bakery and Loch Fyne smoked salmon arrives from the Western Highlands of Scotland via the **Teesdale Trencherman**, more properly known as Johnny Cooke-Hurle of Barnard Castle.

23 Wheelgate, Malton, N. Yorks
☎ 01653 694448
Open: Mon-Sat 8.30am-5.30pm
Thur 8.30am-4pm

MORLEY

Antonio's Delicatessen
Love and marriage to a Leeds girl brought Antonio Jazoli from Sicily to sunny Morley. Sandwiches, too, range in spirit from Sicily with mozzarella, tomato and basil to homely egg mayonnaise. There's crisp Italian bread, wholemeal and French sticks which arrive fresh daily. Also seafood salad in olive oil, kabanos, pepperoni, roast beef and genuine Reggiano Parmigiano.

61 Queen Street,
Morley, Nr Leeds, W. Yorks
☎ 0113 238 1819
Open Mon-Sat 9am-5pm

NORTHALLERTON

Lewis & Cooper
The name in gold leaf is still there. The old wine and whisky signs are in place. Lewis & Cooper opened in Northallerton in 1870 and although the stock may have changed, the spirit of

traditional service remains. This is a food emporium, a grocer as we would fondly imagine all good high street grocers once were but really weren't. It is probably heartily fed up of being called the Harrods of the north because it's something else: old fashioned, charming, stuffy, impeccable, illogical and extraordinary, all in the space of as many shelves and staff. It is Lewis & Cooper. There's nowhere else quite like it, a certifiable Yorkshire treasure. There are 25,000 different lines from vanilla pods to vintage port. They roast their own coffee, keep 150 different cheeses and 120 marmalades. *Nobody* needs to keep 120 marmalades. Then, there is the purest and priciest saffron. In case something is not in stock, they promise they'll try to find it and a battered exercise book notes customers' requests for obscure items: Tasmanian leatherwood honey, Canadian white peas and Bulgarian Rodina tomatoes. While one member of the Lewis family still sits on the board of directors, the last link to the founders, day to day management is carried out by Tony Howard, who began in the business with Lipton's of Harrogate and is only the fourth general manager of Lewis & Cooper this century. Threatening to become the first women managers of

---

HAMPERS & CHAMPERS

Lewis & Cooper supply the ultimate hamper for Christmas or to send to a loved one anywhere in the world. Their De Luxe version costs £145 and contains: Lewis & Cooper Beaumet Brut champagne, fruit cake and fruit nut mix, Asbach Uralt brandy, Gold Dish ox tongue, Epicure king crab, petit-pois, mixed vegetables, white seedless grapes, glacé fruits and blossom honey 'hedgehog', Becas venison soup, Jenson's goose paté, Wiltshire Tracklements apple and sage jelly, Bahlsen biscuits, Gale's lime flower honey, chocolate Bath Oliver biscuits, Arran mustard with herbs, Arran tomato, garlic and almond relish, Roka cheese biscuits, Jackson's tea caddy, Shepcote petit fours, Lyons ground coffee bags, Noel's green olives, Mini Chubby Tree crackers, Lindt Marguerita milk chocolates, Hider Tiffay's assorted liqueurs, Scott's orange marmalade with Teacher's whisky. There are ten other hamper selections, including one of exclusively Yorkshire produce. Other hamper contenders are **Patrick's** *of Hessle.* **Haley and Clifford** *of Leeds and the* **Teesdale Trencherman**.

Lewis and Cooper are his twin daughters on the payroll, Bettina and Victoria. Tony Howard champions local producers. Some, like part-time bee keeper and honey maker **Trevor Swales**, are very small. Plum puddings are baked by Mr Bush, a retired grocer from Sheffield. An Easingwold baker makes the revered Lewis & Cooper fruit cakes. They stock every conceivable nozzle and piping bag for cake decorators. They are also still one of the region's last emporia to deliver grocery orders, within a 20 mile radius, just like a good grocer should. 'Of course, it's totally uneconomic in this day and age', says Tony Howard. 'But it's all part of the image. If we stopped doing it, people would complain that Lewis & Cooper were not what they were'. That, of course, is unimaginable.

92 High Street,
Northallerton, N. Yorks
☎ *01609 772880*
Open: Mon-Sat 8.30am-5.30pm

Selby's

A conventional delicatessen selling a selection of cooked meats, wholefoods and regional, British and European cheeses. The upstairs kitchen makes lunchtime sandwiches and caters for weddings, christenings and, being this part of the world, shooting parties.

6 Market Row,
Northallerton, N. Yorks
☎ *01609 773928*
Open: Mon-Sat 9am-5pm

OTLEY

Gloucester's

A small, attractive shop packed with wholefoods, delicatessen items and first rate locally baked cakes. In particular, beware the lemon drizzle cake, a light sponge soaked in a concentrated lemon syrup. There's chorizo sausage, patés and **Pepper Ar-**den game pies. Strong points are Italian – Parma ham, olives, quick polenta, arborio rice, pasta flour, Balsamic vinegar, and sun dried tomatoes – and cheese, including an unpasteurised farmhouse Cheddar, oak smoked Wensleydale, local **Ashdale** goat's cheese and many more. Notably helpful and enthusiastic.

5 New Market, Otley, W. Yorks
☎ *01943 466935*
Open: Mon-Sat 9am-5.30pm

PILSLEY

Chatsworth Farm Shop

The Chatsworth Farm Shop is not in Yorkshire and never was no matter what map or boundary rubric used. But it is only 12 miles from Sheffield and is worth breaking the rules for. It has one of the best quality cheese counters in the area with over 70 different Irish and English cheeses, many of them farm produced and unpasteurised. The Chatsworth estate farms supply milk for cream, yoghurt and ice cream. The authenticity of the free range eggs is confirmed by the chickens that forage amongst the picnickers down the road at Chatsworth House. Fresh meat is a prime area of distinction. The butchery department has Q Guild status, the meat industry's symbol of quality, and includes lamb from the Duchess of Devonshire's prize-winning flock of Jacob sheep. The 'Duke's Favourite' sausages, an all meat pork sausage with liver and white wine, are fine. The estate's own honey cured bacon is excellent. The shop has a vast range of game, fresh and frozen: wild duck, partridge, wood pigeon, rabbit, venison, guinea fowl, pheasant and poussin. Bread, scones and cakes are produced in a bakery behind the shop. Besides parkin, fruit cake and plum pudding are old fashioned children's favourites such as chocolate covered cornflakes, rice crispy slice, coconut pyramids and flapjack. Yearnings for high tea with nanny perhaps? But for something really different, try an Innes loaf. This sourdough bread was developed by Hugh Inge-Innes Lillingston at his farm in Tamworth, Staffordshire. It takes five days to make and is baked in an ancient wood-fired bread oven. The result, a firm, chewy loaf with a distinctly sour flavour costs an equally sour £6 a loaf but they do weigh in at about 4lbs and are cut down into quarters. The original inspiration for the shop came from the Duchess of Devonshire, who has long balanced a commitment to quality produce with a highly developed financial acumen. You can't miss the crested mints and pricey biscuit tins. But credit for the day to day running of the shop, the searching out of new products and the maintenance of standards must go to Sandy Boyd who came to Chatsworth from the Surrey dairy specialists, Loseley Park. For him this is no tourist clip joint but a high class repository of good food which flourishes on the patronage of its year-round, hard core customers.

Stud Farm, Pilsley,
Bakewell, Derbys
☎ *01246 583392*
Open: Apr-Oct Mon-Sat 9am-5.30pm Nov-Mar 9am-5pm Tue from 9.30am Sun 11am-5pm

RIPLEY

Hopkins-Porter

The name and ownership of this shop, set rather splendidly in the grounds of Ripley Castle, still confuses people. Many who fondly remember the Farnley Farm shop near Otley, run by Anthony Porter, not surprisingly believe he still owns this too. Not so. He sold out nine years ago to run a wholesale operation in Boroughbridge. The shop today is owned by Mervyn and Catherine Moorse and they've kept the name. Although reduced in range and diversity since its heyday, it can still offer decent cheese and some interesting cooked meats. Mervyn Moorse has always supported **Shepherd's Purse** cheese maker Judy Bell and is rewarded with supplies of her popular ewe's milk Yorkshire Blue and, when it's available, her rarer cow's milk Newsham Blue. Their own label Ripley Castle Wensleydale is made by the **Wensleydale Creamery** at Hawes. There's Colston Bassett blue Stilton, a clothbound English cheddar and a matured Devon Oke. The deli counter has a strong selection of continental sausages, salami, Cumbrian dry cured bacon, smoked duck breast, chicken and chicken wings, cooked Cumberland sausage and paté. For pudding, try **Brymor** or **Yorkshire Dales** ice cream or Catherine Moorse's home made treacle tarts.

Old Station Shop, Ripley Castle, Ripley, N. Yorks
☎ *01423 771466*
Open: Tue-Sun 9am-5.30pm
closed 4.30pm in winter

RIPON

Fresh Cut
Andrew Strickland was 10 years with the Happy Eater chain before taking over Fresh Cut, perched in the gallery of Ripon's petite shopping arcade. A good move, for he now provides Ripon with much happier eating from this lovely delicatessen. Primarily an ambassador for British cheese, he stocks **Botton**, blue Stilton from Long Clawson in Leicestershire, Appleby's Cheshire, Mrs Cross's **Cotherstone** and Wensleydale from **Fortmayne Dairy**. There are two standard block cheeses and a different cheese is promoted each week. It might be Pencarreg, a wonderfully ripe unpasteurised Welsh Brie, or a Somerset Camembert. The continental side includes mild or mature Italian Pecorino. Bread rolls and sandwiches are, as the shop name implies, fresh, cut and filled to order and turned round fast. There are home made salads, salami, Parma ham and cooked meats sliced on the spot. Flans are made locally and come sweet, filled with fruit, or savoury with fresh salmon and asparagus.

Ripon Small Shops Arcade, Duck Hill, Ripon, N. Yorks
☎ *01765 600972*
Open: Mon-Sat 9am-5pm
Wed 9am-2.30pm

SCARBOROUGH

Gianni's
Sip a cappuccino, contemplate the Italian wines and the olive oils, choose a pizza-to-go and observe Gianni Bisi making the pasta. Just like mama used to make, perhaps? Not quite. 'She made it all by hand', he grins, as twirls of pasta come out of the machine in the shop window. Well, Modena which Gianni abandoned to improve his English and marry a local girl, has plenty of pasta makers. Scarborough's gain.

14 Victoria Road, Scarborough, N. Yorks
☎ *01723 501724*
Open: Mon-Sat 9am-5.30pm

SCUNTHORPE

Suszczenia's
Polish Michael Suszczenia has been here for 20 years and claims to sell the items you can't get anywhere else. There's scant competition in Scunthorpe to threaten the offer. But in his disarmingly crazy delicatessen, he will find you lumpfish caviar, mushroom ketchup, sesame oil, pickled walnuts, rye bread, noodles, rice and much, much more.

Scunthorpe Market, Food Hall, High Street, Scunthorpe, S. Humbs
Open: Mon-Sat 9am-5.30pm

SHEFFIELD

Beau Deli
David and Karen Beaumont have progressively extended their range in this delicatessen since taking over in 1991. There are 20 kinds of salami and 50 different cheeses. Ham and cheese are understandably their best sellers but they also stock haggis, Pumpernickel (German rye bread), Beluga caviar, Japanese rice wine and the full range of Tiptree jams. They plan next to produce their own pies and pastries.

477/479 Glossop Road, Sheffield, S. Yorks
☎ *0114 266 2235*
Open: Mon-Fri 8.30am-6.30pm
Sat 8.30am-6pm

Kung Heng
A lack-lustre Chinese supermarket that stocks most of the oriental basics in tins, jars or packets but few fresh ingredients. There is meat and fish in the freezer and some woks, chopsticks and kitchen equipment.

London Road, Sheffield, S. Yorks
☎ *0114 258 6652*
Open: Mon-Sat 10.30am-5pm
Sun 12 noon-5pm

STOKESLEY

Stokesley Delicatessen
Prepared foods are a highlight of this popular High Street deli. Spinach roulade, mushroom and walnut parcels and samosas are offered along with cooked meats and patés. Cakes and gateaux can be ordered in advance. Organic bread comes from the **Larchfield Community** at Hemlington. Kath Brown promotes cheese with a different tasting for her customers every week and she is one of the few stockists of the fresh, unwaxed cheese from **Farndale Dairy Goats**.

64 High Street, Stokesley, N. Yorks
☎ *01642 711320*
Open: Mon-Sat 9am-5.30pm

TADCASTER

Little Deli

Loyalty to classic Yorkshire cheese and dairy is the stamp of The Little Deli. Their counter holds Richard III Wensleydale, smoked Wensleydale, Swaledale, Coverdale and **Brymor** ice cream. They also operate a sandwich service.

3 High Street,
Tadcaster, N. Yorks
☎ *01937 835290*
Open: Mon-Fri 9am-5.30pm
Sat 9am-5pm

TICKHILL

Taylor's of Tickhill

Osbert and Bessie Taylor took over this shop opposite the old Buttercross in 1946. Then, food was rationed and customers could bring their own jug to be filled with ale. Now, three generations of Taylor's run the business and, although it has expanded to become a self-service store, it still has the atmosphere of a traditional family grocer. Regulars can pay on account, have groceries delivered to the door and are usually on first name terms with sons Roy and John and grandson Christopher. There are all the usual grocery staples. Pies, bread and roast meat are baked on the premises. Fruit and vegetables are bought locally whenever possible and John Taylor supplies Yorkshire honey from his own hives. Osbert, who runs the cheese counter, keeps a good selection of farmhouse cheeses including Nantwich prize winners. You can buy almost anything from cornflakes to quails' eggs and, within reason, if they don't stock it they'll get hold of it.

9/10 Market Place,
Tickhill, S. Yorks
☎ *01302 742355*
Open: Mon-Thur 8.30am-
12.45pm & 1.45pm-5.30pm
Fri & Sat 8.30am-5.30pm

WAKEFIELD

Fayre Do's

Mango and African mint tea with honey can't fail but to stand out from the excellent choice of tea and coffee served in the tiny upstairs café, which properly deals in real leaves and strainers. Downstairs is a selection of salami and cooked meats with Yorkshire cheeses the mainstay of a cheese counter.

13 Silver Street,
Wakefield, W. Yorks
☎ *01924 291200*
Open: Mon-Sat 9am-5pm Wed
9am-3pm

YARM

Bon Appetit

Louise Anderson keeps delicatessen, cooked meats and cheeses but only the most resolute will avoid being derailed by her home made cakes, baked in the kitchen above this popular and friendly side street shop. Victoria sponge, apricot or redcurrant frangipane and toffee crunch cake lead the attack.

3 Danby Wynd, Yarm, N. Yorks
☎ *01642 787878*
Open: Mon-Sat 9am-5pm

YORK

Good Food Shop

This small but well stocked delicatessen makes good neighbours with **Melton's** restaurant next door. There is usually a reliable collection of British and European cheeses. There are plenty of cooked meats, free range eggs and speciality jams and mustards. But cakes are the thing here. Fresh or from the freezer, there are treacle tarts, curd tarts, chocolate mud pies and much more and they will make almost any kind of speciality cake to order.

9 Scarcroft Road, York
☎ *01904 637445*
Open: Mon-Sat 9.15am-5.30pm

Lawrie's

Housed in a 13th century half timbered building in the middle of York's open market, this large delicatessen is run by David and Jill Lawrie who moved across the road from their unhappily named cheese shop 'Choosa Cheese'. There's plenty of everything here, baskets stuffed to the rims, different counters, jams, chocolates, continental cakes and biscuits, almost too much for its own good. There's an exhaustive range of cheeses from Yorkshire, England and the continent (disappointingly not all trimmed or in prime condition considering their cheese specialist background). Also cooked meats, quiches, sandwiches, pies, pickles and an upstairs café.

2 Jubbergate, York
☎ *01904 653845*
Open: Mon-Sat 8am-5pm

Stéphanes

Mustards, dried mushrooms, speciality sandwiches and a selection of Yorkshire regional cheeses just about hold their own under the unending tourist waves. Not really the ideal location to buck the tide but handy for **Scott of York** virtually next door who still produce genuine York ham.

77 Low Petergate, York
☎ *01904 659556*
Open: Mon-Sat 9.30am-5.30pm

More worthwhile delicatessen
can be found in the following
*shops in the **Cheese & Dairy***
chapter:

***Boroughbridge**, Cheese & Co*
***Brighouse**, Czerwik's*
***Grimsby**, The Larder*
***Harrogate**, The Cheeseboard*
***Ilkley**, Burrell's*
***Knaresborough**, Farm Dairy*
***Scarborough**, The Cheeseboard*
***Settle**, Market Pantry*
***York**, The Food Emporium*

10

Markets

The markets of Yorkshire and Humberside are now officially tourist attractions, according to some optimistic glossy brochures. Anyone cancelling their Tuscan villa for a tour of Yorkshire and Humberside's 100 or so markets is in for a chastening experience. Certainly, there are historic buttercrosses, bell-ringers and the majestic Kirkgate market in Leeds but it is also a trip through some of the worst of modern Britain. West Riding municipal architecture hit rock bottom with its 1960s market hall horrors (see Keighley's and die). Many stalls are a nightmare of nylon and plastic with synthetic food to match. By definition, markets deal in the cheapest and, too often, the poorest food. Cheap meat can only come from factory farms. The battery chicken and her battery eggs rule alongside the shrink-wrap cheese and the ocean stick. So what are the rewards? The sea bird eggs and the horsemeat stalls may have gone but there are still unique foods and genuine regional specialities to be found alongside rich and funny characters. There are some great fishmongers, Eastern European delicatessens, Asian, Caribbean and conventional fruit and vegetable stalls. This may be the last generation of haslet, weasand, pig bag and cow heel but it is in the soot-blackened halls of the industrial towns that they can still be found. The wooden stalls and canvas awnings of the gentler country markets can still deliver distinctive baking and local cheeses. Either way, market day in Yorkshire remains an indestructible part of the British social fabric with its unbroken formula of food piled high and sold cheap.

MARKETS

BARNSLEY

Charter Market Hall

Six days a week Barnsley's modern covered Charter Market Hall is packed. It's cheap, it's cheerful and it's bristling with life and energy. Fruit and vegetable stalls predominate, fiercely competing not just on price but in the glory of their display. There are great mountains of sprouts and potatoes. Spotlights pick up the shine on the carefully constructed pyramids of Mackintosh reds. Prices are some of the lowest anywhere and **Superfruits** have the best selection: all the staples plus aubergines, fennel, chillies, sweet potatoes and lychees. Many Yorkshire markets still have a tripe stall. Barnsley supports two: **Spencer's** and **Gosling's**. Four generations of the Gosling family have sustained the business since 1877. James and Margaret Gosling are among a dwindling band of tripe dressers (washing and bleaching their own tripe) in the country and they will be the last in their family. 'There'll be no more after us', says Margaret. 'Not many people buy tripe now, only old people.' At 72p lb tripe is high protein and cheap. Piles of

pure white honeycomb and thick seam are displayed with cow heel, pig bag (stomach) and elder (cow's udder), cooked and pressed to produce a soft, light orange paste that can be sliced and fried in butter. More traditional northern delicacies are to be found at **Clamp's.** They have a wide range of cooked meats including polony (minced bacon), savoury duck (pig's hock with herbs and breadcrumbs) and black puddings. **Albert Hirst Jnr.** (Tue, Wed, Fri, Sat 8am-5pm) has bulbous rings of shiny black puddings piled up high on poles on his counter. In post-industrial Barnsley they come with apple and cream, garlic or fat free. To his amazement, Albert is selling them to smart restaurants as starters; a renaissance, one suspects, that is some way from a revolution. He also sells fresh meat, sausages in natural skins, boiled feet, pig's chap (face), boiled pig's tails at 20p, polony, savoury duck, potted beef, brawn (pig's head), pork dripping, 120 dozen pork pies every week and the legendary, Barnsley chop (see below). With two more Albert's in the male line, the inheritance is secure. The fish market has half a dozen

stalls. **Mitchell's** (Tue, Wed, Fri, Sat) run by David O'Neil has the biggest selection. Fresh uncooked langoustines, oysters, halibut, salmon trout and whole salmon are all at bargain prices. David O'Neil keeps up good natured banter in true market tradition. He'll tell you if the fish is fresh, frozen or defrosted; will clean and gut; and advise you how to cook it. He has relentless energy and good humour despite getting up at 3.30 a.m. for his thrice-weekly drive to Manchester's wholesale fish market. Upstairs are the cafés. **Oldfield's Original Pie and Pea Stall** has no pretensions. Queue at a hatch for a steaming bowl of pie and peas and a cup of tea for 70p, with chips an additional 20p. Functional seating. No frills. The outdoor and covered markets (Wed, Fri and Sat only) have a few fruit and vegetable stalls.

May Day Green,
Barnsley, S. Yorks
Covered market: Mon-Sat
9.30am-5pm Closed Thur

BEDALE

Bedale Market

A charming country market operates on both sides of Bedale's main street. Its food provision is dominated by **Carrick's**. John runs a well stocked fruit and vegetable stall (main entry p51), with fancy lines of chanterelle mushrooms and baby sweetcorn as well as all the basics. Good soft fruit comes direct from local farms in the summer months. Next door Peter and David Carrick operate a fish van (main entry p12), with the best range of fish for miles. It's guaranteed bone free and comes fresh each day from Hull.

Market Place, Bedale, N. Yorks
Outdoor Market: Tue 8am-5pm

THE BARNSLEY CHOP

Not exactly a delicacy, this regional cut – the two boned, lamb chop weighs in at over a pound. They are said to have first appeared in 1849 at the town's King's Head Hotel to feed hungry farmers. Albert Hirst sealed their fame by serving up 75 one and a half pounders when the Prince of Wales opened Barnsley's Town Hall in 1933. Jane Grigson rated one of Mr Hirst's Barnsley's the best lamb chop she had ever eaten 'the outside being crisp and dark, the inside sweet and tender as butter.' Albert Hirst Jnr. still sells them in the market and out of town the trencherman's dream cuisine of Brooklands motel at Tankersley still keeps the faith with the biggest chops of all.

BRADFORD

Rawson Market

Bradford's main food market is really two markets combined. Rawson Market leads into the James Street Fish Market. The main market is a busy, thriving mix in the old tradition. Vendors used to shout their wares but the market managers stopped it because it was too noisy. Nevertheless, there's plenty of chatter between the stall holders and the customers, some of it real old fashioned bargaining. In the main hall are dozens of butchers and even more fruit and vegetable stalls. Choose with care, especially meat. Some lamb is actually mutton, some has been frozen then thawed out. Competition keeps the prices at rock bottom and you get what you pay for. **Fruit Basket**, with three stalls in the market, has good produce with an interesting specialist selection. Kohlrabi, celeriac, persimmon, passion fruit and fresh figs are all at prices well below the supermarkets. For yams, sweet potato and plantains, try **Agatha's** West Indian stall tucked away in the middle of the meat market. **Hey's Tripe Shop** sells honeycomb tripe, cowheel, pig bag and other odd animal components. Elsewhere are rabbits, hares, chickens, game and, at Christmas, the cheapest turkeys. Look out, above all, for Napoleon and Irena Puc's delightful **Slavia Stores** (main entry p112), tiny but quite simply one of the best continental delicatessens in the region. Whether it's blutwurst (black pudding), kabanos (smoked sausage) or any of the 300 types of cooked meats they stock, the Puc's will dispense it. They have rye bread from Bradford's prize **Kolos** Ukrainian bakery and one thousand and one items to go with it. One day the shelves really will collapse under the combined weight of Greek olive oil, German cakes, Italian pasta, and Polish cream fudge. The Puc's have been serving Bradford's 12,000 expatriate Europeans for 38 years, a magnetic presence on the Bradford food scene. **Pie Tom's**, the unique pie and pea stall that has been a market institution for more than a century is no more, at least neither in name nor decor. New owners have lost the legal right to use the name and the sawn off church pews have been repainted in cream and lemon, doing nothing for the atmosphere. The old sludgy brown went unerringly well with steaming dishes of pie and peas, the black puddings and mugs of tea. No doubt this characterful little café will continue to be Pie Tom's whatever they do with the paint pot (open: Mon & Tue 8am-3pm, Wed 8am-1pm, Thur, Fri, Sat 8am-5pm). Three families dominate Bradford's fish market: **Quirk's**, **Priestley's** and **Burn & Hill**, clocking up nearly 200 years of service between them. Bradford's ethnic mix ensures a wide range of fish from far off oceans. It's the place to come for octopus, red snapper, parrot fish, silver pomfrets from India and the garfish with a backbone that turns an alarming green when cooked. There is an abundance of fresh fish from British fleets, plenty of mussels, crabs, whelks and winkles in season and the odd lobster. The quality can be variable but on the whole the quick turnover ensures freshness.

Rawson Place,
Bradford, W. Yorks
Covered market: Mon-Sat
8.30am-5pm Wed 8.30am-1pm

BRIDLINGTON

Bridlington Market

A traditional open air market with a handful of fresh fruit and vegetable stalls: **Hewitt's**, **Arthur Jackson** and **Reg Witty**, who also sells duck eggs. **Natural Wholefoods**, run for 14 years by Sharon Havercroft, is just that – a wholefood stall selling unsulphured apricots, Lexia raisins, pulses, herbs and spices.

King Street,
Bridlington, N. Humbs
Outdoor market: Wed & Sat
9am-5pm

CASTLEFORD

Market Place

The Castleford and Allerton Mutual Industrial Society Limited 1871 has been refurbished and renamed The Market Place. But for all its gentrification, this is still Castleford covered market where **Schofield's** sell dripping sandwiches beside a sign advising: 'Slim with tripe – high protein, low carbohydrate'. Schofield's have been selling tripe, pig bag, gelatinous cow heel and black pudding on Castleford market since 1876. The stall pays tribute to some curious northern fancies: weasand, a long coffee coloured tube turns out to be windpipe. Thick seam and honeycomb tripe, black pudding, pork dripping and chip fat are at least recognisable. Neatsfoot oil claims to cure rheumatism, arthritis and aching joints. The latest generation stallholder, Nigel Schofield acknowledges that tripe is a dying trade but hopes diversification into cooked meats will save the business. More familiar fruit and vegetables can be found at **Davison's**. There are three fish stalls. **Bethell's**, related to the stall in Leeds Market, **Lane's** and **Granville's** each stock the basics of haddock, cod and mackerel. **Newboulds** have free range eggs and **Nature's Store** have room for some wholefoods among all the pills and potions.

Market Place,
Carlton Street, Castleford,
W. Yorks
Covered market: Mon-Sat
8.30am-5pm

OFFAL & OFFCUTS

The market stalls and pork butchers of Yorkshire and Lancashire represent virtually the last stand of offal and offcuts. Nowadays, most people can afford better cuts or are simply too squeamish. There is, however, a long and honourable history of putting every last piece of the slaughtered beast to profitable use; in the case of the pig, 'everything but the squeal'. Here is a glossary of some of the weird and wonderful bits still on public sale in Yorkshire:

Black Pudding: a sausage made with blood (fresh ideally) with oatmeal, lard and seasoning. It is packed into a natural skin made from intestines or an artifical skin. Boiled, fried or baked.

Brawn: a jellied mould made from pig's head (no brain) and a rich jellied stock reduced from the ears, nose and tail. It is left to set and turns out to form a glistening mound for slicing.

Chitterling: small intestine of pig which has been 'dressed' (cleaned and par-boiled) before sale.

Cowheel: cow's foot, which when cooked has a lot of bone and gelatinous flesh.

Elder: cow's udder, cooked and pressed inside a membrane of bronze jelly, sliced and eaten cold.

Haslet: a meatloaf of pork offal, lard, onions and caul (fat from the pig's internal organs).

Neatsfoot: cow's foot. Neatsfoot oil is a by-product claimed to relieve rheumatism and arthritis or used for softening leather.

Oxtail: the bony tail of a cow. It makes a rich stew or soup.

Pig Favours: pig bag (stomach), pig chap (face). Trotters make a gelatinous stock. Boned and stuffed pig's trotters are appearing on fashionable restaurant menus. Tail, mostly gristle, should go into the stock pot with ears and snout.

Polony: red coiled sausage, made of minced pork, cereal and spices.

Saveloy: a thick sausage made with pork and pork fat, seasoned, sold cooked or raw, formerly contained brains.

Savoury Duck: pig's hock mixed with herbs and breadcrumb. Sometimes rolled into balls and wrapped in caul fat (faggots) or baked in a tray and sold in slices.

Tripe: stomach lining of ruminants like cows. Smooth 'thick seam' comes from the first stomach, the preferred 'white honeycomb' from the second stomach.

Weasand: long and brown, the windpipe.

White Pudding: a sausage made with oatmeal, stock and leeks. No blood.

It's all a dying and largely unmourned trade. Contrary to popular belief elsewhere, northerners do not get by solely on a diet of tripe and onions, for all that there are claims that tripe is low in carbohydrate and high in protein. Indeed, an unscientific survey for this book established that most modern tripe buying was for the dog. But as the stalls disappear do not worry that the offcuts will be thrown away. They will still be eaten. They have long been prime constituents of The Great British Banger.

DEWSBURY

Dewsbury Market

The freshly painted Victorian market hall retains its fine cast iron rafters while the outdoor market with its wooden stalls remains delightfully unchanged, alive with character and atmosphere, a West Riding market at its best. The food stalls begin at the top end of the open market with some semi-permanent fish shops. **Percy Jubb** has mussels, crabs and cheap oysters along with a regular selection of fish, jointed chicken, turkey and rabbit. **Lightowler, Coe** and **Pape's** (also at Huddersfield Monday market) all have a fair selection of fresh fish. There are queues for **Ramshaw's** fruit and vegetables but best of all are **Baig's**. They specialise in Asian produce and while there are plenty of carrots, potatoes and oranges there are also trays of root ginger, bundles of cheap and tangy coriander, three varieties of chilli and heaps of the freshest little aubergines, not much bigger than a walnut. Mooli, cadoo, fresh coconut, guava and juicy, ripe Pakistani mango all make a fabulous display. Mr Baig buys from both Manchester and Bradford wholesale markets and his produce sells quickly so it's dependably fresh. He also has stalls at Wakefield market on Monday and Thursday and Batley on Friday. **Half Acre Eggs** sell cheap trays of eggs – useful for batch baking but there's no sign of free range. **Pickles** sell eggs and cheese. Dewsbury sustains two tripe stalls, **Hey's** and **Gothard's**, but the market's meat favourite, judging by the queues, is **Cross's** (main entry p25), an old established pork butcher where the staff work at breakneck speed in what is no more than a wooden kiosk and where the food is cheap and satisfying but put the heart check-up on hold – roasted pig's feet, brawn, polony, haslet,

ham shanks, spare ribs, roast pig's cheek, pork pies still warm from the bakery and a favourite northern spread for your bread, 'mucky fat' (dripping infused with gravy). The queues swell to 30 or more for Cross's pride and joy – hot roasted belly pork. When the van arrives at 11 o'clock sharp, the sweet smell of roast pork wafts over and trays are transported shoulder high through the crowd: an authentic Dewsbury ritual.

Cloth Hall Street & Corporation Street, Dewsbury, W. Yorks
Outdoor market: Wed & Sat 9.30am-4.30pm
Covered market: Mon-Sat 9am-5pm Tue 9am-1pm

DONCASTER

Doncaster Market

A huge market with over 300 stalls selling everything from carpets to calabrese. For the food lover, the best finds are inside but the outdoor market offers plenty of competitively priced fruit and vegetable stalls. Signs that say 'own grown' do not necessarily mean home grown but, more likely, grown on the huge commercial farms in Lincolnshire. There are plant stalls with cabbage, calabrese and carrots ready for planting. At the end of the day there are some remarkable bargains to be had – a huge tray of plums for £2.00. Look out for **Drury's** organic vegetables. The Indoor Market has stalls selling haslet, black puddings and polony and there are plenty of butchers for fresh meat. **Gibson's** sell cheese but the gem of the hall is **Scicluna's** (main entry p112) delicatessen, a tiny shop run by husband and wife team Nigel and Josephine Cooke (née Scicluna). (Open: Mon-Sat. 8am-5pm. Mon and Wed 8am-1pm). Originally from Malta, the Scicluna's have had stalls on Doncaster market for 15 years. This one is packed floor to ceiling

with an international selection of fine foods: Polish, German and Hungarian meats, Parma ham, unbleached Polish rye bread, poppyseed cakes, fresh Parmesan and four different kinds of olives. They have gherkins, pickled herrings and Californian, Jalapeño and Greek chillies. At Christmas, they somehow manage to cram in even more with continental biscuits and German and Italian cakes. The customers reflect the international flavour of the groceries. Slavs, Spaniards, Italians, Greeks and Poles have all found their way to this little shop for reminders of home. The old fish market has been transformed. If it lacks some of the atmosphere it once had, better access to water and refrigeration means a higher standard of hygiene. Begin on the shellfish stalls where mussels, lobsters, crabs and clams are displayed. There are traditional little saucers of shelled whelks, cockles and winkles to be eaten at the counter with salt and vinegar. Chas. Morgan's **Crab Stall** has dressed crabs, undyed kippers, boiled cod's roe and the staples of cod, haddock and plaice. **Albert Boyd** takes the prize for size and variety. Although still retaining the original name, it is run by the mother and son team of Sheila and Mark Jackson. Sheila buys the widest variety of fish available. On any day of the week, she will have silver hake, rainbow trout, huss, gurnard, whiting, squid and octopus. Whole conger eels are a yard long – £4 each or three for £10. 'You have to skin and gut them yourself at that price', says Sheila. Not a task undertaken lightly. There are rabbits and hares still in their coats, sold with or without heads. Pheasant, wild duck and partridge come in season. Champion crab dresser for Boyd's is Ted Ash, whose knowledge of fish earned him The Guardian newspaper's accolade as 'an encyclopaedia of fish'. Sheila also has a small fish stall on Selby market on Monday and Tadcaster on Thursday.

Market Square,
Doncaster, S, Yorks
All markets: Tue, Fri, Sat
8am-5pm

EASINGWOLD

Easingwold Market

A small market huddles around Easingwold's Buttercross. The fine Georgian houses that surround the square make the setting one of the most charming in North Yorkshire. There is hardly a handful of food stalls – two sell fruit and vegetables and a fish van drives from Thirsk but **Sandra Bates'** cheese stall (main entry p63) is the best reason to go. Her vast range here and at Thirsk market on Saturday includes most of the Yorkshire cheeses as well as a broad selection of continentals.

Market Place,
Easingwold, N. Yorks
Outdoor market:
Fri 8.30am-5pm

GRIMSBY

Freeman Street Market

Freeman Street was once the very heart of Grimsby. After a good trip, with money in their pockets, the fishermen and their families would head for its shops, pubs and cafés. Today, the fishing industry and the close knit community that lived in the terraced houses that clustered around have all but evaporated but Freeman Street Market survives with the flavour and feel of a traditional covered market. Properly, there is a handful of fish stalls although none is spectacular. **Fred's Fisheries** has as wide a range as any. One delicacy found here but rarely seen outside of the Grimsby and Hull hinterlands is cod cheeks, little morsels of tender cod, painstakingly picked from the head of the

fish. As well as cod's cheeks, **Lyn & Sandra's Fisheries** have skate knobs (the same piece taken from a skate) among a selection of good, fresh fish. For no nonsense fish and chips, the romantically named **Pea Bung Café** has sit down or takeaway. There are plenty of fruit and vegetable stalls. **Arundel's** has the best selection.

Freeman Street,
Grimsby, S. Humbs
Covered Market: Tue, Fri, Sat
9am-5pm

Freshney Place Market

Grimsby's soulless new market has none of the atmosphere of Freeman Street and fewer food stalls. **Fred's Fisheries** has a branch here. There is **Jenkin's** butcher for black puddings, brawn and real pork scratchings. **Seymour's** have cooked meats, pies, continental sausage, **Kolos** rye bread and a genuine regional speciality: stuffed chine. Chine is a piece of boned salt pork stuffed with plenty of parsley, simmered then cooled with a weight on top and served cold in slices. Jane Grigson records how in 1870 the French poet Paul Verlaine came to work as a schoolmaster in Stickney, Lincolnshire and observed that stuffed chine was a dish quite peculiar to Lincolnshire. No change there.

Market Hall, Billing Lane,
Grimsby, S, Humbs
Covered market: Tue, Thur, Fri,
Sat 8am-5.30pm

W.I. MARKETS

*There are 17 Women's Institute markets in Yorkshire and Humberside, all selling home-made cakes, biscuits, breads, some fresh produce and their famous jam It is not necessary to be a W.I. member to buy at or bake for the markets. For details see the **Baking** chapter p84.*

GUISBOROUGH

Guisborough Market

Guisborough's attractive market runs along both sides of the wide main street and is brimming with good fruit and vegetable stalls and some interesting extras. **Trueman Teln's** fish stall sometimes includes sea trout and potted crab meat. **The Cheeseman** (main entry p63), with his straw boater and mock Georgian caravan, is a fixture of the North Yorkshire markets at Guisborough, Leyburn and Northallerton. A cheese vendor for 22 years, Coverdale's Don Morrison stocks around 150 different cheeses. Continentals include Pecorino, Parmesan, Gruyere, Vignotte, St. Agur and closer to home are North Yorkshire's own cheeses: Ribblesdale, Swaledale, Cotherstone, various Wensleydales and a good Lancashire from the Trough of Bowland. The bright green and white striped awning of **Chapelbeck Herbs** is easy to spot and has all the pot grown herbs for planting out. The best in wholemeal bread and cakes comes from a stall run by the **Larchfield Community** (main entry p47) based at Hemlington. The community is run on similar lines to **Botton Village** (main entry p56). It, too, is part of the Camphill Village Trust. The aim at Larchfield is to develop employment opportunities for mentally handicapped adults and training schemes for local people with special needs. They run their own bakery and send to market a fine wholemeal loaf made with molasses and sunflower seeds as well as cakes and biscuits made with organic flour. Arrive early to avoid disappointment since the stall packs up at 3pm and may be sold out even earlier

Market Place,
Guisborough, N. Yorks
Outdoor market: Thur & Sat
8.30am-5pm

HALIFAX

Borough Market

Heavy wooden swing doors with polished brass handles lead shoppers into an old style West Riding market hall with a vaulted ceiling. Unfortunately, that's where most interest ends. The basic stalls are largely threadbare and uninspired. The **Egg Shop** has free range eggs and **Roy's Continental Stores** stock Baltic sausage, gherkins, salted herrings and speck, high fat bacon. Cheap butchers run along the edge and standard fruit and vegetable stalls are ranged in the centre. Step outside for a row of good fish stalls on Albion Street. **Doyle's** (main entry p13) is easily the best .

Albion Street, Halifax, W. Yorks
Covered Market: Mon-Sat
9am-5.30pm

HUDDERSFIELD

Queensgate Market

Queensgate Market Hall is a dispiriting 1960s building and there's not much inside to lift the heart with the gleaming exception of **Winn's** fresh fish (main entry p15). There is always a dazzling multi-national rep-

resentation on its big sloping counter with queues and excitable business to match. Try croaker, silver pomfret, grouper, red mullet, pandora snapper or Malabar snapper. There is a tremendous range of more familiar names from British waters: hake, grey mullet, whole salmon, monkfish, squid, skate wings, lemon sole, whole coley, herring roe, oysters, whelks, winkles, Arbroath smokies, natural smoked haddock, finnan haddock, John Dory, herring fillets and smoked salmon. Elsewhere in the market is **Colletta's Nut Shop** for muesli, rice and dried fruit. **Continental Foods** have continental sausages and salami and are a source of salt cod. Along with familiar fruit and vegetables, **Rhodes Brothers** have West Indian plantains, cocoa, pumpkin, dasheen and yams. **Meeres** have a few organics among their conventionally grown fruit and vegetables.

Princess Alexandra Walk,
Huddersfield, W. Yorks
Covered market: Mon-Sat
9am-5pm

Monday Market

Despite being known as the Monday Market, this market act-

ually operates every day except Wednesday (bric-a-brac Tue & Sat). Half of the stalls are under the restored Victorian canopy of the old wholesale market and the rest are outdoors. **Pape's** fish stall also stands on Dewsbury market. The tripe shop stocks neatsfoot oil, allegedly a cure for rheumatism and bruises; more plausibly of use in softening leather. A West Indian fruit and vegetable stall has salt cod. **Wood & Sons** have a fish shop on the edge of the market with trevally, herrings, sprats and codling.

Brook Street,
Huddersfield, W. Yorks
Covered & Outdoor market:
Mon, Thur & Sat 8am-5pm

KEIGHLEY

Keighley Market

Keighley's charmless market hall has precious few good food stalls. The **Accrington Stall** offers the widest choice of fruit and vegetables. Otherwise, each greengrocer appears to have a speciality:**Wilson's** stock yellow tomatoes and persimmon; **Smith's** have ripe mangoes. For fish there is **Joe Narey**. **Buon Appetito** is a delicatessen with Italian cheese and continental sausage. Butcher **Jack Scaife** sells dry cured bacon and frozen game.

Low Street,
Keighley, W. Yorks
Covered market: Mon-Sat
8.30am-5pm Tue 8.30am-1pm

LEEDS

Kirkgate Market

See over

Kirkgate, Leeds, W. Yorks
Open: indoor market
Mon-Sat 8am-6pm
Wed 8am-1pm
Outdoor market
Mon (second hand clothes)
Tue, Thur (Flea market)
Fri, Sat 8am-6pm

HUCKSTERS

In the last century the rural markets of North Yorkshire were valuable outlets for the produce of local farms. Men known as 'hucksters' travelled round the Dales and Moors collecting farm produce to sell either locally or at the big markets of the West Riding. Alternatively, farmers would go to market themselves, loading up the cart with fruit, vegetables, eggs, butter, honey and, maybe, some chickens and pigeons before heading for the markets of Whitby or Hawes. Farmers' wives took butter to market, carefully shaped into blocks by wooden Scotch hands or in rounds bearing the stamp of their farm or decorated with leaves and flowers. Once, 7,000lbs of butter were sold in a single day at Hawes market and it was not unusual for 3,000lbs to be sold on market day. Cheesemakers took their cheeses to the famous Yarm Fair each October where they could sell it on to cheese agents or factors.

KIRKGATE MARKET

With 500 indoor stalls and a further 300 outside, Leeds Market is the biggest in the country, a riot of Flemish facades, Venetian domes and art nouveau detail. Sadly, the billiards room and palm court of the original design never materialised but in 1993, after years of neglect, an £8 million renovation scheme finally restored the buildings to their former glory. The cast iron shop units and the Corinthian columns were freshly painted. So, too, the clock whose original centrepiece was transferred to Oakwood in 1912 where it stands today.

Everything fairly buzzes with life and colour. Flowers, plastic and real, are on the first stalls to greet you and the pile it high, sell it cheap philosophy is contagious, whether it's shell suits or shellfish. Don't waste time looking for rocket or radicchio – there is nothing fancy here. Fruit and veg. stalls are fast and furious with bravura displays and hardly a penny between them. For the widest range, **Ronnie Bretherick** in Row 3 has celeriac, sweet potatoes, and Chinese pak-choi. The fresh meat stalls are not for the fainthearted. A whole aisle is dedicated to meat, with a dozen butchers in their doorways enticing you in for the bargain of the day. The sinister sounding **Wildblood's** sell boiled ham, tongue and various cooked meats. Like the meat, poultry prices are rock bottom. There's not a free range chicken in sight. **Foster's** are game dealers and they usually have duck and rabbit. **Stanley's**, opposite, also sell duck eggs and game.

The splendid fish market, with spotlights that make the ice and the fish sparkle, is down a dank alley before the New Market. Dominated by three family firms, **Ramsden's, Bethell's** and **Welham's**, the market has had scant competition from the rest of Leeds for years. On a winter Saturday, Arthur Welham had red bream, gurnard, jacks, lemon sole, strawberry grouper, Dover sole, turbot, red snapper and grey mullet. He supplies the Leeds Chinese with live crab, fresh squid, octopus and huge cuttlefish, dripping with black ink. Ramsden's had oysters, fresh water dabs, sprats, herrings, mackerel, trout and coble-caught haddock from Whitby. Bethell's had good looking turbot and sea bass.

The New Market, built in 1975 as a temporary structure after the great fire, is still there, a gloomy cavern of a place. Row H has **Spice Corner** selling West Indian vegetables and spices. **The Egg Box** sells free range and tiny pullet eggs. You can also pick through a 'seconds' tray (eggs with cracked shells) or take your pick from the ungraded box. **The Continental Food Store** is a useful delicatessen. Cockles and mussels, oysters and winkles can be bought at **Hayes** in Row A. Eat them at the stall, traditionally with salt and vinegar or with a squeeze of lemon and a dash of tabasco. They will also dress crabs while you wait. **The Nut Shop** has mountains of pecans, walnuts and cashews, salted or plain, broken or whole; dried fruit and all the paraphernalia for cake decorating. There are more nuts at **Brooksbank** in the main market.

The Outdoor Market at the bottom is cheaper still. This is where Michael Marks of Marks and Spencer set out his first penny bazaar. The stall holders here can let rip and if there's nothing for a penny, there is certainly quick fire banter and sharp selling. They undercut their neighbour and artfully sell you two pounds of lychees you never knew you wanted. There is a West Indian stall with dasheen and eddoes, yams and plantains. Finally there are itinerant sellers with no stall at all, just a sorry box of tomatoes or a tray of mushrooms. This is food for the poorest purse. We're only 200 yards from the swish new wave restaurants on the riverside but we could be on different continents.

NORTHALLERTON

Northallerton Market

Northallerton operates a lively twice weekly open market down both sides of its broad main street. Food stalls include cheese from **The Cheeseman** (main entry p63) with his 150 varieties. There are wholefoods, fish and greengrocers. The best of these last two belong to the **Carrick** brothers who have been serving North Yorkshire's country markets for 64 years. The big green fish van is run by Peter & David Carrick (main entry p12) and their brother John Carrick has the bright and breezy fruit and vegetable stall next door (main entry p51). The Carrick's can also be found at Bedale, Tue; Northallerton, Wed, Sat; Ripon, Thur; Leyburn, Fri; and Richmond, Sat.

High Street,
Northallerton, N. Yorks
Outdoor market: Wed & Sat
8am-5pm

OTLEY

Otley Market

There has been a market in Otley since 1222. Today it surrounds the old Buttercross which was once the trading centre for the butter, cream and cheese of nearby farms. Now, it houses a few wooden benches, a resting place for weary shoppers. The setting is picturesque and the market supports some 60 stalls that ex-

---

MARKET HOURS

Trading hours are variable, especially on outdoor markets. Many stall holders will begin trading before the times stated here. In winter or if trade is poor, traders are liable to pack up early. Treat printed times with caution.

---

tend along Kirkgate but the food is largely drab. Regulation fruit and vegetable stalls predominate; there is a decent wholefood stall that has good quality **Suma** products and **Baines Cheese Van** (main entry p65) calls with its cheeses and delicious soft oatcakes.

Market Place & Kirkgate,
Otley, W. Yorks
Outdoor market: Tue, Fri, Sat
8.30am-5pm

RIPON

Ripon Market

There's more tradition in the history than the food here. The market is 886 years old. Ancient custom is maintained by the ringing of a handbell every Thursday at 11am to mark the opening of the market although it will already have been trading since around eight o'clock in the morning. The tradition dates back to Ripon's history as a corn market, when farmers would attempt to start trading before the tax man arrived to take his two handfuls of corn from each sack. Today, there are more plastic household goods than honest regional foodstuffs. The **Carrick** brothers are here with their lively greengrocery stall (main entry p51) and large fish van (main entry p12). **Ian Holmes** brings local and continental cheeses from Richmond. There is a useful wholefood stall selling dried herbs, spices, rice and pulses, some unremarkable fruit and vegetable stalls and that's about it for historic Ripon Market.

Market Place, Ripon, N. Yorks
Outdoor market: Thur & Sat
9am-4.30pm

SCUNTHORPE

Food Hall

Scunthorpe market is generously endowed with greengrocers, befitting a parent county with such an industrial strength in vegeta-

ble growing as Lincolnshire. There are plenty to choose from but **Law's** probably have the widest selection. Fresh fish from Grimsby can be found at **Cribb's** or **Elkington's**. Both have plenty of choice. Anything you can't get elsewhere, which in Scunthorpe means quite a lot, can be found at **Suszczenia**, or so its owner claims. White coated, Polish Michael S. has been here for 20 years and his delightfully chaotic delicatessen stall has lumpfish caviar, mushroom ketchup, sesame oil, pickled walnuts, **Kolos** rye bread, noodles, rice, pasta and much more. It's all supposed to be there somewhere. **Christine's** egg stall is actually run by Doris and Doreen. They sell free range goose and duck eggs, sagely advising enquirers: 'Duck eggs are like hens' eggs only a bit stronger.' Then they fall about laughing and admit they've never tried them. **Pocklington & Son** (also at Ashby and Hull markets) make treacle, syrup, curd and coconut tarts, cakes, pasties and cooked meats and the definitive regional dish, Lincolnshire stuffed chine.

High Street,
Scunthorpe, S. Humbs
Covered market: Thur-Sat
9am-5pm Butchers Mon-Sat

SEDBERGH

Sedbergh Market

Sedbergh market has declined over the years from twenty stalls to half a dozen and now only **Ralph Strickland** rates a mention. He buys fresh fish from Fleetwood for Sedbergh and Kirkby Lonsdale markets. Cod, haddock and plaice are the mainstays but depending on what looks good on the quayside and wholesale market, there may also be monkfish, rainbow trout, Manx kippers and dabs.

Sedbergh Car Park,
Sedbergh, N. Yorks
Outdoor market: Wed 9am-4pm

SELBY

Selby Market

Selby Market spreads itself along Wide Street and behind the Londesbrough Arms Hotel into Market Place. There is the usual handful of fruit and vegetable stalls, some good looking plants from local market gardens and a couple of fish vans. No rosettes to be awarded here but there's some fun to be had at **Crow's** poultry auction (see below), held every Monday behind the Londesbrough Arms. Competing with Crow's is a pantechnicon equipped with microphone where cheap frozen meat and chicken is auctioned with macabre efficiency. A heap of joints is thrown on to the scales. You can guess at the quality but the weight and price are impossible to calculate before the meat is pushed down a chute and into a waiting carrier bag – sold, wrapped and delivered to the hapless bidder, all in the space of 30 seconds.

Market Place and Wide Street,
Selby, N. Yorks
Outdoor market: Mon 8am-4pm

SETTLE

Settle Market

Quite the best stall is **Dales Pantry**, a small cake stall run by a young, self-taught cook, Rachel Anderson. She has been baking flat out for the last two years to finance her greater love in life, horses. With commendable entrepreneurial skill, she has set up a special kitchen (to comply with hygiene regulations) at the family farm in Cowling, near Keighley, and bakes throughout the week for her market stall, for Settle's **Market Pantry**, for the Bolton Abbey Pavilion and her local Post Office at Cowling. Descending coach parties make a beeline for wholemeal honey and date loaves, chocolate cakes, shortbreads, flapjacks, carrot cakes and chewy butterscotch biscuits. **Priestley's** (main entry p63) sell 45 different cheeses with four different Lancashire's: mild, creamy, tasty or strong from the award-winning Rhodes of Carron Lodge, near Preston.

Market Place,
Settle, N. Yorks
Outdoor market: Tue 9am-5pm

SHEFFIELD

Castle Market

There are two parts to this modern covered market. In the main market there is little to get excited about, with only a handful of food stalls concentrating on cooked meats and fruit and vegetables. **Castle Fruit and Salad** is a self-service stall. **Grant's**

Groceries sell Caribbean food like white and yellow yams, dasheen, cocoa, hot round peppers and salt fish. **Castle Nut Bar** is a source of loose nuts. Upstairs from the main market, the light and airy Meat and Fish Market is a much livelier affair, especially on Friday and Saturday. Butchers stand in the aisles selling big bags of 'meat for the week' for £5. **Ellis** pork butcher's have pork chops, sliced belly pork and small lean joints. **Patrick's** or **Slattery's** also look the part for meat. Two fish stalls, side by side, **Whittington's** and **John Firth's** both sell tiny saucers of cockles, whelks and winkles to be eaten at the counter with salt and vinegar. John Firth boils his own crabs in the big metal vat at the back of the shop and tells of one customer who bought a live crab off him to keep as a pet in the fish tank at home. Fresh fish and poultry are at **Smith & Tissington** or **Wood & Wragg**. **Bruno's** delicatessen sell **Kolos** rye bread and a wide range of continental sausages. **Continental Stores** are good for West Indian vegetables.

Exchange Street,
Sheffield, S. Yorks
Covered market: Mon-Wed
8am-5pm Fri 8am-6pm
Sat 8am-5.30pm

SKIPTON

Skipton Market & Black Horse Market

Skipton's outdoor market has always been extremely popular. Visitors come to High Street by the coachload for some dedicated shopping. Which made the Council's decision to ban the Thursday market, even though traders had been coming unofficially for years, thoroughly mysterious. Damaging to the permanent shopkeepers, said the Council, but Thursdays in Skipton are now worryingly free of shoppers. On its surviving mar-

---

CROW'S POULTRY AUCTION

Every Monday at 10.30 a.m. sharp, Crow's auctioneers hold a live poultry sale behind Selby's Londesbrough Arms. Birds of every type and hue are placed in boxes around the edge of the ring. Bidding moves swiftly through ducks, geese, hens, even rabbits and budgerigars. The wooden shed in the corner of the yard, reminiscent of a railway booking office, turns out to be Crow's offices. Bidders pay their dues at the ticket window, surrounded by posters of mallard and muscovy. It's all over by lunchtime and the afternoon is dedicated to a motley collection of lawnmowers, bicycles and so called electrical goods – although some look as if they should be kept as far from electricity as possible.

ket days, Skipton has two major fruit and vegetable stalls. **Hailey's** fish van (main entry p20) comes on Friday and George Hailey always has good fresh Grimsby haddock and cod and the best of the rest of the catch on board. **Priestley's** (main entry p63) have recently added Skipton to their list of Yorkshire markets. While their cheese stall has no shortage of mass produced vacuum packed cheeses, they do have four classy Lancashire's from Carron Lodge. Their arrival is competition for Janice Edmundson on **The Cheese Stall** (main entry p66) which is tucked away behind the pub in Black Horse Market along with the Wednesday, W.I. market. Her best selling cheese is also a Lancashire, from Singleton's dairy at Longridge, near Preston.

High Street, Skipton, N. Yorks
Outdoor market: Mon, Wed, Fri, & Sat 8am-5pm

Black Horse Market, High Street
Covered market: Mon, Wed, (Thur in summer), Fri 9am-4pm, Sat 9am-4.30pm

TODMORDEN

Market Hall
The Victorian market hall is a mighty stone edifice, perfectly suited to the unbending character of its contents. **Bailey's** tripe stall is a severe example of the genre and **The Crumbly Cheese** (main entry p67) is no more frivolous. It sells traditional oatcakes; its cheese selection is monochrome and when it comes to discussing the origins of its crowning glory, a truly definitive Lancashire, the stubbornness of Mr Hodson's staff would test the will power of the Spanish inquisition. It hurts to praise his cheese but it is excellent.

Burnley Road,
Todmorden, Lancs
Covered market: Wed-Sat 9am-5.30pm

WAKEFIELD

Fish & Meat Market
Mick Wood's fish stall is the star of Wakefield's fish and meat market. Pushing 70 years of age, Mick Wood is still going strong in his clogs and long white apron, presiding over a fish empire that takes in a second wet fish shop on Barnsley market (run by son Christopher) and two fish and chip shops at Langdale End and Monk Bretton near Barnsley (run by his daughter Jane). He always has a huge range of fish that might include lemon sole, Dover sole, monkfish, oysters, hoki, skate wings, herrings, small whole haddock, redfish, mussels, smoked sprats, turbot, brill and squid. In the summer, fresh crab comes from Bridlington, Withernsea or Skipsea. **Stephen Horne** runs another good fish stall and **Danka's** delicatessen has cooked meats, polish sausage and **Kolos** Polish rye bread.

Teal Street, Wakefield, W. Yorks
Covered market: Mon-Sat 9am-5pm Wed 9am-1pm

Indoor Market
A characterless 70s building with little to recommend. **Winn's** have loose nuts and **Asquith's** have fruit and vegetables. Outside, in Brook Street, beside the covered market is **Hey's** tripe shop, one of a chain of three shops also on Bradford and Dewsbury markets. They specialise in thick seam and honeycomb tripe.

Teal Street, Wakefield, W. Yorks
Covered market: Mon-Sat 9am-5pm Wed 9am-1pm

Outdoor Market
A lively outdoor market with old fashioned wooden stalls untouched by the developers. There's plenty of shouting to give it an authentic market atmosphere. The fruit and vegetable stalls dominate and offer some good bargains. **Baig's** who also stand on Dewsbury market, have a fine selection of Asian vegetables including tiny aubergines, fresh ginger, mangoes and big bunches of coriander. **Cartwright's**, **Rhodes** and **Sutton's** are three egg stalls fiercely competing on price although there's barely anything between them.

Teal Street, Wakefield, W. Yorks
Outdoor market: Mon-Sat 9am-5pm Closed Wed

WETHERBY

Wetherby Market
Wetherby has a small outdoor market with only a handful of food stalls. There are the standard greengrocery stalls, fish from **Young's** and it's the Thursday stop for **Baines Cheese Van** (main entry p65).

Market Place,
Wetherby, N. Yorks
Outdoor market: Thur 8.30am-5pm

YORK

Newgate Market
Sometimes known as Jubbergate market, this busy open market adjoins the Shambles, which in medieval times was the butchers' market. The stalls change from day to day but there are plenty of good value fruit and vegetable stalls and the permanent fish stalls are excellent. Best is **Cross of York** (main entry p20) who have plenty of choice from rope grown mussels, scallops in their shells, crab or lobster to fresh white fish. On Saturday, Mrs Husband of **Lodge Farm** sells genuine free-range eggs and uses them in her cakes – fruit cake, sponge cakes, date and walnut, Dundee cake, buns and pastries. She will also supply old hens that have stopped laying, for use in soups and stews.

Parliament Street, York
Outdoor market: Mon-Sat 7.30am-5.30pm

POTS & PANS

Yorkshire lacks a truly outstanding kitchen shop, somewhere that stocks everything from an apple corer to game shears, from a full set of 15 Victorinox Swiss stainless steel knives to a classic Bialetti espresso maker. But with some strenuous shopping around and mail order most items can be hunted down.

The Home at Saltaire is the latest addition to the dazzling revival of Salt's Mill. The shop is stronger on Scandinavian designer ware than tools and equipment for the kitchen drawer but there are good quality pots and pans, original coffee mugs and continental glassware. Look out for multi-coloured Adventures of Tintin plates and crockery that might have been filched from a French café in the 1950s.

For the practical, there's **Catering Equipment** in Ecclesall Road, Sheffield, **Kitchen Bazaar** in Goodramgate and **Lakeland Plastics** in Low Petergate, both in York. In the basement of Austick's bookshop in Harrogate, **The Good Cook Shop** supplies cafetière replacements, kitchen gadgets and cake tins for hire. **R.W. Morten** is an old established hardware and kitchen shop in Ilkley that sells knives and jam pans as well as more modern items like pasta machines and olive stoners. Northallerton has the **Complete Cook** in Barker's Arcade and **Lewis and Cooper** stocks every last icing nozzle. **Habitat** continues to offer kitchen equipment at manageable prices with branches in Leeds, York and Harrogate. The nearest **IKEA** for no-nonsense Swedish plates and kitchen paraphernalia is over the M62 at Warrington with a branch opening at Birstall in autumn 1995.

For antiques, **Muir Hewitt** at Halifax Antiques Centre has one of the country's best collections of original Clarice Cliff, Susie Cooper and other art deco luminaries. Elsewhere in the Halifax complex are stalls specialising in old breadboards, chipped enamel colanders and blue and white hooped T.G. Green Cornish ware of fond childhood memory. Best of all for pantry nostalgics is **Kitchenalia** of Longridge in Lancashire. Their old stuff is usually in the best condition for these genres along with modern collections of Emma Bridgewater pottery.

Sheffield's **David Mellor** has made the greatest contribution to modern British cutlery, so it is galling that his northern shop is not in Yorkshire but in Hathersage, Derbyshire, albeit that it's only a few miles over the border. His cutlery is used in Downing Street and on British Rail, in our Washington embassy and in Wormwood Scrubs. It is collected by the Museum of Modern Art in New York and at the Victoria and Albert Museum. His factory, the Round Building in Hathersage is built on the 'footprint' of an old gas holder and has won almost as many awards as the cutlery. Stockists in the region are: **Table Decor**, North Parade, Bradford; **Kitchen Range**, Finkle Street, York; **The Craft Centre** beneath the City Art Gallery in Leeds and at **Cadeaux** in Queen's Arcade. **Shape Design** and **Mark Turner Design** on Abbeydale Road and **Don Alexander** on Ecclesall Road are Sheffield outlets. For other classic Sheffield cutlery see p188. The Hathersage shop sells the full Mellor range. Prices here are lower than elsewhere but it is never cheap. There are top quality stainless steel saucepans, gadgets and a stunning collection of hand made wooden bowls by Liam O'Neill from Co. Galway, baskets by Jenny Crisp and pottery by John Leach (grandson of Bernard Leach) and others and there is a tempting mail order *Catalogue for Cooks*.

11

Tea Rooms & Cafés

Tea from China and coffee from the West Indies were once the exclusive drinks of the rich and privileged. Working families drank water, milk or weak beer. Tea only became popular in the last century when the expansion of international trade brought the price within reach of the poorer citizen and the approval of Yorkshire's temperance societies. In 1886 Charles Taylor, a northern tea blender and coffee roaster, opened a chain of kiosks serving his own blends. Today, Taylor's are Yorkshire's premier tea and coffee merchants and on Stonegate in York is one of Charles Taylor's original kiosks. A young Swiss confectioner Frederick Belmont was a relative newcomer to the scene when he arrived in Harrogate in 1919, reputedly having boarded the wrong train. He was so charmed by the fashionable spa town that he decided to stay and open a tea room which he mysteriously named Betty's. The four branches (and couldn't Leeds do with winning back its lost Betty's?) still set the standard for the region but there are cafés to suit every taste and every purse from the white lace and polished oak to be found in Skipton to the ultra-modern French-style café in the heart of Barnsley. There is a de-consecrated 15th century church in York serving savoury bakes amid the stained glass or there's smoked salmon and caviar in Beverley. In Saltaire alone, take your tea at a boathouse, beneath a Hockney or in the Unitarian chapel. There are herbal devotees and Italian cappuccino specialists. Of the hundreds of establishments making a decent cuppa, many can cook well too. Here is a personal selection, hopefully as rich and varied as the region.

BARNSLEY
Le Croque Café
Black pudding and Barnsley chop jokes wear thin in Barnsley these days. Not only has the town an award-winning restaurant in **Armstrong's** but it also boasts this elegant café behind Pollyanna's, Yorkshire's most exclusive dress shop. Intimidated by the Armani price tags? Then enter Le Croque through the other door in George Yard. Pollyanna is the creation of the vivacious Rita Britton. Like her shop, the café is minimalist grey and white. Gun metal chairs and tables are dressed in pristine paper cloths. Spare white walls have original prints by David Sinclair depicting 'Rita's Alphabet Gateau'. Service by young men in black T-shirts and long white aprons has a touch of the Gallic. At breakfast there are hot croissants filled with smoked ham or smoked salmon and cream cheese. Bread apart, everything is made on the premises by talented young chef Alison Younis. The counter fills up for lunchtime with deep quiches, proper soups, filled baked potatoes, salmon, prawn and spinach plait and different salads. Eat in or take out a frangipane, a lemon tart, chocolate cake, truffle cake or Alison's sophisticated bread and butter pudding, oozing fresh fruit.
Pollyanna's, George Arcade, Market Hill, Barnsley, S. Yorks ☎ *01226 733674*
Open: Mon-& Sat 10am-5 30pm Tue-Thur 9am-6.30pm Thur 9am-7.30pm

BEDALE
Plummer's Tea Room
A pretty white-washed, oak-beamed tea room that serves fresh, warm cheese scones with melting butter and light lunches of lasagne, game pie and Cumberland sausage from Cockburn's, the prize butcher across the street.
Main Street, Bedale, N. Yorks ☎ *01677 423432*
Open: Mon-Sat 10am-4.30pm

BEVERLEY
Beverley Arms Hotel
Sink into the squashy sofas and comfy armchairs for a cream tea in the Shires Lounge. Forte catering with butter and jam in awful plastic sachets but a comfortable place to relax.
North Bar Within, Beverley, N. Humbs
☎ *01482 869241 Open: Mon-Sun 9.30am-5.30pm*

Butler's Parlour
In a town that embraces names such as North Bar Within and Without and a street called Wednesday Market, then a Victorian arcade called '. . . And Albert' raises no eyebrows. A brightly painted wagon and tubs of flowers signpost this arrangement of cute shops for antiques, doll's house furniture, crafts and the tiny Butler's Parlour, almost a doll's house itself. When there's room, they serve an excellent cup of tea made with leaves: Gunpowder, Assam, Darjeeling or Ceylon. There are pleasant cakes and tea breads and 16 varieties of Taylor's coffee. The teas and coffees are on sale next door.
...And Albert, 33 Highgate, Beverley, N. Humbs
☎ *01482 870032/871251 Open: Mon-Sat 10am-4.30pm*

Café Within
Hidden amongst the antique shops of Hawley's Yard, Café Within boasts pine chair rails, ruched blinds and blue and white walls, so spotless it feels as if the decorators have just walked out. If the atmosphere is a touch clinical, the standard of service and food is high. Sandwiches offer smoked salmon and caviar. Ham comes with coarse grain mustard, beef with horseradish and the egg sandwiches are free range. A trolley has cakes, scones, fruit cake and ice cream. There are specials each day and smokers have a room to themselves.
Hawley's Yard, North Bar Within, Beverley, N. Humbs ☎ *01482 861857*
Open: Mon-Sat 10am-4pm

Ginger's Tea Room
There are so many toys and nursery patchworks it's more like stumbling into a crèche than a coffee shop. The genuinely warm welcome to children comes with small portions and high chairs. Grown up's have excellent open sandwiches, light date and walnut scones and their own cakes and puddings. Earl Grey, Ceylon, Lapsang Souchong and fruit teas cost the same as regular Indian tea.
1 Swaby's Yard, Walkergate, Beverley, N. Humbs ☎ *01482 882919*
Open: Mon-Sat 9.30am-5pm

Tea Cosy
Beverley is well endowed with tea shops and this epitomises the English market town classic: oak panels, polished tables, lacy cloths. steaming pots of tea and tempting cakes. The less cosy conservatory and tea garden take pressure off the main café at busy times.
37 Highgate, Beverley, N. Humbs ☎ *01482 868577*
Open: Mon-Sat 10am-5pm Sun 12 noon-5pm

BOLTON ABBEY
Barden Tower
Teas are served in the old farmhouse of Barden Tower. In autumn when there's a good fire going

the polished oak really glows. Beams, antlers and blue willow pattern add to the effect. Morning coffee, afternoon teas and high teas are offered by owners Robert Hodgson and Jo Parkinson.

Bolton Abbey, Skipton, N. Yorks ☎ 01756 720616
Open: April- & May Wed-Sun July & Aug Tue-Sun
Sept & Oct 10.30am-5.30pm

Devonshire Arms

If you don't fancy paying top dollar in the Burlington Restaurant, you can take morning coffee, lunchtime sandwiches or afternoon tea in one of their lounges and absorb a bit of country house living. It all comes elegantly served in silver tea pots and the sofas are soft enough to keep you there all day.

Bolton Abbey, Skipton, N. Yorks ☎ 01756 710441
Open: Mon-Sun 11am-5.30pm

Tea Cottage

From the garden there are views to Bolton Abbey and the river Wharfe and the outside tables allow visitors to enjoy it to the full. Inside, the cottage is pine and pink. Besides hot dishes – gammon and chips and gratins – there are scones, cakes and cream teas. This is a superior option to the Cavendish Pavilion in Strid Woods which has a faultless setting on even the busiest of Bank Holidays but they've botched the refurbishment: the food is unimaginative and the place reeks with unrestricted smoking. Back at the Tea Cottage, be warned: no parking in the narrow road outside and Bolton Abbey car park charges a hefty £2.50.

Bolton Abbey, Skipton, N. Yorks ☎ 01756 710495
Open: winter Sat & Sun 10am-5pm
summer Mon-Sun 10am-5pm

BRADFORD
The Oastler Room

Richard Oastler, the 'Factory King', was the Yorkshire campaigner responsible for reducing the British working day to ten hours. A noble statue stands in Northgate. A less prestigious memorial is the Dralon covered Oastler Room upstairs in Pratt's furniture store. No gastronomic haven but the best Bradford has to offer since the closure of the Life Church coffee shop on North Parade. Useful for a pot of tea and a surprisingly good scone or sandwich.

Christopher Pratt's Furniture Store,
33 North Parade, Bradford, W. Yorks
☎ 01274 725894
Open: Mon-Fri 10am-4.30pm Sat 9.30am-4pm

TAARO

The Trade Association of Asian Restaurant Owners (TAARO) is better known as Bradford and Britain's first curry college. Established in 1991 its aims are to raise the standard of food and hygiene in Bradford's curry houses. TAARO run short courses in basic food hygiene and business skills and a two year full-time course in Asian cooking. From a training kitchen at their headquarters in the YMCA building they run a 25 cover lunchtime restaurant with a short menu of masala, korma, karahi and biryani dishes. Mindful of all the restaurants surrounding them, TAARO remain discreet but this little known curry haunt costs no more than a couple of pounds for a steaming bowl of curry and a pile of chapatis.

YMCA Building, Little Horton Lane, Bradford,
W. Yorks ☎ 01274 742451
Open: Mon-Thur 11am-2pm

CASTLE BOLTON
Castle Tea Room

Part romantic ruin, part English Heritage, part tea room, Bolton Castle was the high point of English 14th century castle building, fine enough to be commissioned for the Chancellor of England, strong enough to imprison Mary Queen of Scots. Sadly, the tea room owes more to a Granada motorway service station than its grand history. Self-service, plastic tablecloths and a fridge with nothing more rewarding than cans of Lilt and Coke in one of Yorkshire's most stunning locations. The tea, cakes and tea breads were fine but this could and should be a memorable tea room.

Bolton Castle, Castle Bolton, N. Yorks
☎ 01969 23981 Open: March-Nov 10am-5pm

CLEETHORPES
Marples Tea Rooms

In a town primarily dedicated to candy floss and fish and chips, Marples is a pleasant tea room for sandwiches and afternoon tea.

Sea View Street, Cleethorpes, S. Humbs
☎ 01472 697188 Open: Mon-Wed 9am-5pm Thur-
Sat 9am-8.30pm Sun 9am-6pm

CONISTON COLD
Coniston Hall

Adjoining Coniston Cold Farm Shop, the café offers simple, honest food at a reasonable price prepared by good home cooks: soup and sandwiches, a couple of hot dishes and a tempting display of home made cakes and puddings. Plenty of space and easy parking although it is a shame to be in such a location and not to have a view of the lake and the Hall.

Coniston Cold, Nr. Skipton, N. Yorks
☎ 01756 748136 Open: Mon-Sun 10am-6pm

CRACOE
Cracoe Café
Hearty winter warmers of Cumberland sausage, ham and eggs or steak and kidney pie are served in this useful café on the way to the Dales on the B6265. Solid oak tables, bentwood chairs, fresh flowers and an open fire all contribute to a pleasant atmosphere. There are proper soups, sandwiches, quiches, tea time cakes, scones and old fashioned puddings.

Main Street, Cracoe, N. Yorks ☎ *01756 730228*
Open: Mon-Fri 10.30am-5.30pm Sat & Sun 10.30am-6.30pm

DENT
Stone Close
Graham Hudson and Pat Barber run a simple, popular café in the lovely village of Dent. A low beamed ceiling, stone flagged floors and an old fireplace underline the warmth of this 17th century listed building. Enjoy proper home cooking. Cakes, scones and flapjacks are available all day. Lunchtime offerings include soups, a three bean salad or old fashioned gammon and eggs, revitalising after a long walk. Taylor's tea includes Assam, Darjeeling and Gunpowder. The big regret for Stone Close fans is the end of evening meals, due to pressure of work.

Main Street, Dent, N. Yorks ☎ *05396 25231*
Open: Mid March-Nov Mon-Sun 10.30am-6pm Nov & Dec weekends only Jan & Feb closed

DEWSBURY
Box Tree Tea Room
In a town drowning in greasy spoons, this haven serves a fine pot of tea and a slice of cake on the top floor of Strawberry Fair china shop. Everything is spotless and smokers have a room to themselves. Crumpets, muffins, scones and toasted teacakes are on the menu. A table displays chocolate, carrot cake and meringues. More filling meals are provided by potato pie and peas, or soups, quiches and salads.

26 Market Place, Dewsbury, W. Yorks
☎ *01924 466089 Open: Mon-Sat 9.30am-4.30pm*

DONCASTER
Sinclair's
The beautiful Georgian facade lures you inside. Wedding lists are formulated amidst the tinkle of fine china and cut crystal. Up carpeted stairs, tea awaits in gentle civility.

Georgian House, 39 Hallgate,
Doncaster, S. Yorks ☎ *01302 367260*
Open: Mon-Sat 9.30am-5pm

Wood's
This tea and coffee shop has been described as the Betty's of Doncaster. Don't be deceived. But in a town short of good coffee shops, it wins a warm welcome. Wood panelling, thick carpets and lace tablecloths frame the cakes, scones, sandwiches and light snacks.

3a Wood Street, Doncaster, S. Yorks ☎ *01302 327126 Open: Mon-Sat 9am-5.30pm*

HALIFAX
Design House Café Bar
Bars and cafés have come and gone at Dean Clough without leaving much of an impression. Now, in taste and style, Design House looks to have the ingredients for a lasting success. It's a classy team. Furniture design is by Philippe Starck of New York hotel fame; management (and white lilies)are by John Leach, the Salt's Mill planner; and food is supervised by David Watson, top chef at the Pool Court when it won its Michelin star. The menu is correspondingly elegant, the presentation clean and uncluttered, the food delicious. There are attractive sandwich combinations in ciabatta: chorizo, avocado and smoked chicken served with their own coleslaw and well-dressed salad leaves; roast ham, mozzarella and sun dried tomato; or, more conservatively, egg mayonnaise and coronation chicken. There are salads of pasta and beans or tomato, feta and olive and simple dishes of warm smoked salmon, Parma ham and gravadlax all served with a variety of rustic and continental breads. At tea time, indulge passion cake, banana cake or chocolate fudge cake with chocolate sauce. Hot croissants, warm brioche and pain chocolat give Halifax a French breakfast. Good quality teas and coffees.

Dean Clough, Halifax, W. Yorks ☎ *01422 383242*
Open: Mon-Fri 10am-6pm Sat & Sun 10am-5pm

HAREWOOD
Runners & Riders Restaurant
Harewood House's tea for the masses. The stable block is now run by Michael Gill, owner of **Pool Court** at 42 The Calls in Leeds. But don't expect a gourmet menu for this is a functional family café that provides for the thousands passing through the bird garden and adventure playground. Black chairs and cheerful plastic tablecloths sit oddly with traditional horse racing paraphernalia on the walls but this self service café raises itself above the cynical catering usually found at stately homes. There are hot dishes every day: sausage casserole, vegetable macaroni or Yorkshire pudding with onion gravy. Baked potato is for once filled

TAYLOR'S OF HARROGATE

If ever you are invited to taste Taylor's Kopi Luwak coffee, be warned. It may be the finest Sumatran coffee in the world – at £150,000 a tonne it is certainly the most expensive – but Kopi Luwak comes from the droppings of the common palm civet. This interesting cat like beast, *Paradoxurus hermaphroditus* (sic), also gives us a musky perfume from its anal glands. For its coffee bean trick it feeds on the finest, ripest cherries in the coffee plantation. The undigested beans are then collected with the droppings and made into what the Japanese and Sumatrans consider to be the finest coffee in the world. It's a good tale but Kopi Luwak doesn't actually figure in Taylor's regular coffee list: 'On hygiene grounds' is the official explanation of buyer Michael Riley. That list does include 26 different coffees, 27 teas and tisanes and 11 special rare teas. With Kenya Peaberry, Japanese Green Gyokuro or Broken Orange Pekoe, Taylor's indisputably offer some of the best tea and coffee to be found anywhere in the country.

Tony Wild, son of chairman, Victor Wild is credited with raising Taylor's profile from unsung regional roaster to a nationally known coffee and tea blender. Tony's global treks in search of the finest Arabica coffee are certainly colourful. He went by motorbike to Yemen for what was christened the 'Heights of Araby' and sailed to remote St. Helena where he bought up the entire island crop. Dubbed by some as the Indiana Jones of coffee, cynics in the trade have talked more of heights of hype than of Araby. Taylor's have certainly got good mileage out of the publicity and happily admit that the entire coffee crop on St. Helena amounts to just nine 60 kilo bags. Over half of Taylor's coffee is sold to other shops including Marks & Spencer and Sainsbury. It is served in all the Betty's cafés and in Taylor's of Stonegate, York

Pagoda House at Starbeck on the outskirts of Harrogate, is where Taylor's consignments arrive from all the romantic corners of the world: teas from the Dimbula Valley, Sri Lanka; from Northern Rwanda's Mountains of the Moon; from China, Japan and India. The blending of their tea, to suit the local water, has made Taylor's Yorkshire tea both popular and famous. Coffee beans have crossed continents to be roasted and blended into their top selling World's Best, Café, or High Mountain blends. Unblended beans come from estates in Sumatra, Cuba, Jamaica and the Celebes in Indonesia. Everything about coffee is volatile. Tasting is all-important and Taylor's lay cups out along a marble slab for tasters to suck, slurp and spit into copper buckets in a well honed ritual. Only by tasting a range in this way is it possible to identify a coffee's characteristics, says Michael Riley : 'Kenya coffee has high acidity, a fine fruit flavour. Compare that to Java which is a very full bodied, smooth earthy taste but with no acidity.'

Today, Betty's and Taylor's are the same company after amalgamation in the 1960s. Tony Wild has moved out of the business but the search for new tea and coffee continues. A rare Galapagos Island coffee is the latest on the list followed by a Puerto Rican, Yauco Selecto Peaberry. The peaberry is reckoned to have the finest flavour: 'Only 5% of beans will be the perfectly round peaberry. It's a good coffee with a winey flavour.' Asked to choose his favourite coffee, Michael Riley opts for Kenya. 'The quality varies with any coffee. You don't choose wine just because it's from France. With coffee you need a good quality bean, but for me, a top quality blended Kenyan coffee is the best of all.'

Taylor's of Harrogate, Pagoda House, Harrogate, N. Yorks ☎ 01423 889822

interestingly with cream cheese, herbs and walnuts. Well flavoured tomato soup comes with a hint of Pool Court styling – a garnish of croutons and fresh cream, a credit to any half decent restaurant let alone a busy café. There are well prepared salads, sandwiches and a children's menu. On sunny days there are tables and canvas umbrellas outside in an attractive courtyard. Plans are under way for Sunday lunch and evening meals. The only blot was painfully slow and inexperienced service, hopefully now sorted.

Harewood House, Harewood,
Leeds, W. Yorks ☎ 0113 288 6225
Open: April-October Mon-Sun 10am-4.30pm

HARROGATE
Betty's Tea Rooms
Betty's flagship tea room and shop is on the top corner of Parliament Street. Its italic insignia and the municipal flower beds outside are defining emblems of Harrogate and the long queues are testament to Betty's enduring popularity. At weekend peak times the crowds are wearing enough to defeat the original intention of a relaxing interlude. Once settled, the prizes are intact. All the tortes, éclairs and cream cakes sold in the shop are served in the café. Old fashioned favourites are revived in buttery cinnamon toast and hot pikelets. Yorkshire traditions are upheld with warm fat rascals, toasted Yule loaf, parkin, curd tart and buttered banana and walnut loaf. Try out one of their rare coffees with a top of the range Jamaica Blue Mountain Peaberry or a speciality tea. There are grills, rarebits, salads and sandwiches and a popular children's menu. Some whingers complain at Betty's high prices - £2.50 for a pot a tea and a toasted teacake. Take account of the setting, the people-watching (classic Harrogate dowagers still abound), the invariably charming waitress service under pressure, the high standard of food, even a pianist in the early evening, and regard it all as one of Yorkshire's timeless treats.

1 Parliament Street, Harrogate, N. Yorks
☎ 01423 502746 Open: Mon-Sun 9am-9pm
Branches at Ilkley, Northallerton and York

The Green House
The easy-going vegetarian café at the back of the environmental shop has a vegetarian menu that offers a main course and either soup or dessert for £5.00: mushroom or ratatouille pancake, lasagne, served with roast potatoes, salad and a glass of fruit juice.

5 Station Parade, Harrogate, N. Yorks
☎ 01423 502580 Open: Tue-Sat 10am-3.30pm

Pasta Romagna
Besides selling good pasta from what is principally an Italian delicatessen, James Walker serves what one customer claimed was 'the best cappuccino in England.' He will also serve you a slice of pizza with authentic tomato and mozzarella topping straight from the oven.

53 Cold Bath Road, Harrogate, N. Yorks ☎ 01423
564160 Open: Mon-Sat 9am-6.30pm Sun 10am-
3pm

The Tent Room
There are, of course, places other than Betty's to take tea in Harrogate. Casa Fina furnishing store is one. Swathes of dark green fabric create the tented ceiling; bamboo chairs complete a cool setting. It can certainly prove less crowded than their more famous (and frantic) neighbour down the road. At breakfast time there is 'Café Complet': coffee, croissant, toast or roll, and orange juice. The changing blackboard menu moves on to Granary toast, muffins, a cream tea or slice of cake. Lunchtime offers a real soup of carrot and orange or Scotch broth, followed by barbecue chicken with savoury rice or nut roast and onion sauce.

Casa Fina, 21-22 West Park, Harrogate, N. Yorks
☎ 01423 505871 Open: Mon-Sat 10am-5pm

HOWDEN
Bridgegate House
A spotless wholefood shop and café sells well made sandwiches, savouries and cakes all made by Lesley Webb, a former cookery teacher. Everything is vegetarian but she doesn't shout about it in case it puts people off. The bakes, quiches and cakes are top quality. Sadly, she plans to sell up.

15 Bridgegate, Howden, N. Humbs
☎ 01430 431010 Open: Mon-Sat 9am-4.30pm

HUDDERSFIELD
The Blue Room
Solid wooden tables, Chinese parasols, an art nouveau fireplace and a comfortably tatty sofa give Cath Oldham's vegetarian café in lovely Byram Arcade an easy going, slightly exotic ambience. The menu is vegetarian with some fish dishes. Leek and potato soup with roll, cheese and lentil gratin, cottage cheese, potato and lentil salad. Puddings include pancakes with sugar and lemon or hot chocolate fudge cake. For tea, there are sandwiches, wholemeal cakes and scones. Breakfast is served up to 11.30am.

Byram Arcade, Huddersfield, W. Yorks
☎ 01484 512373 Open: Mon-Fri 10am-5pm Sat
9am-5pm

ILKLEY
Betty's Tea Room
Each of Betty's branches has its distinguishing architectural and decorative features. As the years roll by they look less like the daring modern art they began life as and take on the patina of worthy old antiques. At the Ilkley Tea Room, don't miss the stained glass and the French marquetry hunting scene mural. Meanwhile, the queues, the chocolate roulade, éclairs and the glistening fruit flans are dependably the same here as at all Betty's branches. An expanded tea room has taken off some of the pressure but customers quickly fill the space available to savour classic high teas and light meals. There's a genuine welcome for children: bibs, beakers and high chairs to throw food and tantrums from.

32-34 The Grove, Ilkley, W. Yorks ☎ *01943 608029*
Open: Mon-Sun 9am-6pm

INGLETON
Curlew Crafts
Yorkshire has more than its share of shoddy craft shops and tourist tat, but Chris and Sandra Bonsall have managed to combine a quality art and craft shop with a delightful café. Everything is baked on the premises and the sandwiches and jacket potatoes are supplemented by daily specials. Expect three kinds of soup, their own liver paté or an original brie and broccoli pie made with filo pastry. Loose leaf tea and long forgotten childhood drinks of dandelion and burdock or sarsaparilla are served on bold, flowery tablecloths. The walls are filled with original etchings from Piers Browne and Mary Farnell, photographs by Geoff Farnell, paintings by Deidre Borlase and Barbara Tomlinson and wood cuts by the renowned Daleswoman, Marie Hartley. Even she, says Chris, sometimes drops in for afternoon tea.

Main Street , Ingleton, N. Yorks ☎ *01524 241608*
Open: Mon-Sun 9am-6pm Closed Wed in winter.
Closed throughout Jan

KIRTON IN LINDSEY
Mount Pleasant Windmill
Jane White's wonderful baking is shown to good effect in the tea room at Mount Pleasant Windmill. All her mouth-watering cakes illustrate the versatility of the mill's organic flour with chocolate, date, apricot and walnut, carrot cake, coffee and walnut. The lightest wholemeal sponge with raspberry filling ends fears that wholemeal flour makes cakes that are heavy and dull. And there's the magnificent sight of the great sails of one of the region's last working windmills. Plans are well in hand for a brand new bakery opening Easter 1995. In the meantime, visitors can buy Mount Pleasant's excellent flour and a selection of wholefoods from the shop.

Kirton in Lindsey, South Humbs ☎ *01652 010177*
Open: Fri 1pm-4pm
Sat, Sun & Bank Holidays 10am-5pm

LEEDS
Kendal Moore
A simple café behind this popular delicatessen in the Headingley district of Leeds. Light snacks, sandwiches, patés and salads, in fact everything that is temptingly displayed in the shop window is available in the café. It also has a lively Sunday morning breakfast trade with coffee, croissants and newspapers.

74 Otley Road, Leeds, W. Yorks ☎ *0113 278 3439*
Open: Tue-Sun 9am-10pm

MASHAM
Mad Hatter Tea Room
Quaint tea rooms run by Mrs Boshier on the handsome market square. She has two rooms; one decorated with cricket memorabilia, the other in dainty blue and white. Soups and bakes are the mainstays of the savoury menu. There are scones with fruity jam and every morning new home made cakes are set out on her old piano.

2 Church Street, Masham, N. Yorks
☎ *01765 689129 Open: Mon-Sun 10am-5pm*
Closed Thur

MIDDLEHAM
Nosebag Tea Shop
Fat Rascals, Wensleydale apple cake and Yorkshire curd tart are regional tea time specials prepared by Peter and Sally Swales in the Market Square. All time children's favourites include banana sandwiches, Marmite soldiers and cinnamon toast. The combination of peanut butter with marmalade is less traditional or local.

Market Square, Middleham, Leyburn, N. Yorks
☎ *01969 22688 Open: Easter-Nov Mon-Sun*
10.30am-5pm Closed Thur

MIDDLESBROUGH
Filbert's
The three foot African carving that stands sentinel at the door of Filbert's is the first sign in a town of take-aways and burger bars that there is an alternative. Away with the laminated menu, this may not be haute cuisine but it does serve real food. With bright yellow emulsion, original art by local painters, fresh cotton tablecloths and healthy pot

FISH & CHIPS

'You can't get much meat for threepence but you can get a lot of fish and chips.'

George Orwell, The Road To Wigan Pier, 1937

O rwell lived in Leeds when he wrote much of his classic of northern working class poverty and could not have failed to notice how central fish and chips were to the daily life of the city. Even today, the Leeds Yellow Pages list 334 fish and chip shops from **Summat Fishy** to **The Oldest Fish & Chip Shop In The World** in Sandy Old Lane, Yeadon. There are unresolved contenders for the title of the *first* Fish & Chip Shop In The World, argued between supporters of the extinct Granny Duce's of Bradford, Malin's of London and an Oldham tripe dresser but what is beyond doubt is that Leeds and its hinterland comprises the heartbeat and the headquarters of the fish and chip world.

Here, in Meanwood, are the headquarters of the National Federation of Fish Friers and its training school. Here, the editorials of the Fish Friers Review fight the corner of fatty frying against the health police. Here, from Beeston, comes the beef dripping that is the first crucial distinction between Yorkshire frying and the solid vegetable fat of Lancashire. Here, for a century, has been the world headquarters of frying ranges, with six rival manufacturers in their heyday. From Ross Foods at Heckmondwike or the wholesale fish market at Pontefract Lane in Leeds comes endless haddock to supply the chippies of West Yorkshire.

In Headingley, Bretts and **Bryan's Modern Fisheries** gently competed for the title of the best loved establishment of all. Now, Charlie Brett is dead and his delightful shop closed. The immaculate garden can still be seen from North Lane but not the panelled interior with its wild animal posters, Alice's treacle pudding and the ghost of John Arlott. Bryan's (est. 1934) misguidedly dropped the Modern from the neon in their latest modernisation but the Weetwood Lane takeaway and restaurant can still define timeless haddock and chips, malt vinegar and mushy peas, bread and butter and a righteous pot of tea, all under a gleaming tile tableau of seagulls over the Yorkshire coast.

In town, **Nash's Tudor Restaurant** on Merrion Street is a startling 1960s timewarp, a quarter deck of diving helmets, plastic fish tanks, ships' wheels, nautical charts and seamen's knots. It is surprising not to be piped aboard. Forgotten stars from The Good Old Days have signed the wall; they sell prawns by the half pint, shark steaks and it's been in the same family since Louise Nash started commercial frying over a coal fire in 1919. Connoisseurs of the fishnet and Neptunalia school of fish and chip restaurant should also visit **Craven's** of Lowtown, Pudsey. Up Roundhay Road, **Oakwood Fisheries** has the most elegant black and aluminium art deco exterior and shining stainless steel interior in Leeds.

Further out at White Cross, Guiseley, is **Harry Ramsden's**. Few purists would give this tourist attraction top marks for value or taste but it has never seriously been disputed as the most famous in the world. In 1936, nobody put carpets in a chip 'oile, much less chandeliers and a mural of an ocean liner sailing into the sunset. Harry Ramsden did. Cousin Harry 'Sooty' Corbett played the piano. Ramsden's was a baroque wedding cake in a brick warehouse shell, having started out in 1931 in a typical wooden lock-up. Harry celebrated 21 years in the business with a stunt that put him in the Guinness Book of Records. For a day, he sold meals at their original price of 1/2d, drawing queues five miles long and shifting 10,000 portions. He thrived particularly on the textile mill trade, bulk delivering lunch packs for local firms. He was a most particular man: fish had to be dropped skin side up, fried for five minutes exactly in fat at an optimum 350 degrees. His day was made when someone lost a penny in the turnstile he had installed for his toilets. Harry was bought out in 1954. He opened smaller shops in Shipley and Wetherby but the glory days were over. When he died in 1963, the Bradford Telegraph and Argus could not resist the headline: Goodbye Mr Chips. Harry Ramsden's name lives on in twelve branches stretching from Blackpool's Golden Mile to Heathrow Airport and Hong Kong with plans underway for Melbourne, Singapore and Cardiff.

Fish and chips have been the food fuel of the industrial north since the Victorian railways linked up with Grimsby and Hull to distribute their record landings. They provided protein, carbohydrates and vitamin to the poorest families and through two world wars. Fish and chips, said Churchill, were 'The Good Companions'. From a peak of 30,000 shops there are now under 10,000 but 70% of the population still has fish and chips every three months amounting to 50,000 tons of white fish a year. In Hull, it is consumed at rates 50% higher than the national average, paving the way in 1993 to Britain's first 'drive thru' fish and chip restaurant, **The Hudson Bay Clipper Company**, or the matey H.B.s as they like to be known, at Willerby's red brick shopping park near Hull. Experiments with Winnipeg Wedge potatoes were smartly dropped in favour of traditional chips but other sacrilegious modern touches like portion controlled cod fillets, pea fritters instead of mushy peas and frying in vegetable oil have sustained through seven day openings.

The south bank of the Humber has highly regarded restaurants with **Leon's Family Fish Restaurant** of Alexandra Road, Grimsby, resolutely serving haddock over cod, and **Steel's Cornerhouse Café** of Market Place, Cleethorpes. But the best coastal town for fish and chips is unquestionably Whitby. **Trenchers** on New Quay Road has a 'fun-pub' style with Tiffany lamps and buttoned banquettes. Apart from excellent haddock, there's plaice, skate, seafood casserole and fat, fresh crab sandwiches. But nearby, on Pier Road, appropriately overlooking the fish market, is many people's contender for the best of the lot, the **Magpie Café**. Its floral carpets and signed celebrity photographs can grate but the batter is perfect and while there is plenty of prawn, crab and lobster, the fish to order has to be the freshest conceivable cod or haddock or plaice. The tea is made with leaves and served by the friendliest of Yorkshire ladies.

There are chippies like **Scott's Fisheries** of Highstone Lane, Ward Green, Barnsley that specialise in Yorkshire scallop fish cakes (cod sandwiched between two potato slices and deep fried) or Bradford's **Lister Fisheries** on Lilycroft Road which must be the first self-proclaimed Halal chippie in the country, eschewing beef and pork in its oils to respect both Hindu and Muslim sensibilities. **Bizzie Lizzie's** of Swadford Street, Skipton is an award winner of the Sea Fish Authority for its all-round quality and hygiene. This guide has not the slightest intention of counting let alone sampling the thousands of fish and chip shops in the region. The best is probably the one close enough to home to save the batter going soggy and the chips sticking together before you unwrap them in front of the TV.

plants, the place is as easy going as the food: tomato and mozzarella tart, Brazil nut roast, leek and cheese lasagne or leek and cheese roulade all made in the viewable kitchen. There is nothing wildly innovative just robust, generous and excellent value vegetarian food at around £3 per main course. Dishes come with minted potato salad and a few leaves. Crumbles, sticky toffee pudding and bread and butter puddings fill any gaps. Bread is home made and wines are organic.

47 Borough Road, Middlesbrough, Cleveland
☎ *01642 251506 Open: Mon-Wed 12 noon-7pm*
Thur-Sat 12 noon-11pm

NORTHALLERTON
Betty's Tea Room
The smallest of the Betty's chain but the menu, the standards and the popularity are in synch with the other branches. It takes resolution to ignore the cakes, biscuits and chocolate both on the way in to the café and on the way out.

188 High Street, Northallerton, N. Yorks
☎ *01609 775154 Open: Mon-Sun 9am-5.30pm*

PICKERING
Mulberries
Whether it's one of their delicious cakes or apple pie served the Yorkshire way with a slice of Wensleydale, the food is excellent. At lunchtime there are generous bowls of macaroni cheese, sandwiches or patés. Most popular of all is the daily choice of two splendid soups. The Stilton and onion is rich and creamy, garnished with proper croutons and spring onions, served with a warm bread roll and a generous portion of real butter. A café with its act together.

Bridge Street, Pickering, N. Yorks ☎ *01751 472337*
Open: Mon-Fri 10am-3pm Sat 10am-4.30pm

RICHMOND
King's Head Hotel
Log fires, chintz sofas and a selection of cakes and scones on the sideboard make the Clock Room the best bet for afternoon tea in a town with a surprising dearth of decent food.

Market Place, Richmond, N. Yorks
☎ *01748 850220 Open: Mon-Sun 10.30am-5pm*

RIPON
Fountains Abbey Visitors Centre
It takes some architectural nerve to build alongside Fountains Abbey. The peerless setting of the 12th century Cistercian monastery is a World Heritage Site. Its controversial new neighbour is an austerely modernist visitors' centre. Carbuncle or café courageous? The National Trust defends its creation: 'Perhaps some would have preferred a neo-classical stable block.' The airy self-service dining room deals quickly and efficiently with the thousands of visitors. Alongside hedgehog or caterpillar shaped sandwiches, come changing facilities, baby foods, high chairs and plenty of room. There are clean lines of light ash furniture with matching salt and pepper mills, elegant blue and white crockery and through the big windows a tantalising long distance view of the Abbey itself. Grace Elford manages the catering with enthusiasm for local food: local cheeses, Yorkshire Country Wines, and fresh produce bought in Ripon. She describes her cooking as 'down-to-earth British with a twist', featuring interesting combinations like chicken and apricot pie or turkey and chestnut casserole. There is a vegetarian dish and a wholesome soup every day. Open sandwiches are lively and original: prawn and chive with a lemon dressing, nut paté with salad, roast ham and apple. They are served with apple and raisin chutney, organic bread and a salad and fruit garnish. For dessert, there's bread and butter pudding or fresh fruit flan. All the cakes and biscuits are made on the premises but the greatest demand is still for scones with jam and cream.

Fountains Abbey, Ripon, N. Yorks ☎ *01765 601003*
Open: winter Mon-Sun 10am-5pm
summer 10am-6pm

Studley Royal Tea Room
There are tea rooms at either end of the Fountains Abbey estate, neither perfect but both with merit and superb locations. Here, a cream house is set between a duck filled lake and formal gardens. Tea and coffee, a selection of soups and open sandwiches, baked filled potatoes, cakes and scones and daily blackboard specials are served.

Studley Royal, Ripon, N. Yorks ☎ *01765 604246*
Open: winter Mon-Sun 10am-5pm Closed Fri
Nov-Jan summer 10am-6pm

The Warehouse
Above a craft shop in Court Terrace, it's an ideal pause after touring Ripon Cathedral. Oak beams and white washed walls set off old farm implements, stripped pine, blue and white crockery and flowery table cloths. The menu is safe but sure with Stilton and celery soup, sandwiches, filled baked potatoes and quiche. A long table offers a help-yourself selection of scones and buttered tea breads, flapjack, chocolate cake and carrot cake.

Court Terrace, Ripon, N. Yorks ☎ *01765 604665*
Open: Mon-Sat 9.30am-4.30pm

RIPPONDEN
Upperview
This self-proclaimed 'country tea room' on Ripponden's busy A58 may not have the perfect 'country' setting but it does have some old fashioned 'country' cooking. Barbara Green owns the gift shop on the ground floor and the smells of baking soon tempt you upstairs to her café. Rich tea time fruit cakes, bread and good soups, casseroles and vegetarian dishes are all made on the premises. Dinner every Friday offers authentic home cooking. Bring your own wine.

242 Halifax Road, Ripponden, W. Yorks
☎ 01422 823316 Open: Mon, Tue, Thur, Fri
10am-5pm
Wed 9am-1pm Fri 10am-4.30pm & 7pm-9pm
Sat 9am-5pm Sun 1am-5pm

SALTAIRE
Saltaire Boathouse
Selected for its location more than its food. On a sunny afternoon this little boathouse is a delightful spot for tea and scones by the river Aire under the shadow of Titus Salt's mighty mill.

Victoria Road, Saltaire, W. Yorks ☎ 01274 590408
Open: Mon-Sat 11.30am-2.30pm & 7pm-11pm
Sun 11.30am-2.30pm

Saltaire Unitarian Chapel
The remarkable Unitarian chapel in Salt's model village is well worth a visit, especially at organ practice. From 12 noon every Sunday, cups of tea and home made biscuits are served in the Sunday School. It's basic with plastic chairs and tables but on sunny afternoons the doors open onto the canal and it's a fine place to chat with Saltaire's locals, who will proudly tell you all about their still extraordinary village and church.

Victoria Road. Saltaire, W. Yorks
No 'phone
Open: Sun 12 noon-5pm

Salt's Diner
The food at this American style soda fountain cum restaurant on the second floor of Sir Titus Salt's magnificent Italianate mill is not quite as spectacular as it should be to match the setting but it's cheap and cheerful enough and it's most impressive to be among the great stone and iron skeleton of the mill. It helps to like Hockney with his primary colour blown-up Yorkshire snaps on the wall, a latest exhibition usually next door and the permanent collection below in the 1853 Gallery. The Hockney designed menu is bistro basic with a nod to New York: pizza, bagels with cream cheese and smoked salmon, salad niçoise, caprese salad, scrambled egg with smoked salmon and salt beef. Desserts are typified by carrot cake and Häagen Dazs ice cream. Salt's Diner is unlicensed, as Sir Titus would have insisted, but there are low alcohol beers, peach cream soda, root and ginger beers and fresh fruit milk shakes. The regeneration of Salt's Mill, such a brilliant addition to Yorkshire life, has been totally financed by Jonathan Silver, who made his fortune in menswear and has installed the Hockney's, an ever encroaching bookshop, another 10,000 square feet of men's fashion, the diner and, latest of all, a classy kitchenware and ceramic showroom. There are huge fresh white lilies everywhere, classical music and, often enough, Jonathan himself behind the till.

1853 Gallery, Salt's Mill, Saltaire, W. Yorks
☎ 01274 531163 Open: Mon-Sun 10am-6pm

SELBY
Benedict's Tea Room
A Rayburn as part of the interior decor might be taking the ambience a bit far but this 20th century icon of good living exudes the required warmth of a country kitchen. Then there's the exposed brick, the terracotta tiles and a profusion of greenery. Only the searingly hot chicken stroganoff hints at a microwave too. Kathleen Elsworth's tea room, situated in one of Selby's loveliest streets in the shadow of Selby Abbey, is actually a delight. Her homely dishes, simple soups and sandwiches are spot on. Fruit cakes and pies sit invitingly on the sideboard. The delicatessen near the entrance is small but handy for speciality tea and coffee and French country wines.

4 Abbey Place, Selby, N. Yorks ☎ 01757 706856
Open: Mon-Sat 9am-5pm

SETTLE
Country Style
Tucked away to one side of an antique shop, wicker baskets and antiques take up half the space but then come cakes, Taylor's teas including Darjeeling, Earl Grey and herbal. Light lunches are served all day but the fruit bread, the sticky flapjacks, toasted teacakes and an ever changing range of cakes are the real calling cards.

Kirkgate, Settle, N. Yorks No phone
Open: Mon-Sun 10am-5pm

Liverpool House
Anyone stepping in might be tempted to make an offer for the crocheted tray cloths, the antique jelly moulds or even the ancient gas stove. However, none is for sale. They were left to Brenda Nolan by

ROASTERS & BLENDERS

Coffee is the world's second most valuable traded commodity after oil. Britons drink 3.7 cups of tea a day in sales worth £550 million. Tea and coffee are necessarily political. They are grown in the Third World and drunk by the First. Buying takes place in the arcane world of commodity auctions under a pricing system that would baffle a chancellor. Big commercial producers have long been criticised for unethical practices: tea companies for the exploitation of workers, coffee growers for deforestation and pesticides that damage the environment and their workers' health. Anyone wincing at the price of tea and coffee in Britain may reflect on the true price of producing it.

Cafédirect, committed to ethical marketing, buys quality arabica coffee direct from small co-operatives in Cost Rica, Peru, Mexico and Nicaragua. They visit the growers, make advance payments, provide longer contracts and pay above market price for the coffee. To sell at a sensible price, shareholders receive modest returns and the company has lower staff and advertising costs. Cafédirect is now in Oxfam shops and the major supermarkets of Yorkshire and Humberside. Ethical trading in tea is proving more difficult as it is produced on large estates dominated by a few powerful interests. The use of casual labour makes the industry open to exploitation. Typhoo, sensitive to the criticism, have pledged to buy only from producers committed to decent pay and conditions. **Taylor's**, Yorkshire's premier tea and coffee importer, try, they say, to buy direct from growers and do visit the estates.

Leaving aside **Betty's** and **Taylor's**, Sheffield is probably the best place to hunt down tea and coffee. Few people walking up Charles Street can fail to be attracted by the wonderful smells that waft their way out of **Pollard's Tea & Coffee** as the raw coffee beans gently turn from green to brown in the splendid black roaster placed cleverly right in the middle of the shop. The names are as evocative as the smells. There's Old Brown Java (strong and full), Kenya Peaberry and Mysore Indian (medium) and Costa Rica and Nicaragua (mild). Most expensive at £12 per pound is Puerto Rican Yauco Selecto. The staff are happy to advise on the different roasts and there are back-up leaflets on coffee making. Pollard's sell all the jugs, filters, cafetières, Moka and Atomic espresso and cappuccino machines, even the Ibrik for Turkish coffee.

Their tea repertoire is equally impressive: Bewley's Irish from Dublin, Keemun China, the classics of English Breakfast, Earl Grey, Lapsang, Assam, Darjeeling and Ceylon and a wide range of herbal teas. High above the counter, Pollard's have arranged their ornate old tea bins bearing the dreamy names of outposts of the tea empire: Kandy, Nuwera Eliya and Dimbula. Pollard's, established in 1879, pre-date both Betty's and Taylor's. The **Traditional Heritage Museum** on Ecclesall Road recreates their West Street coffee shop from the turn of the century. The modern Pollard's are now installed in Meadowhall and continue to supply shops and restaurants throughout South Yorkshire.

The **Proper Coffee House** on Sharrowvale Road is another plus for Sheffield. A tiny, unkempt shop with an outsize roaster stocks Cafédirect, organic coffees and it is a northern outlet for Whittard of Chelsea's rarified teas and flavoured coffees. Lands Lane, Leeds has a branch of **Whittard**, too. The best of the rest might be the **Tea Caddy** in Bar Street, Scarborough. Carole Parkin has a comprehensive choice of tea and coffee in an attractive shop. Coffees include pale Indian, black cappuccino, Black Sack, mature Indonesian and Casablanca. Teas include Gunpowder Green and Slippery Elm.

an aunt and have been incorporated into the decor of this listed 18th century town house close to Market Square. Coffees, teas, lunches and evening meals are prepared with consummate skill and imagination. There are Wensleydale cheese and date sandwiches and more familiar hot bacon ones. A sandwich, a scone with jam, a slice of cake and a pot of afternoon tea will leave your purse only £3.50 lighter.

Chapel Square, Settle, N. Yorks ☎ 01729 822247
Open: Mon, Tue, Fri, Sat 10am-5pm
Sun 2pm-5pm Dinner by arrangement

SHEFFIELD
Café Monde
Bortsch, chicken in ginger, vegetable chilli are among some original offerings in this relaxed and slightly bohemian city centre café. It is pleasantly furnished with ceramic floor tiles and light ash tables and a self service counter of stripped pine. Generous slabs of fruit cake, chocolate brownies and carrot cake are served with Taylor's coffee, herbal or regular tea.

119 Devonshire Street, Sheffield, S. Yorks
☎ 0114 275 9254 Open: Mon-Sat 8am-7pm

Just Cooking
Between West Streeet and Charter Square, it's self-service, it's city centre and it's undeniably functional but it's also a blessed change from the themed chain eateries and pub microwaves that dominate central Sheffield. The quality of the cooking has won many devotees. It specialises in good value salads, pies, quiches and vegetarian dishes. Hot meals are typically beef goulash, steak and kidney pie or heavily sauced chicken; roulades and cheesecakes for dessert. They also provide takeaway and outside catering.

Carver Street, Sheffield, S. Yorks ☎ 0114 2 727869
Open: Mon, Tue, Thur, Fri 10am-3.30pm Wed
10am-7pm Sat 10am-4pm

SKIPTON
Herbs Vegetarian Restaurant
A health food shop with a wholefood vegetarian restaurant upstairs. The heavily pined restaurant serves good quality food: potato and herb soup with sesame croutons, warming vegetable casseroles with garlic bread and flans such as leek and Stilton or asparagus and tarragon. There are some interesting salads and delicious cakes and puddings: toffee and walnut tart, lemon and almond cakes, crêpes filled with ice cream and bilberries. The three course special is good value or you can have a pot of tea, with real tea leaves, and a slice of

buttered fruit bran loaf, which despite its worthy name is seductively sweet and moist. The staff happily served a little boy with a glass of water and a plain biscuit and took time out to discuss the stegosaurus (the original vegetarian) with him.

10 High Street, Skipton, N. Yorks ☎ 01756 60619
Open: Mon-Sat 9.30am-4.45pm Closed Tue

Rafters
Built literally in the rafters and eaves of a restored corn mill, Rafters enhances its dramatic location with polished oak tables, rough stone walls and discreet use of copper and lace, a haven run with understated charm and efficiency by the Holloway family. Sally, self-taught and accomplished, cooks straightforward casseroles and savoury bakes to support the sandwiches and soups at lunchtime. But her talent lies primarily in cakes and desserts: Pavlova's, white chocolate éclairs, delicious pear and almond tart, chocolate roulade and lemon tart. A host of fruit pies, cakes and scones are baked fresh each day. Sally's mother Barbara takes charge of the customers and the rest of the family do the shopping, wash up and generally muck in. The pottery on sale is by the Holloway's other talented daughter Jo.

High Corn Mill, Chapel Hill, Skipton, N. Yorks
☎ 0756 700265 Open: Mon-Sat 10am-5pm
Closed Tue & Sun

SLEIGHTS
River Garden Café
A simple timber built tea room situated on the banks of the river Esk amid colourful gardens. Inside the tables are simple and basic and tea and cakes are dispensed self-service style from a hatch in one corner. Cakes and hot dishes are only average. The point here is to sit on the riverside watching the ducks and feeding the tame sparrows. Look out for the life-like grey squirrel sculpture.. There is a croquet lawn and garden centre for further diversions.

Sleights, N. Yorks ☎ 01947 810329
Open: hours variable, please 'phone ahead

SWINSTY
Swinsty Tea Rooms
A fine place to stop after a walk around Fewston or Swinsty reservoir. Situated between the two, this lovely stone house and garden opens at weekends for home made cakes, scones and pots of tea and soft drinks that can be taken in the conservatory or outside on the terrace.

Swinsty, N. Yorks No 'phone
Open: Sat, Sun and Bank Holidays only 11am-5pm

WHITBY
Shepherd's Purse

Passing from the cheese and wholefoods, through the scented candles and Indian prints of the gift shop, you come to the Shepherd's Purse self-service café, cheerfully run by a young team of vegetarian cooks who make whatever takes their fancy using ingredients from the shop. It might be broccoli, mushroom and leek bake or pasta and seaweed. There are sticky cakes and equally sticky puddings, a fresh soup every day and big bowls of salad. Good wholesome stuff.

95 Church Street, Whitby, N. Yorks
☎ 01947 820228 Open: Mon-Sun 9.30am-5pm
Jan & Feb closed Mon & Wed

YORK
Arts Centre

Soothing medieval music plays and the old bell ropes still hang from this de-consecrated 12th century church. The oak tables look almost as old. The plastic stacking chairs do not. Soup comes with freshly baked soda bread; rich winter casseroles with dumplings and baked potato. Baguettes are filled with Stilton and walnut, coarse meat or smoked mackerel patés. Scones include orange and lemon or sultana and cinnamon. Enter through the same door upon which a priest once attached a written diatribe against Henry VIII – and was executed for it

St. John's Church, Micklegate, York
☎ 01904 642582 Open: Tue-Sat 10am-5pm

Betty's Tea Room

If Harrogate is the flagship of the Betty's fleet, then York is the transatlantic liner. The l930s wood panelling and the art deco stained glass deliberately echo the glamorous heyday of the steamships and were installed by craftsmen from the Queen Mary. Queues to damn the expense and go on board are as long as ever. The same counter range and menu operate throughout the chain so the food and drink, upstairs and downstairs, all match up to Betty's usual high standard. Sandwiches, salads, grills and rarebits – the latter made with Theakson's famous Old Peculier ale – are served throughout the day and evening. There are excellent toasted muffins, cinnamon toasts and hot pikelets but above all, leave room for the cakes. Trolleys, piled high with éclairs, tortes, roulades and all manner of elaborate conversation stoppers, ply constantly between the tables, followed by countless pairs of eyes. Maybe I'll have one after all...

6-8 St. Helen's Square, York ☎ 01904 659142
Open: Mon-Sun 9am-9pm

Café Impressions

Post-modern pedestal tables, black tubular chairs, Le Monde on sticks and often all pervading cigarette smoke: very French and naturally inhabited by arty types using the dark room or on photographic courses at the Impressions gallery. The café makes espresso and cappuccino, serves savoury croissants filled with salmon, or sweet ones with banana and whipped cream. There are sandwiches, filled baguettes, quiches, salad, baked potatoes and soup.

29 Castlegate, York ☎ 01904 654724
Open: Mon-Sat 9.30am-5pm Sun 10am-4.30pm

Capaldi's Coffee Shop

For a reviving shot of caffeine after a tour of York Minster call at Capaldi's coffee shop on nearby College Street. They serve a strong espresso and cappuccino, their own Italian ice cream and a few cakes. Florence this is not, but given a sunny afternoon and some pavement tables and it could almost be. Coffee is for sale together with the cafetières and all the coffee paraphernalia.

12 College Street, York ☎ 01904 631417
Open: Mon-Sun 10am-5pm

Liberty's

Make it up two flights of steep stairs to the top floor of the Liberty's store in York and you will be rewarded with an excellent tea room. Stripped wood floors and comfortable banquettes are naturally upholstered in Liberty's inimitable style. The morning starts with a pot of tea or cafetière of coffee with a variety of scones: apple and cinnamon, fruit or cheese or perhaps some toasted fruit loaf. Lunch is served from 11am onwards and always features home-made soup and a daily special. In summer, it might be salmon; in winter, chicken Kiev. It's served with salad, baked potato and a glass of wine or fruit juice. To follow there is invariably apple pie and cream, strawberry tart or a cream cake. Tea time offerings include a cream tea with the usual scones, jam and cream or the opportunity for a blow-out on the full-scale afternoon tea, which comes on a tiered plate stand with sandwiches, scones, cream cakes and strawberry tarts and, of course, a pot of tea. Great after a day's shopping in York although the queues can meander down to the floor below.

15 Davygate, York ☎ 01904 610021
Open: Mon-Fri 9.30am-5pm Sat 9.30am-5pm

National Trust Tea Rooms

Trustworthy food, well prepared and efficiently served. Metallic tables and elegant ash sideboards sit easily alongside the restored brick fireplace, willow pattern plates in typical NT style and stunning colour photographs of the kitchens at Castle Drogo in Devon. Smoked haddock and prawn pie, mushroom nut and tomato bake and tuna, pepper and sweetcorn flan all come with seasonal vegetables. In winter, there is swede, turnip, broccoli and baked potato with a generous knob of butter; in summer, something lighter. Cakes, trifles, crumbles are reliable as is the perennial favourite and now fashionable treacle sponge and custard. Children have their own choice of teddy bear biscuits or spaghetti hoops. High chairs, bottle warming and baby foods are available. In recent years, the standard of the tea rooms at National Trust properties has steadily improved. Most can be recommended.

30 Goodramgate, York ☎ 01904 659282
Open: Mon-Fri 9.30am-5pm
Sat 9.30am-5.30pm

St. William's Restaurant

This self-service restaurant in the beautiful building of St. William's College is a short step from the Minster for even the most coach-bound tourist. The interior decor is almost as timeless as the medieval stones: Habitat circa 1970. At busy times the pressure begins to show but they manage to turn out reliable soups, salads, sandwiches and hot meat and vegetarian dishes. Gooey cakes and puddings are popular at tea-time. The open courtyard is a particularly pleasant spot on a sunny summer afternoon.

College Street, York ☎ 01904 634830
Open: Mon-Sun 10am-5pm

Sesame Café

Don't expect frills in one of the cheapest cafés in Yorkshire, a vegetarian café at the Rudolph Steiner School in Fulford. Aimed principally as a facility for parents, the public are welcome so long as they are prepared for long wooden benches in a rather tatty classroom overrun by toddlers. It's at its busiest between 12.30 and 1.15pm when the school use it as a take-away. Service is minimal. Queue at a hatch and clear up afterwards. For wholesome veggie food at bargain prices, it's hard to beat. Home made soup 60p, baked potato with cheese 80p, cheese and potato flan 60p while the pasta bake shoots up to £1.00. Jennifer Aitkin cooks with a team of parents and ex-pupils. They use organic ingredients wherever possible and can provide outside catering as well as cakes and frozen meals to order.

York Steiner School, 30 Fulford Cross, York
☎ 01904 610770 Open: Mon-Fri 9am-3.30pm

Spurriergate Centre

St. Michael's is a redundant church that has been given new life as a café. If lunch with the Nine Order of Angels and the Tree of Jesse, depicted in 15th century stained glass, appeals then this is the place to say grace. Even the altar is there, complete with the Ten Commandments and the Apostles' Creed on the ornamental screen. With grand civic pomposity, St Michael's magnificent 18th century doors record the names of the city's mayors. The food is fine: soups, baked potatoes, savoury bakes and a selection of scones and cakes but the awful food lamps and school meals counter sadly damage the dramatic effect. Profits go towards Christian charitable projects in the city.

St. Michael's Church, Spurriergate, York
☎ 01904 629393 Open: Mon-Sat 10am-5pm
Closed second Tuesday of every month

Taylor's Tea Rooms

Charles Taylor was for many years the northern agent for a London tea company. In 1886 he set up as a tea and coffee blender on his own account. He had noticed how local variations in the water could affect the flavour of the tea and he began creating suitable blends for each area. It's a practise Taylor's continue to this day. He went on to open a chain of 'Kiosks' where coffee was roasted in the shop window and served in the café inside. Taylor's Tea Rooms on Stonegate is one of the original 'Kiosks'. After the war when the popularity of Taylor's cafés and kiosks declined, Taylor's were bought out by their long time rival, **Betty's**. Besides the famous Café blend, served in all the Betty's cafés, Taylor's stock the full range of teas and coffees, selected and blended at their headquarters in Harrogate. Speciality coffees include Jamaica Blue Mountain Peaberry, their most expensive at £25 lb., organic Yemeni Mocha, Puerto Rican or a rare Cuban, Ethiopian or Columbian. Besides the now famous Yorkshire tea and quality Empire teas from Ceylon, Darjeeling or Kenya there are flowery Chinese Yunnan, Rose Petal or Green Gunpowder teas. Scented teas come with cinnamon, mango or orange peel or for real cachet, choose from a small selection of unblended single estate teas, with the estate's name stamped on the tea caddy. In the café above the shop they serve the full Taylor's range and offer the same Betty's menu of tea, cakes and savouries. The first floor offers the Betty's menu from a warren of cosy rooms with low ceilings. Less well known than its sister establishment down the road, it is a better bet for a table without the queues.

46 Stonegate, York
☎ 01904 622865 Open: Mon-Sun 9am-5.30pm

OUTSIDE CATERERS

'Are you lucky enough, wealthy enough and privileged enough?'
Harewood House spokesman, 1994

Very nearly everywhere and everybody is for sale. The Queen's cousin hires out Harewood House dining room for a 'facility fee' of £35 per head. The menus are prepared by Michael Gill's **Pool Court** 'team' at between £35 and £50 per head. 'Gratuities' are set compulsorily at 10 per cent and wines are extra. The implication of the glossy brochure is that it's only for Debrett's sort of people but the small print reveals it as really pitching at industry and the 'launch trade'. Are you lucky, wealthy and privileged enough? The estate office at **Harewood House, Harewood, N. Yorks** ☎ **0113 288 6225** will let you know.

With enough warning and enough wallet, most of the region's top chefs and local delicatessen owners will cater for you at home, aboard a canal boat, on a steam train or in a hot air balloon. You can hire unusual venues from the municipal baths to the Merchant Adventurers Hall; from Ripley Castle to a television studio. You can send for a marquee and fill it with a mobile barbeque or a medieval feast. Children's party specialists bring bouncy castles and individual jellies.

Few big commercial caterers are worth recommending. The flabby quiche and soggy vol au vent mentality still prevails in Yorkshire wedding receptions and corporate hospitality boxes, compounded by mark-ups that cause double takes. Belinda Mordaunt's **Simply Delicious, 12 Market Street, Malton, N.Yorks** ☎ **01653 692725** is a notable exception to the first rule at least. Simply Delicious has adamant principles that food is freshly cooked on site, never re-heated except harmlessly with casseroles, and always served on hot plates. Belinda has cooked bangers and mash for the Princess of Wales and there is an accent on shooting parties and society charity do's. But her enthusiastic team of ten cooks will travel anywhere, feed any number from six to 600 and supply anything from egg sandwiches to fresh salmon in filo parcels with beurre blanc. Each menu is individually designed with the client.

Yoko's who serve Japanese feasts from a suburban house in Harrogate also take their hot plates and happi coats out on the road. **Natureways** of Roundhay Road, Leeds is a vegetarian catering specialist. Willi Rehbock of the **Blue Goose Cookery School, Brookside, Newby, Clapham, N. Yorks** ☎ **01524 251520** also offers outside catering. And there is one individual cuisine that comes only through the outside catering route: Mrs Kalwant Kaur Virdee's **Pinky's, 6 Garmont Road, Leeds, W.Yorks** ☎ **0113 262 5290** uniquely guarantees Indian food cooked as it is in an Indian home.

Mrs Virdee began Pinky's with a modest takeaway operation on Chapeltown Road until driven out by rent increases. Now she cooks private dinners for ten or more and Indian New Year celebrations for up to 300. She always uses fresh ingredients and prepares northern Indian dishes learned at her mother's side in Kenya where she was born. Samosas are freshly made, lamb dishes are assiduously marinated in yoghurt and spices and her biriyani takes six hours to prepare, with layers of rice and chicken that require long, slow cooking. Mrs Virdee's love of food shines through everything she does. Even her chevra – Bombay mix – is home-made with tiny potato shavings, peanuts, cashews, sultanas and chick peas spiced with chilli, turmeric, mustard and cumin.

12

Restaurants

This chapter contains over 100 restaurants in Yorkshire and Humberside. They have been selected to represent a cross section in geography, price and cuisine. When it comes to eating out, the region offers both feast and famine. Leeds, York and Harrogate are well endowed with a wide choice and innovative cooking. Middlesbrough, Hull and South Yorkshire have too few places to recommend. Ethnic restaurants are given a listing where it is felt to be justified by a distinctive cuisine or exceptional cooking but there are a thousand nondescript trattorias, curry and chop suey houses happily untried and untested by this guide. As a general rule, Leeds is safely the best bet for Chinese, Bradford for Indian and Sheffield for Afro-Caribbean food. It's also a general rule that will be regularly broken. This is a personal, even quirky, selection. Naturally, there will be scandalous omissions, great favourites ignored and outdated endorsements. Sorry. Chefs leave, banks foreclose and standards change (for better as well as worse). But hopefully even the most dedicated follower of regional food fashion will find a pleasant surprise in these listings. Whoever eats even half way through it will know that from pub grub to gastrodome, Yorkshire's never been a better place for eating out.

ASENBY

Thirsk, N. Yorks
☎ *01845 577286*
Open: Restaurant
Mon-Sat 11.30am-2pm &
6.30pm-9pm
Sun 12 noon-2pm
Bar Mon-Sat 11.30am-
2.30pm & 6.30pm-9.30pm
Closed Sun evening

Crab & Lobster   Pub

Aah. . . the gourmet magic of the A19! On it's trunk and branches are now three Good Food Guide listings: **McCoys**, **Chapters** at Stokesley and promoted from county round-up to full entry is Asenby's local, once the Shoulder of Mutton, renamed the Crab & Lobster by landlord David Barnard. It's thatched, it's cosy and it sells beer but is it really a pub? David Barnard's own description of bar brasserie/restaurant is about right. There's no tap room and it's no place to hog a table and drink without eating at a weekend lunchtime. Food deservedly dominates. Arrive early for a seat in the bar. Arrive early for the tasty range of free bites: crudités with dips, spicy sausage, miniature quiches and peanuts. The bar menu is chalked on the beams and it's hard to envisage going wrong. Forty dishes of rising sophistication from roast beef and Yorkshire pudding to Indonesian clay baked chicken with banana cream sauce. The choice is imaginative: tagliatelle of scallops, oranges and ginger; herb crusted salmon and tomato with cucumber beurre blanc. Portions are proper and prices around the £7.50 mark. The heavily atmospheric dining room, crammed with dark wood and antiques, is dearer - appreciably so for à la carte. Think restaurant rather than pub and it helps. A welcome development is the fixed price lunch menu at £12.95 and dinner at £19.95. With three courses and plenty of choice at each course it looks like better value. Home made bread comes in chunks of white, brown or dark brown with nuts and seeds. The Crab & Lobster naturally puts you in mind of crustaceans which can sometimes be limited but there's plenty of fish and David Barnard is likely to change his menu at a whim. At the Indo-Chinese edges, a holiday in Malaysia was the inspiration for chicken satay with peanut sauce and his dim sum shames many Chinatown offerings. First rate vegetables and plenty of chocolate puddings. Service is pleasant and efficient. This is a class operation which holds up under pressure. The Crab & Lobster works very hard, perhaps a little too hard. For some, there will be one too many Edwardian leather suitcase and casually hung parasol but never mind. If there was a Crab and Lobster for every Beefeater steakhouse there wouldn't be this book.

BAILDON

15 Westgate, Baildon,
Shipley, W. Yorks
☎ *01274 531596*
Open: Mon-Thur
6pm-10pm
Fri & Sat 6pm-11pm

Conways   Restaurant

The wine bars and restaurants of Baildon village have long flattered to deceive with nobody making a decisive breakthrough in its kitchens. Conways is the nearest yet but it is not worth a major detour to misquote Michelin. It can't quite shake off its suburban origins: the bar downstairs has enough bright pine to send for sunglasses; the beams in the upstairs dining room don't quite go with repro Victorian chairs and the teapot collection. Thumbs down for desiccated rabbit in a hotpot with prunes. Thumbs up for smoked fish, mushrooms cooked in cider in a filo basket, a rich skate from the blackboard, a lovely dish of perfectly cooked small baked potatoes and the beetroot in mustard sauce. All the servings were generous, the vegetables absurdly so.

BARNSLEY

6 Shambles Street,
Barnsley, S. Yorks
☎ *01226 240113*
Open: Tue-Fri 12 noon-
2pm & 7pm-9.30pm

Armstrong's   Restaurant

Armstrong's barely announces itself to a drab town centre street, but once beyond its big, heavy door there is a different world of cool colours and subdued lighting in a long, elegant dining room with a grand piano. This is the place that first lifted Barnsley into the Good Food Guide, indeed brought Barnsley the coveted County Restaurant of the Year, title, even if South

Yorkshire is not the hardest fought region in the competition especially now that the wonderful Peano's has wretchedly closed. Nick Pound, the chef and proprietor, was taught in London by the food writers' current darling Stephen Bull and he has mastered the 'modern eclectic' style that is invariably used to describe his cooking: ingredients and international techniques come together for original and highly successful dishes. Once upon a time restaurants could be categorised bluntly as French or English. Here are influences from North Africa, South East Asia, the Mediterranean and India. Sea bass meets ginger and spring onions. Venison is stir fried with oyster mushrooms and star anise. The tagine of braised shoulder of lamb with cumin and coriander is served with tsatsiki. From Morocco back to Barnsley and a homage to Albert Hirst with a salad of black pudding, poached egg and bacon. There's no mistaking the panache of the cooking and it's well worth the money which is high but not wild.

BARTON ON HUMBER

11 Market Place, Barton on Humber, S. Humbs
☎ 01652 0635147
Open: Mon-Sat 6pm-11pm

Elio's   Trattoria

A pleasant, compact trattoria with a typical, traditional Italian menu which is nevertheless well cooked. The flourish comes with some imaginative daily specials, with the emphasis on fresh fish – mussels in garlic and white wine, brill and snapper. There's a well-flavoured aubergine parmigiana and good home made bread. Vegetarians, and veal lovers are equally well catered for. It's relatively cheap and undeniably cheerful.

BEVERLEY

Station Square
Beverley, N. Humbs
☎ 01482 866700
Open: Mon-Sat 12 noon-2pm & 7pm-10pm

Cerutti Two   Bistro

Housed in Beverley's former railway station, this bistro/restaurant is sister to the elegant Cerutti's of Hull (see p170) and like its partner, primarily a fish and seafood specialist. Cerutti Two has not been visited by this guide but as the Good Food Guide rates it higher than the Hull restaurant, it is obviously worth mentioning.

BILBROUGH

Main Street, Bilbrough, York
☎ 01937 832128
Open: Tue-Thur 12 noon-2pm & 7pm-9.30pm
Fri & Sat 6.30pm-9.30pm
Sun 7pm-9pm

Three Hares   Pub

Any pub that offers a warm salad of chorizo sausage and pine nuts or strips of chicken in cajun spices is definitely taking bar food up a notch. Add another notch for fresh potted salmon with a caper salad and lime mayonnaise or honey roasted ham hock with a meat glaze sauce. Such are the daily treats of Bilbrough's Three Hares, a village pub largely hi-jacked like the village by management class commuters. There's a formal restaurant with starched white cloths and polished glassware but the lunchtime and midweek attraction is the broad based bar menu and blackboard specials. Soup of the day might be creamy broccoli and courgette with croutons but a characterless bread roll. The salmon 'special' has a rich and tasty crab sauce. All the dishes are served with a generous portion of buttery new potatoes and mixed vegetables – crunchy verging on under-cooked. Bread and butter pudding and ginger and syrup sponge and custard are the puddings of the moment. Crème brûlée comes with the twist of a tangy rhubarb base. As pub food goes, the Three Hares is in the premier league – imaginative and seasonal, well cooked and smartly presented. The major let-down is the decor and ambience; copper pans, dried flowers and bland walls. Of course, it's no worse than a million pubs with their hearts ripped out. Of course, none of this matters if the food is this good. Or does it? One suspects the Three Hares would be booming with a more sympathetic setting.

BOLTON ABBEY

Bolton Abbey, Skipton,
N. Yorks
☎ *01756 710441*
Open: Mon-Sun 12 noon-
2pm & 7pm-10pm

Devonshire Arms   Restaurant

Green wellies in the porch, antlers high on the stone walls, famously caught fish in glass cases. The oak furniture is deeply polished. The family portraits are old and dark. The Devonshire Arms has all the right accessories for the sumptuous country house hotel. Indeed, on arrival, everything is calculated to make you feel that the Duke and Duchess of Devonshire will shortly be down to join you for drinks and that upon departure you are signing the visitor's book rather than a vulgar cheque. You can then hire a vintage sports car to tour the Dales or, more wastefully, a helicopter. You can shoot the moor for game birds or fish the adjoining Wharfe for trout or grayling which chef will cook for you with home grown herbs. The food in the Burlington Restaurant is classically based English with an active eye on the cosmopolitan. Roast beef, braised oxtail, salmon and lamb are accompanied by chicken baked Chinese-style in a paper bag, deep fried king prawns in a cinnamon batter and grilled mackerel with black soya beans. The dining room decor similarly goes for a modern interpretation of classic styling. The lunchtime set menu (markedly cheaper than one of Yorkshire's heftiest evening à la carte's) delivered a fine warm salad of liver and bacon and a tasty red mullet and ratatouille starter. Now, where possibly better for roast beef and Yorkshire pudding on Sunday? Wheel on the trolley with full pomp and circumstance. Raise the great silver dome. Alas, the beef ordered rare was conspicuously well done; the replacement two slices came with neither apology nor offer of a compensating third slice; the Yorkshire puddings were too airy. The beef and gravy were eventually up to expectation and, for pudding, soft fruits and berries were beautifully complemented by real mint ice cream tasting of a garden not a bottle. Then, there are any number of sitting rooms with comfy chintz chairs to sink into, browse the Sotheby auction guides, admire the impeccable flower arrangements and wait for the waiter to remember the coffee you ordered. At least one of the staff appeared to mistakenly believe that he rather than the current resident of Chatsworth House was the real Duke of Devonshire. Afternoon tea is probably the best way to sample this country house experience at nursery slope prices.

BOSTON SPA

174 High Street, Boston
Spa, W. Yorks
☎ *01937 845625*
Open: Tue-Sat 12 noon-
10pm

Café Provence   Bistro

White washed walls are given the rough Artex treatment, floors are laid with coconut matting and old kilims. The sun shines out of the oils and pastels of John Holt, a Thirsk artist whose vivid evocations of French country markets and southern landscapes help prop up the Provençal aspirations. If the butcher's bicycle in the hall and the wooden barrel that artfully supports a few autumn apples reminds you of the heavy styling of the Crab and Lobster, you're right. David Barnard has brought much of the sharpness of Asenby to a warren of upstairs rooms in Georgian Boston Spa – and some keener pricing on the mobile blackboard. Starters offered a plate of charcuterie, black pudding with mustard, scallops in filo pastry and game terrine. Only roast crottin (goat's cheese) and beetroot held out any hope for vegetarians. Main course dishes had sausage and olive mash, fish cakes with spinach on cream and chive sauce, indeed, plenty of fish in the shape of sea bass, halibut and scallops. But when a 'trio of fish with taglarene on a herb beurre blanc' arrived, a query into what the trio consisted of won the response: 'Salmon, mackerel and, I dunno, maybe halibut, maybe haddock.' With that, the waitress gave up on the matter. The mystery fish was fine. A generous dish of chunky vegetables hinted at Provence with peppers and aubergines among the carrots and broccoli. The bill when it came was spectacularly wrong. A glass of wine was priced as half a bottle, a jug of tap water apparently cost £1.80. It was all rectified happily enough but when there's a commendable kitchen supporting an agreeable atmosphere, the serving staff really should be able to know the score, both on the money and the food.

BRADFORD

386 Great Horton Road, Bradford, W. Yorks
☎ *01274 571861*
Open: Mon-Sun 11am-1am

Mumtaz Paan House   Indian

Bradford's best curry house is always a contentious issue but can anywhere else boast a glossy illustrated cookbook with all its recipes? Sadly, it's a closed book unless you speak Swedish. A Swedish publisher wanted a definitive curry book and headed not to Bangalore but to Bradford and the Mumtaz Paan. He chose well. From humble beginnings, this excellent restaurant is setting the standard. In 1980, Mumtaz Khan Akbar quietly opened a paan house in a stone cottage on Great Horton Road. His ambition was to offer sweets and paan to his Asian compatriots. Paan houses are popular on the sub-continent where the chewing of paan is a national pastime. It is supposed to aid digestion but among habitual chewers it colours the teeth and gums an alarming bright pink. It also stains the pavement when finally spat out. Paan is a mixture of crushed betel nuts, aniseed, fennel and sunflower seeds all combined with a sour or sweet paste (or tobacco) and wrapped in a tiny parcel made from the aromatic green leaf of the betel tree. Most English palates spit it out fast. After three years Mumtaz and brothers Gul-Nawaz and Rab-Nawaz expanded into the next door fish and chip shop to serve the sort of food they ate at home. Their mother Mrs Akbar worked out the recipes and cooked in her basement kitchen. Dishes were freshly made with Mrs Akbar's own blend of spices with no concessions to Western tastes. Lamb and chicken was served with rice for Bengalis; the preferred naan for Punjabis and Arabs. They offered vegetarian dishes to Hindus. This was no vindaloo and lager joint. The Mumtaz Paan House was catering for its own. Alcohol is strictly forbidden but there are jugs of sweet or salted lassi or fruit juice. In 1992, they refurbished again. In came blue neon and a conservatory with cane furniture and ceiling fans. A touch of Hollywood hit Great Horton Road with telephones at every table for the businessmen (although young Asian yuppies still prefer their mobiles). Happily, Asian women eat here comfortably, with or without men. A pleasing mix of age, race and gender keeps the House lively from 11am through to last orders at 1am seven days a week. By Asian standards, the menu is still short and simple with beautifully flavoured karahi main courses of lamb, chicken, fish or vegetables. The marinated cod is a fiery revelation and the bhel puri has everything bar the kitchen sink: chick peas, potatoes, cucumber, tomato, onion, crisped bread, Bombay mix served with sweet and hot chutney, tamarind sauce and yoghurt and onion. Finish up with falooda, a milk shake with spaghetti slivers in it. There's a gleaming sweet display on the way out and, finally, the paan counter. A new factory now makes Mumtaz dishes for Morrisons, Asda and the Co-op and discussions are taking place with even bigger names. The Akbar family's only regret is that their mother did not live long enough to see the huge success her sons made out of her simple home made curries. She died in 1990 but a plaque over the kitchen door is dedicated to her memory.

A CURRY IN BRADFORD

'Bradford has established a gastronomic colony that compares with New York's Chinatown or the multitudinous Indonesian restaurants of Amsterdam. . . A revolution in Yorkshire eating tastes has occurred.'

Roger Ratcliffe, The Bradford Book, 1990

There are 7,000 curry restaurants in the UK, more than anywhere else in the world including India. There may be more in London and Birmingham but per head of population, Bradford wins hands down. More than 150 restaurants and takeaways service a population of 300,000. Bradford is the undisputed curry capital of Britain. It has its trade associations, its curry trails and its tourist hype. There remain some truly shocking dives; there is an enormous middle range of decent low cost curry houses which are insufficiently distinctive to gain a separate listing (or be authoritatively covered) and there are a handful of superb restaurants, improving all the time.

Perversely, there has never been a great penchant for family dining out or taking away among Bradford's 60,000 Asian origin community. It's not unusual on a Saturday night to find nothing but white faces in a popular city centre curry house. More Muslim and Hindu lads eat out now but British born Asian women are still overwhelmingly expected to perform traditional domestic duties. Eating at home with the family is culturally important. Home cooks are routinely contemptuous of restaurant standards.

The original curry houses of Bradford were established to cater for single Asian men at the outset of major immigration to the city in the 1950s when there were virtually no Asian women to cook for them. The men came to work the newly instituted 12 hour nightshifts of the wool textile mills and send their money home. They lived a twilight existence six days a week, sleeping in the day and frequenting the simple street cafés that sprang up to serve food from home.

There are competing claims for Bradford's first curry house between the **Sweet Centre** in Lumb Lane, the upwardly mobile **Kashmir** in Morley Street and the meshed windows of the **Karachi** in Neal Street. Students caught on first to scooping up a curry with a chapati for next to nothing. Curious middle classes followed and takeaways staying open after pubs closed launched the infamous cocktail of a skinful of lager and a vindaloo. The Karachi remains most curry fans' idea of the quintessential 'Indian': no cutlery, bare walls, chipped formica, tubular metal chairs and, above all, heroically cheap. Ah. . . but remember when you could get a curry there for 30p? Remember when they didn't even have a menu? It hasn't compromised that much. The Karachi remains an authentic Asian working man's café.

When the textile industry collapsed, Indian restaurants mushroomed (the word 'Indian' is used as in the pre-partition sub-continent of all India before the creation of Pakistan and Bangladesh). West Riding Asian families turned to catering as an alternative source of income but through the 1970s ever hotter vindaloos masked poor ingredients topped with oil slicks of ghee. Pre-boiled mutton, chicken or catering pack prawns were added to stock cubes and an all purpose sauce. Like the Chinese takeaway, suddenly every town had one. The authentic flavour of the original Bradford Punjabi creation was dissipated. Not that there ever was an authentic Indian dish of curry and pilau rice. Curry was invented by the British Raj, an anglicised version of the local cuisine. Some say the word curry is adapted from the karahi metal cooking dish, others from a Tamil word for spicy, others again from kari, the South Indian leaf.

Second generation Pakistanis and Indians spearheaded the next advance in Yorkshire restaurants. The now defunct Mandalay in Leeds went upmarket with piano and prices at the top end of the scale. The **Shabab** chain brought new heights of Moghul emperor settings to Huddersfield, Leeds and Harrogate with vast brass jugs and tinkling multi-coloured chairs. Tubular chairs and functional Pyrex were out. The Sabir brothers opened their first **Aagrah** restaurant in 1977 introducing Kashmiri dishes to Pudsey, Shipley, Skipton and Garforth. Everyone should go to Bradford's **Bombay Brasserie** – once. The conversion of the former St. Andrew's church is a telling commentary on religious changes in Bradford. The deck-out is preposterously gaudy but the food's not a patch on its previous incarnations as Omar Khayyam's and Sheikh's. The **Sweet Centre** on Lumb Lane is the only Bradford restaurant that opens for an authentic Asian breakfast. The unique all-women cooks of vegetarian **Hansa's** with branches in Bradford and Leeds became the region's only true Gujarati restaurateurs although **Bharat** on Bradford's Great Horton Road is establishing a growing reputation and claims Gujarat origins despite serving both meat and vegetarian dishes. But it is the **Mumtaz Paan House,** further down Great Horton Road, that is setting the pace for individualistic dishes in the 1990s.

The next development in Bradford's status as curry capital came with **TAARO**, the Trade Association of Asian Restaurant Owners, set up in 1991 as Bradford and Britain's first curry college. TAARO run a two year training course in Asian cooking and short courses on food hygiene. They also organise the annual Hot Stuff chef of the Year competition, won in 1994 by Omar Gulzar Khan chef/owner of **Shah Jehan** on Manchester Road. TAARO themselves run a discreet little training restaurant (so as not to upset the local restaurant owners) serving midweek curry lunches. They also run business skills seminars to tackle the problem of too many low price restaurants under-cutting one another with the inevitable failure of one or more.

Despite these innovations, most Indian restaurants are at heart more interchangeable than dedicated curry fans would have you believe, a British amalgam of all regional styles and ingredients. Certainly, anyone travelling in India and Pakistan would see virtually nothing in common between Asian street food and the curries back home – other than a continuing need for vigilant kitchen health inspection on both continents. One simple rule on the sub-continent is that the North is meatier and bread based; the South progressively hotter, vegetarian and rice based. Drinking water to put out the chilli fires won't work anywhere.

Much confusion still reigns. Glossaries of Indian restaurant food are notoriously inconsistent. So are menu translations and spellings. One street's balti is the next's karahi. There are blatant contradictions like tandooris without a tandoor and instant biryanis. The fun is in the exploration and discovery of an ever-changing scene and maybe even talking to the staff for longer than it takes to order and pay the bill. The bill, in turn, invariably confirms that there's still no better value on the market.

BRADFORD

32 Manor Row,
Bradford, W. Yorks
☎ *01274 720371/720335*
Open: Sun-Thur 12 noon-
2pm & 6pm-midnight
Fri & Sat 6pm-1.30am

35 Westgate,
Huddersfield W. Yorks
☎ *01484 422775*
Open: Sun-Thur
6pm-11.30pm
Fri 6pm-midnight

BRADFORD

North Park Road,
Bradford, W. Yorks
☎ *01274 492559*
Open: Mon-Fri 7pm-
9.30pm Sat 7pm-10pm

BRADFORD

113 Oak Lane, Bradford.
W. Yorks
☎ *01274 490176*
Open: Mon-Sun 11.30am-
2am

Nawaab · Indian

Pervez Akhtar, head chef at Nawaab, won the 1993 Hot Stuff Award organised by Bradford's Asian Restaurant Owners Association and voted by an all Asian jury with his Murgh Makhan, a chicken dish marinated in spices, yoghurt and cream and baked in a clay oven. Top chef or not, Nawaab is definitely in the top flight of Bradford restaurants that have left the cheap, cutlery-free zones far behind. Murgh Makhan is on the menu and available for take-away. The former bank is always a fun place to eat with its great china elephant and rip-roaring business at peak times. There's a comprehensive menu with some fish specialities in addition to the familiar classics, murgh, gosht, tandoor and chef's specialities which include an unusual shahi murgh, a chicken and cheese dish. The take-away menu loses a little eastern lustre with chicken nuggets and chicken Kiev. Outside catering available.

Restaurant 19 · Restaurant

Restaurant 19 is housed in one of Bradford's minor 'brass castles', a sandstone pile with high ceilings, ornate plaster work and a scattering of Victorian effects. North Park Road is on the boundary of Lister Park and Cartwright Hall and chef/proprietor Stephen Smith worries that the proximity of 'notorious' Manningham Lane puts people off. Don't be. Manningham Lane's pretty tame from a moving car and there's Michelin-starred food waiting. Whatever the real value of a 1994 Michelin star, there were still only three in the entire region and this is the least expensive. Certainly, the creativity and the cooking would stand out in any company. The winter menu has Stephen Smith's hallmark dishes of warm salad of ox tongue with celeriac and casserole of rabbit and ham hock. The apparently plain English meats (a harking back to the offal stalls of Bury and his northern roots?) have new life confidently injected into them. Fish comes fresh every day from Blackpool and features strongly. So do Mediterranean flavours. Tender beef fillet is distinctively served with toasted polenta, Parma ham and Gorgonzola. If this is peasant cooking, make us all poor. The menu makes few concessions to vegetarians but dishes will be prepared with advance warning. Restaurant 19 is guided by seasonal produce in composing its menu. It promises more vegetable starters with asparagus and artichokes in spring and summer. Sweets often come with memorable combinations: prune and almond tart is served with an Armagnac and prune ice cream. Rhubarb and ginger crème brûlée goes with rhubarb sorbet. The fixed price menu is £26. It's all a far cry from Stephen Smith's background in City and Guilds, school meals and canteen catering yet amazingly this is his first restaurant. In a decade it has gone from strength to strength, winning West Yorkshire County Restaurant of the Year in the Good Food Guide and warm write-ups from every critic who matters. There should be no stopping its progress and reputation.

Shiraz · Indian

Mohammed Gulbahar has taken the Shiraz upmarket with more emphasis on the restaurant than its origins as a sweet centre. A long menu takes in the house speciality Balti Gosht and some unusual vegetable curries which include not just lentil or spinach but pumpkin, okra and red beans, either alone or for an extra 20p combined any way you want. Late night revellers should appreciate the 2am finish.

BRADFORD

110-114 Lumb Lane,
Bradford, W. Yorks
☎ *01274 731735*
Open: Sweet Centre Mon-
Sun 8am-11pm
Restaurant 12 noon-
midnight

Sweet Centre & Restaurant   Indian

The Sweet Centre is one of Bradford's oldest restaurants, established for 30 years on Lumb Lane with the same chef as when it opened in 1964. It's a popular place for breakfast. Stools line the long counter and from 8am to 12 noon you can order a Pakistani breakfast of fried chapatis and chick peas. The restaurant next door, popular with English and Asian alike, is an odd mix, halfway between plush restaurant and basic caff. There are ornately carved chairs at plastic topped tables. Fancy plaster work adorns the walls but there are no knives and forks. As a Muslim restaurant no alcohol is served but they do not object to customers bringing their own. An otherwise conventional menu reveals a handful of outlandish dishes: brain curry speaks for itself; paya curry is made with sheep trotters. There is also fish curry, quail curry and a range of balti dishes served in metal bowls.

BRIDLINGTON

West End Pier,
South Cliff Road,
Bridlington, N. Humbs
☎ *01262 674729*
Open: Mon-Sun 11am-
11pm

Blue Lobster   Fish Restaurant

Fishing boats and crabbers land at Bridlington harbour daily and most of their catch promptly does a vanishing act. There's precious little evidence of fresh seafood in Brid's bars and restaurants. Mike Baron's Blue Lobster is the obvious exception and in true Bridlington seaside style it's a pretty obvious place. Set on the harbour edge, the best views are upstairs away from the smoke-filled bar. The furnishings are over the top pseudo-rustic and the menu is almost big enough to paper a small bathroom. It does offer some useful illustrations and descriptions of fish and seafood as well as listing the dishes. There are lobster thermidors and scampi provençales but the best comes from the seafood least tampered with: half a dozen oysters on ice, a platter of smoked salmon, oysters, prawns and fresh salmon, fresh lobster salad or lobster grilled with butter or garlic. Bridlington's finest, dressed crab, is served simply with bread and butter. The **Blue Lobster** also doubles up as fishmonger, specialising in local crab and lobster.

BRIGHOUSE

6-8 Bradford Road,
Brighouse, W. Yorks
☎ *01484 715284*
Open: Mon-Fri 6pm-
11pm Sat 7pm-late
Lunches in Dec

Brook's   Restaurant

Brook's is quite a shock to the system in the heart of worthy old West Riding Brighouse. It's an entertaining restaurant to be in and a very good one to eat at. Every Brighouse should have one and too few do. Darrell Brook (ex-Savoy) plays old jazz records, pins unusual and original paintings on the walls and places fine old Victorian furniture on the polished wood floors. There are tasteful black blinds and tongue and groove panels. It is almost pointless to describe menu or food because Brook's point of greatest pride is in changing the menu weekly and never repeating itself. This seemingly reckless policy actually works. You rarely hear a bad word said about the food. Try to picture what you might eat from what you won't: duck and pistachio galantine; tartlet of lamb's kidneys and chipolatas in red wine; tagliatelle and mushrooms tossed in a creamy carrot sauce; snapper with five spices; pigeon breast with ginger sauce. All come with the mini bouquetière of vegetables, one item on the menu that could change for the better here as at many other clever kitchens. Have all these bright regional chefs no confidence in cooking seasonal vegetables with the same creativity they put into meat and fish? Desserts return to top post-modern form with Brook's bread and butter pudding and biscuit with mascarpone, cream and caramel. Coloured crayons are provided to decorate the paper tablecloth and service was slow enough to tempt a threatening version of The Last Supper.

BURLEY IN WHARFEDALE

78 Main Street,
Burley in Wharfedale,
W. Yorks.
☎ *01943 864602*
Open: Tue-Sat 6pm-10pm

David Woolley's   Restaurant

You'd think from some of the rave reviews and loud supporters of David Woolley's restaurant that the finished article had been finally located in his elongated cottage on the main road through Burley in Wharfedale. Familiar Dales watercolours and ruched curtains win few points for artistic impression; being hurtled through the courses is no way to reward a prompt arrival and wherever you sit the noise and after-shave from the next table mingles with your meal. This is a cramped restaurant – for width and height. If it is as relentlessly full as David Woolley claims, he could surely afford to jettison a table or two in the common good. The sauces that accompany the range of fish, game and meat are distinct, assured and potent. If you pack in a rich starter and rich dessert on either side, the whole lot can stop you in your tracks. It's strong stuff with a particular long suit in fish. No quarrels here. It would be worth trying the fixed price £12.95 menu for three courses to establish a taste for the place before graduating to the full blown experience. Starters feature carrot and coriander soup and pan fried lamb's kidney in spinach. Main courses offer the likes of boned leg of duckling and fish in saffron and white wine.

BYLAND

Byland Abbey, N. Yorks
☎ *01347 868204*
Open: Mon-Sun 10am-
2.30pm & 6.30pm-11pm

Abbey Inn   Pub

Directly opposite Byland Abbey and with a pleasant garden, the Abbey Inn has a privileged setting. Six years ago the interior had a dramatic makeover. Conventionally enough, the warren of rooms have stone-flagged floors and exposed beams. Then the scene becomes progressively surreal with a collage of old farm machinery, mismatched tables and chairs, butter churns, stuffed birds and assorted monkish relics and regalia. The blackboard menu calms down with food well above pub grub average: ham and chicken liver paté, wild boar paté, battered haddock, vegetable pie, mushroom stroganoff, boned and rolled chicken stuffed with apricots. Puddings include banoffee pie, white and dark chocolate mousse or bread and butter pudding.

CHAPEL LE DALE

Chapel Le Dale,
Nr. Ingleton, N. Yorks
☎ *01524 241256*
Open: Mon-Sat 12 noon-
2.30pm & 7pm-9.30pm
Sun 12 noon -2.30pm &
7pm-9pm

Old Hill Inn   Pub

Surviving Whernside in the rain or even emerging triumphant from Gaping Gill demands a piping hot bath, a roaring fire, comfy old settees and substantial warming food. Step into the Old Hill Inn which has been reviving bedraggled travellers since 1615. John and Sue Riley's bar menu and specials turn up the heat. There's been Madras or a vegetarian thali with three curries of chick peas and lentils, pepper and okra and, hottest of all, mushroom and aubergine served with rice and poppadoms. Other interesting choices featured jugged hare, spinach and lentil bake. Good going for a quiet weekday lunchtime. More conventionally, they do lasagne, chilli con carne, pizza and a children's menu. A recently opened and more genteel dining room can't hold a candle to the warmth of the bar. Sadly, the Riley's put the Old Hill Inn up for sale but until then it's business as usual.

CRAYKE

Crayke N. Yorks
☎ *01347 22614*
Open: Mon-Sun residents
only

Halfway House   Bed and Breakfast

To win the English Tourist Board's award for the best bed and breakfast in the land you need a bit more than Laura Ashley prettiness in the bedroom and a free fill-up of fresh orange juice at breakfast. Belle Hepworth has a lot more at the rambling red brick Halfway House - gardens, views, tennis court, springboard location for the North York Moors but above all, the food. It's not quite the point of B and B but you could go just for the meals.

Belle Hepworth is a self taught cook who looks for quality fresh ingredients. She offers a no-choice dinner menu but, with warning, she will avoid any particular dislikes. Be prepared to talk to other guests. Everyone, including the Hepworth's, sits together at the long oak table to eat by candlelight in the panelled dining room. Her style is traditional English: roasts, pork fillet in various guises - wrapped in pastry with plum sauce or with mushroom, sherry and cream – duckling, pheasant with all the trimmings, gammon and Cumberland sauce. Salmon, trout and scampi provençale all appear on her menus. Starters may be soups or salads; puddings may be pavlovas and crumbles. Cheese and biscuits. Breakfast has freshly squeezed orange juice, a sideboard with cereals, muesli, Greek yoghurt, fresh grapefruit and dried fruit compote. There's also a cooked breakfast and toast, croissants and warm bread rolls before you stagger off.

EAST WITTON

East Witton, Nr Leyburn, N. Yorks
☎ *01969 24273*
Open: Mon-Sun 12 noon-2.30pm & 7pm-9.30pm

Blue Lion   Pub

The Blue Lion in the almost too perfectly preserved village of East Witton has always been an amazing pub. Former landlady Bessie Fletcher kept the front door locked, only allowed in people she knew and served her privileged regulars with beer from a jug until her death in 1990. When Paul Kline moved in, there was no electric light and next to no plumbing. The place was derelict. His restoration was so unusually sensitive for a Dales pub that he is warmly applauded for preserving the old flag-stones that he actually installed himself. Oak settles, log fires and careful restraint with horse brass and hunting scene make the bar satisfyingly dark and warm. With food to match, it's a leading contender for the best all-round pub in the Dales. The chef John Dalby is given a free hand in the kitchen and produces sophisticated dishes to high standards. Local produce is reflected in the long blackboard menu behind the bar. In season, game predominates. Roast partridge comes on a bed of creamed leeks and a madeira sauce. Wensleydale wild boar, reared in West Witton, is served braised in red wine and marsala. There is always a variety of challenging fish items like coley with ginger, pimento and spring onion butter. All main courses arrive with a plate of mixed vegetables. There is a host of hot and cold starters. The best sellers are leeks in cream sauce with smoked bacon and Wensleydale cheese or home-made ravioli of smoked chicken, tomato and wild mushroom with pimento, tomato and thyme butter sauce. Puddings at the Blue Lion are notable, best of all because you can order all of them. For £5.95 you can taste the chestnut and Armagnac parfait, sticky toffee pudding with butterscotch sauce and home-made banana sorbet, lemon mousse with orange sauce and orange buns, glazed lemon tart and on and on ... Not surprisingly one order and two spoons is by far the commonest response. Apart from the public bar, there's a more formal restaurant or an elegantly proportioned private room where a party of 12 or so can enjoy a leisurely Sunday lunch from a polished mahogany table. Summer diners can sit in the garden under the apple trees.

FARNLEY TYAS

Farnley Tyas, Huddersfield, W. Yorks
☎ *01484 666644*

Golden Cock   Bar/Restaurant

Eighteen months ago, the father and son partnership of Phillip and Dominic Kirkup moved from the Woodman at Thunderbridge, poached chef Simon Shaw from **Leodis** in Leeds and set up in this restored Pennine stone pub. Their bar is regularly busy with customers tucking into steaming bowls of mussels or something tasty from the long blackboard menu. The dining

Open: Mon-Sat 12 noon-
2.30pm & Mon-Thur
7pm-9.15pm
Fri & Sat 7pm-10pm
Sun 12 noon-3.45pm
Closed Sun evening

room offers a surface formality with beige damask cloths, burgundy napkins, burgundy and cream drapes with tie backs and pelmets. An exotic vine, trailing fat black grapes, turns out to be not quite the real thing but it's a smart, comfortable dining room. The staff are welcoming and helpful but never intimidating. It's the food that is taken seriously. The menu offers sea bass, salmon, turbot and tuna or fillet steak, duck and pigeon. Colour comes from the crostini of goat's cheese, spinach and mâche salad, the beef carpaccio with shavings of Parmesan, the chicken with coconut and coriander with korma sauce. A main course salad niçoise was expertly produced with fresh warm tuna on top of sliced tomatoes, hard boiled egg with the black olives, green beans, sliced new potatoes artfully filling in round the sides and all dressed in a worthy olive oil. There are steaks for traditionalists and three vegetarian options. Puddings offer the ever popular crème brûlée or toffee pudding and more unusual roasted pears with honey ice cream.

GOATHLAND

Goathland, Nr Whitby,
N. Yorks
☎ *01947 896486*
Open: Restaurant Mon-
Sun 7pm-8.30pm
Sun 12 noon-1.30pm
Bar Mon-Sun 12 noon-
2pm & 6.30pm-9pm

Mallyan Hotel   Bar/Restaurant

Local produce is often claimed by restaurateurs but rarely fully delivered. The Mallyan Hotel is confident enough of its sources to publish them. Fish is from Whitby, the fresh from Crook's wholesalers, the smoked kippers from **Fortune**'s of Henrietta Street. Goat's cheese is from nearby **Dog Tree Bank Farm**, game from Studforth Farm, wholefoods from **Suma** and vegetables from Leeds Wholesale Market. Their excellent beef is home cured, their sauces and chutneys home made and bottled. The menu shows the dual courtesy of crediting all the staff and inviting the diner into the kitchen. All these encouraging signs are borne out in the cooking. Peter and Judith Heslop's food has even won a gushing write-up from The Times food critic Jonathan Meades who is notorious for rarely venturing outside London, much less liking what he finds there. Find here a naturally strong hand in seafood: Whitby plaice with glazed banana, brill with galingale (a nutty French root) and lemon leaf sauce, local squid marinated in lime with home made tartare sauce. If you've got local, flaunt it. Local lamb cutlets are accompanied by Mallyan crab apple jelly. Who else makes bilberry and apple pie with Yorkshire picked bilberries? Even the mushrooms are sometimes local blewitt. The man from The Times never made it past the bar menu and the light, almost stately dining room is a minor shock after acclimatising to the snug, brown bars. Peter (ex-Dorchester) and Judith are both professionally trained chefs and genuine wine lovers. You will enjoy a highly principled meal but not a stuffy one. The surrounding countryside is forever glorious, especially when the late summer heather turns vividly purple, and if the once peaceful village of Goathland will never be quite the same after Yorkshire Television's hugely popular Heartbeat series, the tourist buses all park at the other end of a long village. The Mallyan Hotel is in fine fettle.

GOLCAR

Acre Mill, Knowl Road,
Golcar, Huddersfield,
W. Yorks
☎ *01484 654284*

Weaver's Shed   Restaurant

Golcar goes back to the Domesday Book, Acre Mill goes back to the 18th century and Yorkshire diners have been going back to the Weaver's Shed for 21 years. It's been a dependable fixture in the Good Food Guide for a decade despite changing ownership and it continues to please even if the upsurge of new restaurants has seen some catch and others surpass it. Weaver's Shed is no longer quite at the cutting edge. The 1970s mill

Open: Tue-Fri 12 noon-
2pm & 7pm-9.30pm
Sat 7pm-10pm
Closed Sun & Mon

conversion job has had something of a fierce lift since the new owner Stephen Jackson took over. So, too, has the cooking style of dinner-party British set by Peter and Kate McGunnigle. Under Jackson's direction, who incidentally works in the kitchen as second chef, the menu is moving gently into a new era. Jackson describes it as a mixture of eclectic, Italian and modern British. Smoked duck in citrus vinaigrette or spicy chicken and leek in a custard tartlet was followed by delicate halibut with cream and herbs and venison in pepper sauce. Silver service vegetables were worthy and well cooked - mashed swede and carrot, beans, cauliflower with tomato and new potatoes. The advance promise of all produce coming fresh from local suppliers was most plausible at this stage of the meal. Puddings include that Yorkshire favourite banana and toffee pudding. The plate of four cheeses failed to offer a Yorkshire cheese, disappointing given their stated pride in an 'unrivalled' selection of British farmhouse cheeses. The bread is home made, the service homely and the prices demand high standards. A new innovation has been to invite guest chefs to cook for the restaurant. To date visiting chefs have included David Wilson from the Peat Inn, Fife; Shaun Hill from Gidleigh Park, Devon; and Brian Turner, happy to return near to his Halifax roots, from Turner's in London.

GRIMSBY

Haven Mill, Garth Lane,
Grimsby, S. Humbs
☎ *01472 346338*
Open: Mon-Sat 10am-
3pm Wed-Sat 7.30pm -
11pm Closed Sun

Granary   Restaurant

Converting a grain mill into a restaurant was all the rage in 1979 but The Granary on the first floor of Haven Mill has weathered well. If some of the furniture is due for re-upholstery, it helps with the unstuffy, comfortable feel of the room. Considering it's Grimsby, the price of the fish sharpens matters up but at least it's there - smoked halibut with dill sauce, fresh crab salad and skate. Meat eaters are well catered for with brawn as an unlikely starter, followed by steaks or cajun chicken casserole. Nice unpretentious place, neat cooking.

GRIMSBY

2 Cleethorpes Road,
Grimsby, S. Humbs
☎ *01472 342257*
Open: Mon-Sat 12 noon-
1.30pm & 5.30pm-6.30pm
Sun 5.30pm-6.30pm

Danish Mission   Danish

After five years as missionaries in Nigeria one might hanker for plummier assignments than running a seamen's hostel in Grimsby but Fini and Lisa Iversen are a charming young Danish couple who are clearly made of the right stuff. As well as providing a home from home for Danish seamen, they've propelled the dining room into a Good Food Guide listing. You don't have to be off a Danish container ship to eat here although the Iversen's politely remind that it is primarily a home before a restaurant. The £4 buffet lunch - smörgasbord is smörrebröd in Danish and amounts to a lot more than the literal translation of bread table - has been well logged by local office workers. There are eight to ten different dishes laid out every day, both hot and cold: marinated herrings, of course, mackerel, tuna, cold roast beef, ham and salami, smoked pork loin and salad. Hot dishes might be a chicken casserole, forloren hare (meat loaf), hakke bøf (beef burgers) and fricadella (meat balls), served with rice and potatoes. The Iversen's make their own traditional dark rye bread and there are simple puddings or a biscuit to finish off. Meal times are tight so there's little time to catch up on all the latest available Danish books and newspapers. Discard any lingering image of a dismal hostel for beached old sailors. This is clean, simple and comfortable. It is Danish after all. Look out for the sign on Cleethorpes Road that says Sömandshjemmet – Danish for Seaman's Mission.

ETHNIC EATING

There used to be an Australian restaurant in the outback of Bradford called Billabong. Long gone now but the dedicated follower of foreign food can still locate some weird if not always wonderful ethnic cuisine within the county boundaries. This essay travels rather than recommends. Indian, Chinese, American, French and Italian places are far too commonplace for special mention.

Meanwhile, you can sample smörgasbord at the **Danish Mission** (p163) in Grimsby and if it's to your taste you can stock up with more Danish produce at George Herd's Ship's Stores nearby. You can wolf Bavarian in Pocklington at the **Bayernstubl-Zillertal**. It's mainly a krabben (prawn cocktail) and steak place but it has its share of bratwurst and bockwurst sausage, rolmops heringe, and the various schnitzels come with jager (hunter's sauce) of wine cream and mushroom or a knoblauch (garlic) gypsy sauce. With 24 hours notice they will prepare a Balkan fleischplatter, a varied selection of cooked meats.

With the closure of Elland's Barcelona, the region lacks a truly Hispanic dimension. **The Mediterranean** on Sheffield's chic Sharrowvale Road village has dedicated regional Spanish evenings, a set of 17 tapas from wolfish to onion tortilla and main courses of zarzuela, a fish stew with eight different seafoods, and stuffed roast saddle of kid with cous-cous and minted sauce. Service and desserts can be indifferent. **La Cucard** in Middlesbrough claims Spanish and French credentials. Amid the potages and moules marinières come guacamole and paella. **Fino's** of Harrogate has won awards for its tapas but large portions make it difficult to sample across the range. **Monkman's** of Ilkley (p172) and **Sous le Nez en Ville** in Leeds (p179) both do good tapas selections as sidelines. For countries with such vivid national cuisines as Lebanon and Turkey, there's scant sign of more significant exports than inner city doner kebab spits. Rodley's **Olive Tree** is not only the best Greek restaurant around by far, it also does eastern Mediterranean and Maghreb specialities.

Mexican restaurants (faithful to their country of origin) are much of a muchness. Established spots include **Cocina**, Bradford; **Aztec**, Dewsbury; **Pancho's**, Doncaster; **Caliente** and **Salsa Mexicana**, Leeds; **El Sombrero**, Sheffield; and **Salsa Posada**, York. **La Bamba** of Sheffield claims Chilean burritos and Argentinian fish although not that nation's more famous steaks. **La Fiesta Mexicana** on Bishopthorpe Road, York is a useful take-away and delivery service run by the Colman's who have travelled extensively in Mexico. Tacos, burritos, tostados and chimichangas with chillies, refried beans and salsa. **Frazer's Wholefood Emporium** of Harrogate (p103) is outstandingly the region's best stockist for authentic raw materials of the Tex Mex persuasion.

Huddersfield. Leeds and Sheffield are the natural bases for a Caribbean scene that is finally improving after a long spell in the doldrums. **Queensgate Market** (p129) in Huddersfield has West Indian ingredients at **Winn's** for fish, and **Rhodes Brothers** for vegetables, and **Spice Cuisine** restaurant, en route to Honley, offers an unbeatably cheap Sunday lunch of saltfish cakes, spiced curried goat, baked trevally fish and jerk pork for £4.99. In Leeds, **Dr B's** is run by Barnardo's for training young people in catering. Don't ask if they're all orphans as the Duke of Edinburgh once did on a visit to Chapeltown.They're not. There's the Jamaican national dish of saltfish and ackee, yams, plantain, Caribbean chicken and mango juice all served with elaborate politeness under project leader Victor Shaw. Glenn of homely **Glenn's** on Beeston Road has a direct line to Leeds Market for kingfish and swordfish. He adds creole and cajun influences and, from his home islands, Cayman Kai chicken, heavily flavoured with fresh coriander. The combination of his massive 'Fiesta' table with Hunslet's local Old Fart brew is enough to precipitate a B and B booking upstairs.

Sheffield has three main Afro-Caribbean contenders. **Calabash** is the most comprehensive, a big red joint on London Road, with a long suit in both vegetarian and fish dishes. There's maluse (steamed vegetables), cariola (vegetables in garlic); sunsplash bakes (seasoned yam and sweet potato cakes). Red sea bream comes in coconut sauce; the escoviche fish is lightly fried and saltfish comes with the spinach-like callaloo. Broomhill's West African **UK Mama** is small, colourful and original with egusi soup of melon seed and herbs, payala Afro-Spanish style seafood, beef and mushroom 'moi-moi' black eyed beans, Johnny cake fried dumplings, meat tagine and a West African 'Combi' of mixed vegetables in stewed fish sauce. Nigerian chef Sam Okotie runs **Sarah's** at Hillsborough with a mixed Caribbean and European menu.

Thai, Malaysian and Singaporean food has not travelled particularly well to Yorkshire and the region has nowhere up to top Soho standards. Sheffield's **Bah Nah** offers stir fries and curries amid set menus and artificial flowers. **Sala Thai** in Headingley is the most enterprising in range with 70 plus dishes and the most ostentatious with its national costume/air hostess tight silk skirt service but off hand management. The less affected downtown Leeds duo of **Thai Siam**, charmingly run by the Wudtavee family, and **Mai Thai** are more back to basics with curry pastes, lime leaves, lemon grass, sharp peanut sauces, pomfret fish and Thai pudding.

Leeds' **New Asia** has some 20 Vietnamese dishes on its menu. The Chinese ingredients are largely familiar. The distinction comes with a lot of vermicelli and odd items like Mia Nuong Tom, which is grilled sugar cane in prawn meat stuffing. Sowerby Bridge's well established **Java** has the Indonesian field to itself and boasts weekly deliveries of banana and pandan leaves from the far east, exclusive Indonesian spices and lots of coconut milk and sambal sauces. Outside the main Japanese listings, the sushi at **Matsui** in Scarborough has been recommended for good value.

Leeds is the unchallenged capital of East European migration in the north east with significant populations of Estonians, Latvians, Lithuanians, Ukrainians and Poles. There are cultural centres and clubs dotted around Bradford, Halifax and Huddersfield but, apart from the notable exception of Chris Kwiatkowski's **Partner's** in York (p197), the most traditional eating out is concentrated around Chapeltown in Leeds. The **Adriatic Hotel** does varied East European dishes and there are authentic Polish kitchens at the **Polish Catholic Centre** (evenings only) and **Milan's Club**, where Polish RAF flyers still sometimes gather at the bar over Zywiec beer and Bison vodka. The fare here is exceptionally hearty: stuffed pancakes, Polish sausage, a heavily hammered and breadcrumbed pork cutlet, and pirozki – a pasta pie crammed with curd cheese and served with fried pork fat. Only Milan himself is not Polish. Nor is he Italian. He's from the former Yugoslavia.

HALIFAX

Dean Clough, Halifax, W. Yorks
☎ *01422 383242*
Open: Mon-Fri 12 noon-2pm Mon-Sat 6pm-10.30pm

Design House   Restaurant

John Leach the managing director of Design House food complex at Dean Clough pulled off something of a coup when in late 1994 he lured chef David Watson from the Michelin-starred Pool Court to launch the café, deli and restaurant at Dean Clough. The massive Victorian edifice was once the biggest carpet factory in the world, set to become another decaying ghost of the West Riding's industrial heritage until the enlightened millionaire Ernest Hall converted it into a business park and installed the Contemporary Art Gallery, businesses large and small and brought the leviathan back to life. Bold blue and orange curtains divide café from restaurant with the flexibility for either to expand if required. Furniture design is by Philippe Starck, better known for avant-garde Manhattan hotel interiors than restored carpet mills. The blue and orange is reprised in the ultra modern sofas. Lights, mirrors, white lilies and blue glass add up to an attractive restaurant and bar. Still, it's a shame that there are no views and little sense of the grandeur of the location. Elegant simplicity marks David Watson's first menu, with no more than six choices at each course. There are genuine vegetarian alternatives throughout and high quality ingredients consistent with the high ability in the kitchen. Begin with aubergine and pesto Genovese tart or venison with roquette and Parmesan. Main courses have calve's liver in citrus sauce or roast pigeon with a contemporary parsnip mash and gin and juniper sauce. Finish with caramelised apples and pears, melted chocolate mousse or a rare savoury, deep fried Cashel Blue cheese with a herb salad. No dish costs more than £9.00.

HAROME

Harome, Nr. Helmsley, N. Yorks
☎ *01439 770397*
Open: 11.30am-2.30pm 6pm-11pm

The Star   Pub

Harome is about as thatched a village as Yorkshire can boast and it has the coach parties to prove it. The Star happily surrenders most of this trade to its larger rival pub and carries on in its Olde English way: thatch, whitewash, old oak and miner's lamps. Only the skittle alley is missing. As ever with unspoiled old pubs, it's more fun to eat in the bar than the more functional dining room. The food is superior pub fare: carefully cooked steak, chicken laced with cream and brandy and changing blackboard specials. The potted crab was piled high with fresh meat and a juicy claw. The garden is spacious and there are plenty of distractions for children.

HARROGATE

3 Royal Parade, Harrogate, N. Yorks
☎ *01423 503034*
Open: Mon-Sun 6pm - 11pm

Café Fleur   Bistro

This relaxed bistro has no great pretensions in repertoire, decor or price, almost approaching a canteen feel in its big square room, but it's hit a spot with Harrogate diners for its early-bird menu at the bargain price of £5.95 for three courses before 7.30pm. By 7pm it's buzzing and the big window serves to attract more trade as the evening wears on. Portions are hefty though not always accurate. A generous salad of bacon and croutons needed more olive oil, which was supplied on request. A main course pasta was sufficiently drenched in garlic to floor a passing Frenchman.

HARROGATE

5 Montpellier Gardens, Harrogate, N. Yorks
☎ *01423 502650*
Open: Mon-Sat 12 noon-2.30pm & 7pm-10.15pm

Drum & Monkey   Fish Restaurant

Saturday lunchtime at the Drum and Monkey is one of the great eating out spectacles of modern Yorkshire. The doors open at noon and five minutes later the downstairs bar is full. It's feeding time for Yorkshire's Sandhurst and Sloane wannabes, all in their country weekend fig and in full cry. To be sure of a good seat for this ritual it is sometimes necessary to book weeks in advance. But nobody needs a four wheel drive to enjoy timeless English fish and seafood and wash it down with a steely dry French white. The formula's been rock steady for more than a decade, a Wheeler's of the North menu in a city oyster bar setting. The best bets are the simplest: lobster in its classic manifestations, fresh crab, bisques, mussels, salmon, Dover sole and, naturally, oysters. The preparation and cooking has no truck with passing fish fashions and is straight down the line. There is a dining room upstairs but you can't help feeling you're missing the buzz and the people-watching of downstairs where you can take a bench seat at a marble topped table or sit on a high stool and eat off the slate bar as the orders fly around. The yellow walls look as though they are testimony to years of unrestricted smoking though it's possible they just repaint it that way and if some of the decor is showing a chip here or a fray there, that's fine. The Drum and Monkey is accumulating character not wrinkles.

HARROGATE

1 Montpellier Mews,
Harrogate, N. Yorks
☎ *01423 530708*
Open: Tue-Sun 12 noon-
2pm & 6.30pm-10.30pm
Closed Sun dinner

Millers the Bistro   Restaurant

The region's foodies held their collective breath when Simon Gueller down-graded his restaurant to bistro, ripped out his warm mahogany bar and vivid oil paintings and totally re-worked his menu. Breathe again. The old formulations may have won the reviews and the rosettes but there were also empty tables all too visible, all too often, in the ground floor dining room. The new version is humming. It's cheaper or at least it can be unless you're understandably seduced by the more wondrous dishes (less so by an irritating £1 cover charge). The new design is bright and modern without being spartan. It's more relaxed all round. Chef/proprietor Simon Gueller is an excellent cook in his own right but the initial collaboration with Marco Pierre White (old Box Tree hands together) has added a further dimension. White's 'Risotto of Ink' scores as well in Montpellier Mews as it must in the Canteen at Chelsea Harbour. A dreamy pasta with lobster and basil sauce; smoked salmon with a chive and butter sauce; calf's liver with spinach, bacon and mashed potato all bore the hallmarks of Gueller's kitchen: fine ingredients, punctilious cooking and a touch of flair. Puddings had prune and Armagnac ice cream and a delicate concoction of cream and crushed meringue (in the inevitable puddle of raspberry coulis). The rumours that Gueller and White are launching a new restaurant in Yorkshire have gone quiet, replaced by a new one that Gueller is setting his sights on the already well endowed Leeds riverside. Until those plans bear fruit, Miller's is showing ample class.

HARROGATE

11a Regent Parade,
Harrogate, N. Yorks
☎ *01423 504041*
Open: Tue-Sat 10am-2pm
& 7pm-10pm
Closed Mon & Sun

Tiffins on the Stray   Vegetarian

The magazine table at this pleasant vegetarian restaurant offers The Vegetarian and Country Living and the food holds out a similar mix of discipline and indulgence. A sample of the daily changing blackboard: beetroot fritters with orange sauce, soup and hot herb-filled scones, cream cheese and cashew nut paté, nut roast with Yorkshire pudding, chick pea and spinach curry, stuffed courgettes, all with stir fry vegetables and pancakes filled with fruit purée. Then there are tarts, sticky puddings, muffins and crumpets, home made cakes, home baked bread and flavoured butter. With coir matting and foldaway chairs, it has a light sensible air. Sadly, no Harrogate colonels were spotted picking up the transcendental meditation leaflets. Sadder, Tiffins has recently lost its driving force Liz Coussins. Hopefully, her successor will uphold her high standards.

HARROGATE

23 Hookstone Chase,
Harrogate, N. Yorks
✆ *01423 885611*
Open: Mon-Sun 7.30pm-
midnight

Yoko's — Japanese

A dozen or so Yorkshire men and women seated on the floor at a low Japanese table, wrapped in 'happi coats' and eating hors d'oeuvres to the accompaniment of authentic koto music in a suburban house in Harrogate, is one of the region's culinary collector's pieces. Yoko, born in Nagasaki, has been cooking for 20 years ever since she met and married Yorkshireman Keith Banks. For the last five years, she has been offering genuine Japanese hospitality to parties of eight to 20 from her home in Hookstone Chase. What began as a hobby has developed into a fully fledged business and her customers are curious locals, Japanese ex-pats or visiting business people. There's no need to fear raw fish. It is served only on request and the menu is agreed in advance. From around £20 a head (bring your own wine) these are almost authentic Tokyo prices but it is a memorable Japanese experience that lasts from 7.30pm until midnight. In full kimono regalia, Yoko greets her guests and wraps them in a happi coat. Hors d'oeuvres are taken on the Chinese carpeted floor and then guests are ushered into the main course room for the big event. The Teppanyaki menu offers the evocatively named pine tree course, consisting of fillet steak, king prawns and salmon, all cooked on the special teppanyaki cooking table and eaten straight away with a piquant sauce. The plum tree course has rump steak, prawn and halibut. With all the quick-fire frying that goes on, the reason for the happi coat becomes apparent. 'I was terrified of ruining someone's silk blouse', says Yoko. There are shabu-shabu, sukiyaki, tempura and sushi menus to choose from. Shabu-shabu is thin beef and vegetables, cooked fondue style in a broth and dipped in sauce. Sukiyaki adds soya sauce and sake rice wine to the mix. All the menus are served with Japanese style vegetables, rice and soup. There are fruit desserts and coffee or green tea to follow. Yoko will also cater at your home or office.

HETTON

Hetton, N. Yorks
✆ *01756 730263*
Open: Restaurant
Mon-Sat 7am-9.30pm
Sun 12.15pm-2pm
Brasserie Mon-Sun
12 noon-2pm & 6pm-
10pm

The Angel — Pub/Restaurant

The manoeuvering begins before opening time. People linger outside but not too far from the door. When it opens there's nothing so crude as a headlong rush but certainly a smart trot for the best seats and to ensure a seat at all. Such is the well-won reputation of the 17th century Angel Inn in the moneyed Dales village of Hetton. It would win most polls as the best pub cooking in Yorkshire and not many restaurants can match it either. Bar meals are informal with staff wearing black waistcoats and long white aprons to give the impression of a French bistro rather than an English pub something the Angel clearly cultivates, calling it the brasserie rather than the bar. Fish features strongly with a garlic fish soup which benefits from a rich shellfish stock. Main courses include cod with beurre blanc, red mullet and various shellfish. There's invariably something interesting and different. Mediterranean flavours turn up in a salad of rucola with fresh Parmesan, bruschetta with three toppings and a hot salad of Provençal vegetables. Hearty meat dishes are oxtail braised in Guinness with olive mash or boudin blanc et noir. The restaurant is just as popular and booking is essential. Here there is more sophistication. The Angel's signature dish of fish 'moneybags' stuffed with salmon and cheese sauce, wrapped in filo pastry and served on lobster sauce, runs and runs. Duck, fillet steak, and guinea fowl all appear along with English lamb and a special Friday fish menu. They say that if it's hard to reach the top, it's harder still to stay there. The Angel shows no sign of being knocked off its perch.

HOLMFIRTH

Victoria Square,
Holmfirth, W. Yorks
☎ *01484 689003*
Open: Tue-Sat 7pm-
9.30pm

Le Premier Etage   Restaurant

At weekends, the correct instinct is to drive straight through Holmfirth without stopping and without looking left or right to see the damage that the Summer Wine and wrinkled stocking business has done to an attractive town. Creep back at night. Upstairs at Le Premier Etage is a magical little room with bags of atmosphere and a happy marriage of Gallic flair and West Riding wallop in the cooking, a package that is fast making it one of the best restaurants in Yorkshire. Steep stairs with garlic smells wafting down draw you into a subtly lit corner room overlooking Victoria Square and the river Holme. Old beams and brickwork are cleverly exposed. The mahogany furniture feels right and dotted around is virtuoso hand thrown pottery from the local Booth House Gallery, a spectacular example of which – a fish shaped pot – brings a barnstorming bouillabaisse. The rascasse (scorpion fish), as decreed by scholars of the Marseilles original, was not spotted but there was plenty of the authentic rest, including the bones, and a quantity that was a meal in itself. Such enormous generosity with helpings makes the diner feel guilty for returning fine food to the kitchen and must be counter-productive for management as the appetite for pudding fades. Much of the blackboard was pure Brittany – langoustines, moules, fresh oysters, Co-quille St. Jacques, fresh clams and plenty of garlic. The fishermen of Britain are recognised with large Whitby cock crab, Dover sole and wild salmon. Red snapper came grilled with buttery red peppers, herbs and samphire. The carte has more of the feel of a French country market with piperade and a cassolette; there's Ricard with the fricassée and Dijon mustard in the sautéed ham steak. A salad of leaves with pigeon and smoked ham in warm walnut vinaigrette was positively narcotic and duck breast had a crisp skin while remaining pink inside They were served with another dauntingly sized dish of admirable vegetables. Strangely, amid so much accomplished cooking the puddings were a disappointment. Banana brûlée was cloyingly topped with Demerara and the marshmallow ice cream was a bridge too far. Chef patron Mark Irving is young, talented and visits France regularly to keep on his culinary toes. The commitment to his calling shines through.

HONLEY

6 Westgate, Honley,
W. Yorks
☎ *01484 662066*
Open: Mon-Sat 12 noon-
2pm & 7pm-10pm

Mustards & Punch   Restaurant

The logo is Punch's cap with bells on. Jars of mustard in glass cases decorate one side of this little Pennine bistro and framed Punch cartoons fill the opposite wall. A little studied, perhaps, but the wooden floor boards, marble topped tables and old bentwood chairs combine to create a warm, agreeable atmosphere in which to enjoy food of a far higher order than the laid back wine bar setting it inhabits. Scott Hessel launched out on his own after being named Chef of the Year on a Roux scholarship and serving time at the **Crab & Lobster**. A blackboard menu introduces a cross section of the 90s most fashionable ingredients: black pudding, pesto, polenta, saffron, onion marmalade. Happily, they are not just here for fashion's sake but are put to good use. The wild mushroom tart with pesto and pine nuts had a crisp base and gently sautéed mushrooms but the basil came so finely chopped that it lost its flavour on the way. The mussel and clam croustade was a wonder-fully fishy parcel on a creamy sauce of saffron, muscat and curry. Main course guinea fowl was full flavoured and served with polenta that deftly soaked up the mushroom juice of the sauce. Grilled tuna failed its perennial test: fractionally overcooked is fatally overcooked. Grilled vegetables helped but the pesto again was so subtle as to be thin. No problem, Scott

Hessel dashed off in search of a bowl full without offence. Such willingness to please, high calibre ingredients and accomplished cooking have won Mustards and Punch a rapid, popular and critical following. There are jazz nights, Halloween nights, special dinners for high days and holidays, including Christmas Day. Wednesday is ladies lunch day at an enterprising £15 for two. All the hard work appears to be paying off and it's certainly heartening to see a restaurant alive and busy on a foggy autumn midweek night in Honley.

HORSFORTH

*36a Town Street,
Horsforth,
Leeds, W. Yorks
☎ 0113 258 1885
Open: Mon-Sun 6pm-
10.30pm Fri & Sat 6pm-
11pm*

Paris   Restaurant

The opening of Paris in 1989 can now be seen as a seminal moment in the modern history of eating out in and around Leeds. Up until then there was next to nowhere coming up with exciting European food between the wine bar end of the market and the high priced formalities of the **Box Tree** and **Pool Court**. Even fewer restaurants exploited the possibilities of our native fish. Where before was regularly serving turbot and mullet? Martin Spalding and chef Steven Kendell delivered the goods: bright ideas with the earliest early bird menus for this kind of enterprise. Paris was a swift success, brimmingly full and lively most nights and going from strength to strength with an ever more ambitious fish choice daily chalked up on the blackboard. So successful that Messrs Spalding and Kendell were able to expand their adventures by opening **Leodis** in the Leeds riverside renaissance. Not that Paris has slipped down or out during their moonlighting. Under the custodianship of manager Kimberley O' Rourke, fish remains the big draw but a large à la carte takes in much else that is vegetarian, flesh and fowl: calf's liver with bacon and rösti, duck breast with port and blueberries, guinea fowl, venison, veal and a comforting plate of Cumberland sausage with bubble and squeak. If the cooking is no longer trend setting and the cutting edge of dining room design has moved on, Paris still deserves to be remembered when it finally runs out of its Horsforth lease and moves its tent to the Stanhope Arms at Rodley.

HULL

*10 Nelson Street, Hull,
N. Humbs
☎ 01482 28501
Open: Mon-Fri 12 noon-
2pm & 7pm-9pm
Closed Sat lunch*

Cerutti's   Fish Restaurant

In 1974 when Tony and Tina Cerutti opened their elegant riverside restaurant it was – despite Hull's fishing history – the only show in town. Twenty years on, little has changed and Cerutti's still holds down its reputation as the best place for fish in the city. Set amid the heritage and the Georgian doorways of the Old Town, it enjoys a prime location too. Fish appear in many guises but the plate of assorted grilled fish is hard to beat: monkfish, scallops, langoustine, scampi, plaice and haddock are lightly grilled to delicate perfection with real tartare sauce. The upstairs dining room is light and spacious. Tablecloths are starched to a crisp; glass and silver gleam. Tall windows provide diners a view of the Humber and if life on the estuary is not what it was, there's still the odd passing coaster or ocean going tanker to set off nautical imaginings. The immaculate, formal service fits the mood. A weighty bill returns the mariner to dry land.

IDLE

*7 Albion Road, Idle,
Bradford, W. Yorks
☎ 01274 616587*

Symposium Food and Wine Bar   Bistro/Wine Bar

Another wet Tuesday in autumn, another near empty wine bar. It can't be easy to fill a restaurant in Bradford's outer suburbs every night of the week and the new management appears no more successful than the old. Tables take up most of the floor space and the place is more food than wine. Behind

Open: Mon-Fri 12 noon-
2pm Mon-Sat 7pm-10pm

the big picture window of a fine old chemist's, soft repro lighting, photos of old Idle and stripped wooden floors make for a good looking setting but when it's nearly empty the dining room's too big for warmth and the bar's too small for many passing drinkers. The blackboard meals are not over ambitious and no less tasty for that. Leek and potato soup was thick, full flavoured and made with proper stock. Smoked hors d'oeuvres demanded few culinary challenges but some resourceful shopping for halibut, trout, chicken and venison. Boeuf bourguignon was as rich and robust as it should be, with the meat meltingly tender after long slow cooking in red wine. Monkfish with pesto mash was a nod towards new-look cuisine but the portions of monkfish and even the mash were slight, making a fridge clearing dish of five different vegetables disproportionately large. Strawberry shortcake, banoffee pie and a duo of chocolates were coyly announced as 'Be Carefuls'. Service was brisk to off-hand. But hopefully just an off night.

ILKLEY

37 Church Street, Ilkley,
W. Yorks
☎ *01943 608484*
Open: Tue-Fri 12 noon-
2.30pm & 7pm-10.30pm
Sat 7pm-10.30pm
Sun 12 noon-2.30pm

Box Tree   Restaurant

The fortunes and misfortunes of the region's most famous restaurant could fill a chapter or a TV mini-series. The story begins in 1962 when Malcolm Reid and Colin Long who ran a snack bar opposite Leeds abattoir, bought Box Tree Cottage and with chef Michael Lawson turned a tea room into one of Britain's top restaurants. Along the way they collected a high camp antique collection, plush with gilt and velvet, crammed with oriental artefacts and life-size porcelain greyhounds. Shirley Bassey opened the extension of 1971. A Leeds lad called Marco Pierre White passed through the kitchen in 1979. They earned two Michelin stars and twice won the Egon Ronay accolade of Best Restaurant in Britain. Its prices were legendary, even stratospheric with fine wine. Then, in 1986, Reid and Long bowed out. Having apparently never bothered with accounts or book keeping, they sold the restaurant complete with flamboyant objets d'art for a reputed £1 million. But as head chefs came and went, the recession came and stayed. Pea soup and toasted marshmallow replaced the haute cuisine. The rosettes and the stars fell away. In 1992, the Box Tree crashed with debts of £50,000. Enter Madam Helen Avis, a wealthy, Greek-born businesswoman, hotelier, scholar, aristocrat and all-round time bomb. Within three months, she pulled off a remarkable coup, signing up Marco Pierre White who promptly declared war on Michael Gill and his Michelin star down the road at the Pool Court. Another three months and Marco Pierre had stomped off back to London with Madam threatening to sue him for damage to the kitchen ceiling. In quick succession, Avis went through manager, head chef and pastry chef, too. After such excitement, it's relatively quiet now. Madam Avis's volcano appears dormant although her presence can be oppressive. Most of the antiques are unbroken and the collection of Naviasky oil paintings is superb. The four course £29.95 set menu (exclusive even of coffee) still makes it one of the most expensive restaurants in the region so chef Thierry Leprêtre-Granet is expected to deliver. After canapés and agreeable smoked salmon roulade appetisers, the starters were disappointing. Lasagne with snails and parsley was flat and button mushrooms with coriander and raisins lacked potency. Main courses of tournedos of beef and grilled turbot were far more assured; fleshy and firmly sauced but the portions were miserably petite and the tiny slices and cubes of seasonal vegetable were a nouvelle parody. Excellent puddings helped to fill the gap.

White and dark chocolate mousse with coffee sauce was actually bigger than the main course and poached pear with hazelnuts and pistachio served with ice cream and a toffee sauce punched its weight. The service was of the formal perfectionist school which feels silly on a near empty Tuesday night and leaves the diners curling up under the inspection. The brochure makes fine claims to be recreating the grande tradition of the Box Tree's glorious past. But it can't. Times and tastes have changed. Having recovered some of the disastrous lost ground since Reid and Long departed, the gilded cottage now needs to forge a new house style, forget the overbearing history of a decade of rosettes and accolades and change enough to earn its own fresh laurels.

ILKLEY

60/60a The Grove, Ilkley, W. Yorks
☎ 01943 816477
Open: Mon 7pm-10pm
Tue-Sat 12 noon-2.30pm
& 6.30pm-10.30pm

Monkman's   Bistro

Ilkley residents have known this bistro with its distinctive conservatory frontage in different guises down the years. It's often given off a cliquish odour, doubtless agreeable to paid up members but less fragrant to outsiders. As Monkman's it may prove to have the staying power its attractive position deserves. Certainly, Chris Monkman has some pedigree: Low Hall; the Fountain House, Boroughbridge; Plummers of Bedale. There have been mixed opinions but the cooking has shown itself to be more than competent without being too clever. The tapas have herrings in dill, smoked duck breast, sun dried tomatoes and squid vinaigrette. The enterprising extremes of fish on the blackboard ranged from Faroe Island salmon to gurnard. Baked sliced potatoes cooked in cream were just right and there is a solid raft of sticky and indulgent desserts to follow. There are two evening sittings on Saturday which are capably dealt with and nothing breaks an Ilkley bank account.

LEEDS

42/44 The Calls,
Leeds, W. Yorks
☎ 0113 234 3232
Open: Mon-Fri 12 noon-
2.30pm & 6.30pm-
10.30pm
Sat 6.30pm-10.30pm

Brasserie Forty Four   Brasserie

The vortex of brave new Leeds: riverside setting, world food, no trace of provincial neurosis. It was the first of the Calls district restaurants to get it right and for many it's still the best. After four years the rooms are certainly still striking. Big bright oils on bare brick walls, futureworld furniture on ash boards, exposed piping and cast iron, a slick and jazzy grain mill conversion. Perhaps, the metal swings at the bar are wearing thin (the mechanical negro pianist always did) and one could wish that the view to the Joshua Tetley side of the river had a few more Mississippi steamboats rolling by. . . but all in time. From its debut, the food gave a welcome kick up the city centre backside: exciting amalgams, grilled vegetables, brill and bream and sea bass with Chinese accents; New Zealand wines and Tuscan oils, basil, balsam and sun dried tomatoes. No big news around the place now but revelatory then. The Yorkshire pudding and battered cod lines became a shade too self-conscious but some of the desserts have been knock-outs. Some of the mark-up's for fish that are no great luxury at the market are sharp but the budget 'light and rapid' lunch of any two courses for £7.25, inclusive of coffee, service and VAT, is undeniable value. The small hotel next door is the only place to stay for visiting stars, won over by touches like CD players in every bedroom. With Michael Gill of **Pool Court**, first as a partner and now sole proprietor of Brasserie 44, standards are assured. Add to this the relocation of Pool Court from its rural home to this city centre site, and the overall effect is a revitalising of this quarter of Leeds. Even the rest of the country is noticing. For which, much thanks.

LEEDS

16-17 Kirkgate, Leeds,
W. Yorks
☎ *0113 246 0381*
Open: Mon-Sat 11.30am-
2.30pm & 6pm-11.30pm

Darbar   Indian

This splendid third floor room has an exotic history for dingy Kirkgate. Once a sober clerks' office, it sweated out the early 1980s as a gay disco and now it's the King's court – the Darbar. Check the fancy fretwork, the meeting of Pakistani carpenters and Louis XV in the furniture but above all the lovely hand-painted ceramic tile tableaux of the Dales and Whitby Harbour. Now that Karim Mir and Max Ahmed have set them in white plaster Islamic arches, slap on the preservation order. The cooking is mid to up-market North West Indian, with Bengal and Kashmir specialities. It's strong on Tandoor, Karahi dishes, charcoal grills and breads. Weaker on their vaunted spice and pickle. Check out, too, the buffet lunch, last heard of promising as much as you can eat for £3.95.

LEEDS

60a Street Lane, Leeds,
W. Yorks
☎ *0113 266 6501/6031*
Open: Mon-Sat 12 noon-
2.30pm & 6pm-11.30pm
Sun 12.30pm-3pm & 6pm-
11pm

Flying Pizza   Pizzeria

The legend lives on, almost beyond parody. There are as always the BMWs and Merc's posing outside; the footballer's wives and the year round suntans posing inside. Nouveau riche? Not half. Meanwhile, the port and melon, tuna and beans, steak in brandy, and all the veal dishes roll on down the years, blithely untouched by culinary fashion. Adriano Piazzaroli can afford to smile. He's gone from manager to sole owner and sits on a £2 million a year turnover. It's usually noisy or crazy or both with flying Italian waiters and reliable pizza and pasta. Nobody tampers with this winning formula.

LEEDS

31-33 East Parade,
Leeds, W. Yorks
☎ *0113 245 9707*
Open: Mon-Sat 8am-
11pm

La Grillade   Bistro

Guy Laval has been flying the tricolour for real French food in Leeds for 15 years now; not grande bouffe but brasserie French, above all great steak and great frites. You can flirt around the menu - chicken in tarragon and Toulouse sausages are exciting holiday romances - but you keep coming home to the steak (offered in four degrees of rarity), the utterly French straw chips and the vigorously dressed salads. After all the years in the catacombs under the Wellesley Hotel in Wellington Street, La Grillade has spread its wings impressively in East Parade. You can play at being in France by dropping in for coffee, croissants and a newspaper in the morning or having a glass of red wine on a bar stool in mid-afternoon while the young French staff pose and pout to Parisian standards. The room has an enlarged zinc bar styling that works particularly well and it is not at all derivative of anything else going on in Leeds. Steak apart, all La Grillade's other old tunes still play well; the well-kept French cheeses, the monster crudités and one item that's never left Guy's menu, no doubt as a sly reproach to a Yorkshire he's never totally embraced, his exemplary Normandy boudin noir black pudding.

LEEDS

Shire Oak Road,
Headingley, Leeds,
W. Yorks
☎ *0113 278 4446*
Open: Mon-Sat 7.15pm-
9.45pm Sun 12 noon-2pm

Haley's   Restaurant

Haley's was the 1994 Good Food Guide's County Restaurant of the Year for West Yorkshire – some feat in the face of the tremendous competition. Setting up a discreet private hotel (more for businessmen than lovers) in Headingley when all the smart money was going into new downtown hotels and restaurants took some nerve and deserves its rewards. The spin-off deli **Haley and Clifford's** also enriches suburban Leeds. Chef Chris Baxter (ex Connaught Hotel) takes his food very seriously. His fish is superb and the gravadlax in a trio of salmon is a definitive version. Rendezvous of seafood is another winner. Bring French and Italian dictionaries: salad of roast pigeon on a bed of ficiole glaciole is, of course, lamb's lettuce with sesame seed dressing and there's more in the same modern haute vein. Roast lamb with rosemary and herb crust was less rarefied and the reduced sauce was deep and rich. Textbook service was summed up by the arrival of the 'ramasse-miette', sorry, dustpan. Three flourishes of a silver thingy and the table was ready for the next course - except that not a crumb had been dropped in the first place. There's something about Haley's that puts staff and diners on whispering best behaviour. Perhaps it's the upmarket show home decor with its swags and tie-backs and leather bound volumes and the Roman pomp of its perfect loos. Enjoy them because these prices are tops for Leeds. It's all exquisite, just a little too formal.

LEEDS

72-74 North Street,
Leeds, W. Yorks
☎ *0113 244 4408*
Open: Tue-Thur 6pm-
10.30pm
Fri & Sat 6pm-11.30pm
Sun 6pm-10pm
Thur & Fri 12 noon-2pm

44 Great Horton Road,
Bradford, W. Yorks
☎ *01274 730433*
Open: Mon-Sun 12 noon-
2pm & 5pm-11pm
Sun 12 noon-2pm

Hansa's   Indian

Hansa's is a delightfully run Gujarati Indian restaurant with a string of differences from every other Asian establishment in the region. It neither looks nor tastes like either end of the curry house market. It has a genuine single regional base where others merely pretend. It is wholly vegetarian. It has a warm and welcoming bar with greater ambition than over priced Carling and Côtes du Rhône e.g. Indian wines and champagne. The dining area is a carefully lit, split-level loft which is another welcome change after a surfeit of plush Moghul boudoirs. Instead of Mecca rugs or Taj Mahal calendars there are framed photographs of Hansa Dabhi's family. Hansa had no professional training but decided to open a restaurant after successfully cooking her native Gujarati food at her children's school fetes. Gujarati food, from North West India, is so different from the usual offerings that even the comprehensive descriptions on the menu may need verbal back-up. The easiest way in is the thali, a complete meal with all the pickles, breads and raitas and a glass of lassi. Chickpeas are prominent in several dishes. Extend ambition with masala dhosa, a mixture of spiced vegetables wrapped in a pancake served with sambar sauce and coconut chutney. Ravaiya are spicy stuffed aubergines. The interesting sweet section has vegan options too. Sweet Sev is vermicelli with sultanas, cardamom and almonds or try an Indian-style Knickerbocker Glory. The sister restaurant in Bradford replicates Hansa's virtues of an attractively lit building from the outside and a stimulating meal inside.

LEEDS

38 The Calls, Leeds,
W. Yorks
☎ *0113 245 3870*
Open: Mon-Sun 12 noon -
2.30pm & 5.30pm-
10.30pm

Hereford Beefstouw   Steak Restaurant

Leeds' only Danish restaurant has a novel style in service. It takes ten minutes to explain but once mastered will presumably spare the waiters the bother of speaking to their customers. On arrival you are presented with a card. On it write your table number - indicated by a brass plate embedded in said table. Write down your initials. Now select your steak by its number. Thus 11 is sirloin steak 180gr., 16 is grilled skewer 150gr.. Indicate with a cross how it should be cooked – rare, medium etc., what kind of butter you require – garlic, parsley etc., whether you require chips or baked potato and another cross if you want a salad. Pens are helpfully chained to the tables. They even suggest that you post the menu to a friend, free of charge. Come off it. The staff are a charming team of Danes, Germans and Belgians and, given the chance, customers would no doubt be happy to meet them while they take the order and decode the Maastricht agreement, all of which could done in half the time it takes to explain the gimmick. The Hereford Beefstouw was founded in 1971 by a Danish couple who now operate a

NEW WAVE LEEDS

D raw a line from the bottom of East Parade to Crown Point Bridge. The narrow strip of Leeds real estate between that line and the river Aire has in the last decade witnessed the most dramatic explosion of good restaurants in great settings not just in Yorkshire but probably anywhere in Britain. Six of them are covered at length in their own right on adjoining pages – **La Grillade** for its superior Frenchness (and his chef Renzo has re-opened his old haunt on Wellington Street); **Hereford Beefstouw** for a unique steak lover's experience; **Sous le Nez en Ville**, **Leodis** and **Brasserie Forty Four** for being at the forefront of contemporary British cooking. After 28 years Michael Gill has closed Pool Court at Pool in Wharfedale but has opened up in great new city centre style as **Pool Court at 42**. There are doubtless new arrivals yet to come.

Still in The Calls, there's **Shear's Yard**, a big basement wine bar with night-time live jazz and fast improving modern dishes from menu and blackboard. Yet another scrubbed up warehouse **Sparrow's Wharf** has a succession of rooms and a narrow balcony fronting the Aire. Drinking dominates but the hatch service food with large hunks of bread is fair enough.

The most nervously awaited redevelopment has been **Dyson's** on Lower Briggate, following the closure of the peerless jewellers some years ago. The good news is that the Time Ball Building has survived extraordinarily well with the exterior clock, the priceless carved wood interior balcony and the bevelled glass largely intact. Marriott Hotels, the new owners, can now reinforce their proven architectural taste by raising the food above a superficially slick and detached hotel restaurant level. It's the most wonderful room which should mean as much to Leeds as Betty's does to Harrogate but it hasn't taken off yet. The **Cornucopia Café** in the well of the Corn Exchange and London's **Pizza Express** in the happily restored White Cloth Hall both exploit their privileged historic homes impressively, the latter with an unusual conservatory as well as split level main rooms.

Bibi's is still the pick of a fistful of Italian ristorantes in the bottom half of town, with **Dino's** under the railway station as runner-up. Bibi's has never looked back since leaving Mill Hill for the Roman imperialism of the old Mario and Franco's in Greek Street. Don't expect great subtlety (there is a real gap in the market for a truly individual Italian restaurant) but neither will it let you or your office Christmas party down.

Big business in one form or other has driven all this activity so perhaps it is fitting to champion the smallest and most independent of the restaurants at the bottom of town. **Brigg Shots** is a squashed up room and a half with bench seating, tucked away in Queen's Court, a pretty brick courtyard between Lower Briggate and The Calls. A Brigg-shot is a pot of ale, a noggin of pottage and a trencher of roast beef and was apparently served in local pubs in the days when Leeds Cloth Market was held nearby on Leeds Bridge. Today, the eponymous tureens of soup for sharing are their best known line but Brigg Shots is invisible from any road and too easily forgotten. They've closed at lunchtimes so it may soon be a case of use it or lose it. You could find goat's cheese and figs in filo pastry or hot chicken livers with orange and coriander. There's always a healthy vegetarian choice between menu and blackboard. Nothing flashy but it's an endearing combination of style, modesty and value.

chain of 12 restaurants across Europe. It's steak, steak and then more steak. Vegetarians take heed: the only concession is grilled Baltic salmon and a substantial salad bar. The set up is high church Scandinavian. There's bleached wood from floorboard to pepper mill, 'scrubbed three times in double cream', claimed the waiter with a straight face. Designer glassware and cutlery are IKEA de luxe. With its pipes and girders all hanging out, we have a mini Pompidou Centre to add to the Calls converted warehouse collection. Then there are significant looking hangings of rolling pins and woodworkers tools. The Beefstouw logo turns up relentlessly on pens, tea towels, glasses and sugar cubes. A circular kitchen in stainless steel operates in full view of the restaurant. There's nowhere remotely like it. See it. Try it. Fill in its silly form. The pricy steaks, by the way, are fine, the Hereford being the breed not the town and the meat is imported Danish or Aussie. But why here and why now with all the red meat scares and B.S.E. and vogue Mediterranean diets and concern for the vegetarian in your party? Beefstouw is surely doomed unless, perhaps, under all the designer disguise can be see Homo Tyke, red in tooth and claw, and fighting back. This may be the counter-revolution against the fish fanciers – Restaurant Bloke.

LEEDS

Victoria Mill, Sovereign Street, Leeds, W. Yorks
☎ *0113 242 1010*
Open: Mon-Fri 12 noon-2pm & 6pm-11pm
Sat 6pm-11pm

Leodis   Bistro

Another bend in the river, another stylish conversion. Leodis and Brasserie 44 are doubtless like family members who can't see the facial similarities when everyone else can. The food and wine is inter-continental. The iron and brick of the industrial revolution once more meet matt black, this time with a splash of Miro. Another daring enterprise, another exhilarating result. Leodis is the creation of Martin Spalding and chef Steven Kendell. The two became friends at Thomas Danby Catering College in Leeds and, between them, they have worked the **Box Tree**, Digby's, Maxwell Plum, **Sous Le Nez,** and **Paris** in Horsforth which they also co-own and more recently **La Rochelle** in Menston. There were some wonky moments in the early days of Leodis but the food soon settled into its stride. No surprise with their pedigree that white fish provides a trusty backbone, indeed its own page on the menu, but the choice ventures inland from the North Sea and the Med for oxtail casserole, rösti potato, steamed treacle sponge and bread and butter pudding. Stir fry and tagliatelle keep the air miles going; flourishes come with samphire and morels. The cast list changes regularly. There is a three course budget menu and à la carte prices are slightly keener than that other brasserie down river. Although nominally 'smart dress is preferred' here, there's also a bit more sense of a party going on. Which is finally better? What the hell, the town is big enough for both of them.

LEEDS

19 Lady Lane, Leeds, W. Yorks
0113 245 0520
Open: Mon-Sun 12 noon-12 midnight

Lucky Dragon   Chinese

More Chinese currently eat at the underground barn of the Lucky Dragon than at any other place in town. Whole families, from the very old to the very young, descend on the big, round tables for Sunday lunch dim sum and off the main menu specials. They've been stocking up for the week at Hing Fat Hong supermarket next door but there's no doubt that the Cantonese kitchen here is a magnet, too, having stayed on strong form since it opened three years ago. Chinese menus are available but they are for the determined Sinophile. The secret is to ask what the day's specials are. They may try to discourage you, citing tripe with ginger or duck's feet in oyster sauce but

YORKSHIRE'S CHINESE

There are 8,000 ethnic Chinese in Yorkshire and Humberside and 2,000 of them live in the Leeds metropolitan district. The majority came to Britain from Hong Kong's New Territories in the 1950s when their farms were swallowed up by the city's growing industrialisation. Many were Hakka people with their own traditions and dialect but Cantonese remains the established dialect for education and business.

Unlike the Asians arriving in Britain to work in the textile mills, there was little to offer an uneducated Chinese farmer. In those early days, they turned with considerable entrepreneurial energy to laundry work and in the 1960s to catering and the ubiquitous Chinese takeaway. These small family businesses offered Chop Suey, an anglicised Chinese dish taken from the United States where a stir-fry of anything and everything was served to the coolies building the U.S. railroads.

Today there is hardly a town in Britain that does not have at least one Chinese restaurant or take-away. Many have remained stubbornly with the fried rice and chop suey of those early days. Others, especially in Leeds, serve a modified but still recognisable Cantonese cuisine. Cantonese food has its origins in the rich and fertile area of southern China where fruit and vegetables grow abundantly and where the South China sea is a rich source of fish and seafood. The characteristic oyster sauce came originally from the oysters that thrived in the Pearl river. Cantonese food is based on the stir-fry and the wok and peanut oil is the predominant cooking fat. Less well known are the steamed dishes of prawn dumplings or crabmeat with ginger that are characteristic Hakka dishes. The proximity and prosperity of Hong Kong has added diversity to the Cantonese cuisine but the basic style remains the same. Meat is still considered a luxury in a country that has suffered great hardship and famine. Indeed the resourceful Cantonese have earned themselves a reputation for eating everything on four legs except the table.

You won't find, frogs, snakes or shark's lips in Yorkshire, but with perseverance it is possible to eat authentic Chinese food in Leeds restaurants. The staff may try and dissuade you on the grounds that duck's web, chicken feet and stir fried chicken gizzard are not to western tastes but 'specials' could reveal more acceptable dishes of pancakes filled with scallops or sliced duck with Chinese mushrooms. Sunday is the time when families from all over Yorkshire descend on the Chinese supermarkets of Leeds and take lunch in one of four favourite Cantonese restaurants – **Lucky Dragon** (main entry p176), **Sang Sang**, **Jumbo** or **Maxi's** (main entry p178) – enjoying the treats of freshly killed crab, lobster, cuttlefish or carp.

The **Mandarin** (the Whan Hai until the imperturbable Mr Wong's retirement) is the city's Peking restaurant, a cooking style dominated by vegetables rather than meat with flavourings of rice wine, soy sauce and sesame oil. The upstairs room has not aged well and the Peking Imperial hors d'oeuvres and fish 'squirrel' style sound better than they taste but with 24 hours notice they will still lay on a Mongolian feast or you can simply turn up on the day for tasty Manchurian lamb. Of course, the most famous dish of all is the original Peking duck, its crisp skin and tender meat dressed with spring onions and sweet bean paste, wrapped up in a thin pancake, a recipe virtually unchanged since the Ming emperors brought their court to Beijing in the 15th century .

they could just as easily have exquisite little pancakes filled with scallops or sliced duck. Even if you don't have the tenacity to eat what the Chinese families are eating, there is more than enough to choose from on the exhaustive English menu.

LEEDS

6 Bingley Street, Westport Centre, Leeds, W. Yorks
☎ *0113 244 0552*
Open: Mon-Sun 12 noon-midnight

Maxi's   Chinese

People blink the first time they see Maxi's, a vivid red and green pagoda with golden dragons and lions rampant on Yorkshire bungalow ranch style. Was this passed by the planning committee? Still, set on a particularly rootless spot off the inner ring road amid the fire station, the dog pound, a casino and a Kwik-Fit, we are not in a fragile conservation area. Through the brass embossed doors for a warehouse of Chinese baroque and gaudy reliefs. In the middle, a raised pavilion (with Sky TV) for that special family or business gathering. All this magnificent Hong Kong excess was nervelessly assembled at the height of recession by a consortium of Chinese businessmen. Maxi's seats 100 and has as many main courses but after all the razzmatazz it is still Leeds Cantonese. Blindfolded, you could be at the Lucky Dragon or Sang Sang. Nothing wrong with that. The spicier ends of satay and salt and pepper squid are lip-smacking examples of the genre; the hot plates sizzle and spit; the infinite supplies of crispy ducks are reliably halved, quartered, sauced and pancaked. Dim sum and crab and prawn starters are as tasty as ever and at weekend nights when the great room is full and flying it could be Kowloon not Kirkstall Road. Connoisseurs of the stroppy Chinese waiter, feared locally to be a dying breed, can strike lucky with a couple here. But where is the chef to put his own personal stamp on a Cantonese menu or even surprise items on a blackboard?

LEEDS

42/44 The Calls, Leeds, W. Yorks
☎ *0113 244 4242*
Open: Mon-Fri 12 noon - 2pm & Mon-Sat 7pm-9.30pm

Pool Court at 42   Restaurant

It won't take long for the new Pool Court to be place for executives and ladies who lunch. The colours are black, grey, and white; the shapes are oval and 30s ocean liner. It feels cool and classy. No lounge, no bar but an exclusivity reinforced by just ten tables in one room and a menu that rolls out foie gras, caviar, oysters and truffle oil. After 28 famous years at Pool in Wharfedale culminating in a Michelin, Michael Gill suddenly closed and in November 1994 took over Brasserie Forty Four and this new venture next door. While Pool's chef David Watson headed for Halifax and the **Design House**, the encumbent Jeff Baker was given two restaurants to feed from one kitchen. The Michelin inspectors have been told to stay away for a year until the perfectionist Gill is ready to have his new creation judged. Let them in. The £26.50 three course menu is worth showing off (as doubtless is £37.50 for seven courses). The minestrone of scallops and prawns with pesto was a rewarding invention; the asparagus with wild mushroom and truffle dressing a concentrated hit. A whole roast partridge, exactly timed, had a tingling thyme jus. An exemplary duck breast was raised further by a rich tapenade of olive, anchovy and shredded duck leg enclosed in a miniature pastry case. Vegetables were scarce beyond a well dressed salad and creamy mashed potato. The puddings of panna cotta (baked cream) with macerated blueberries and 'exotic' fruits with sabayon (zabaglione) were finely balanced, excepting the unseasonal strawberry. Quality touches around the edges with amuse geules, honey and sunflower bread, speciality French butter, melting chocolates. Service comes from the Pool Court team, headed by Steve Ridalgh with an easy professionalism.

LEEDS

186 Roundhay Road,
Leeds, W. Yorks
☎ *0113 274 80411*
Open: Mon-Thur 11am-
2.30pm & 5pm-10.30pm
Fri 5pm-11pm
Sat 4pm-11pm
Sun 4pm-10.30pm

Raja's Tandoor · Indian

Bikram Pal Singh has been on an amazing cook's tour since stuffing his first paratha at grandmother's knee in the Indian Punjab. He arrived in England in 1970 and worked in Leeds' original Indian, the Ashoka in Merrion Street. He owned a greasy spoon café in Leeds market, and then managed the Mandalay in its high flying prime. But he and his long-standing chef Harban Singh always hankered after something less pretentious without compromising the food. Raja's is it, the outstanding Indian from the cluster on Roundhay Road. It's clean as a whistle and the open plan kitchen houses a proper clay tandoor. Five inches thick and insulated with sand, it never goes out. The nan, the mixed tandoori, the garlic lamb with fresh coriander show off Raja's at its best. With nothing costing more than a fiver, the road from Mandalay has been worth it for everyone.

LEEDS

115 Otley Road, Leeds,
W. Yorks.
☎ *0113 275 5017*
Mon-Thur 12 noon-2pm
& 6pm-11pm
Fri & Sat 12 noon-2pm &
6pm-11pm

Salvo's · Italian

They have been queuing outside for 20 years now and no one ever seems to mind. This tiny Italian is a Headingley institution. Excellent pizza, decent pasta, whopping portions, square deal prices and an upbeat atmosphere have been the unfailing ingredients since Salvatore Dammone opened up in 1975 after owning restaurants in Salerno and Baronissi. He ran Salvo's with dignity and charm amid the hullabaloo, complemented by his two sons, the ebullient Gianfranco front of house and Geppino in the kitchen. Salvatore died of a heart attack on Boxing Day 1993. His restaurant never rests on its laurels. They redecorate. They keep changing and expanding the 'trading-up' section of the menu, notably with daily fish deliveries from Grimsby. The delivery service has gone as has the city centre restaurant but now it's Gianfranco's jazz club and there's a thriving Sunday night supper club of five course meals based on regional and national cuisines. Salvo's house style is not stamped with any heavy Italian regional authenticity. They call it 'eclectic with a Mediterranean accent'. It's as generous as ever.

LEEDS

The Basement, Quebec
House, Quebec Street,
Leeds
☎ *0113 244 0108*
Mon-Fri 12 noon-2.30pm
& 6pm-10.30pm
Sat 6pm-11pm

Sous le Nez en Ville · Bistro

Relocating from Ilkley and adding 'en Ville' to the name proved a good move for Sous le Nez – and for the Leeds business district. Despite the disadvantages of a characterless cellar dining room, it quickly won plaudits and still justifies them. The bar serves good tapas (six varieties for £6 is prime value) and light meals. The dining room proper has starters of chorizo with lentils and bacon, salmon and sorrel terrine basking in a rich shellfish sauce. Rack of lamb, pork fillet, char grilled steaks all go down well, usually with a modern twist. There is always plenty of fish on the changing blackboard menu as well as some creative vegetarian dishes. Any wine buff will confirm that Sous le Nez (Under the Nose) lives up to its name with a smart, interesting and squarely priced cellar.

LEEDS

Belgrave Hall, Belgrave
Street, Leeds, W. Yorks
☎ *0113 245 3345*
Open: Mon-Fri 12 noon-
2pm & 6pm-11pm Sat
6pm-11pm

Teppanyaki · Japanese

Down the basement steps into a slightly surreal creation of black lacquer and perspex waterworks. Not quite the tatami matting and paper screens of a James Bond film but not bad for Belgrave Street. Madame Butterfly smiles sweetly with the menu as you grimly digest the cost of getting up those steps again. Then, scrubbed up and white gowned you are led into a stainless steel theatre. From another entrance, in comes cook. His white headband with red blob has awful kamikaze overtones. Try to think more martial arts instead. His trolley could launch the Royal Armoury, replete with shining choppers and dangerous looking knives, bottles of brandy and the contents of his fridge. It may look authentic but these chefs are actually Thai, Filipino or Vietnamese. Apparently, Japanese chefs are too expensive. A pristine wooden tray containing the raw ingredients for fried rice is presented to the customer in reverential silence. A nod of approval and the performance can begin: first, a little oil on the long steel hotplate and then the garlic, shoved and worried by two wallpaper scrapers. Onions come next, fried in the centre of the hotplate and then skidded off to a distant and cooler corner to await an encore. The rice is reheated and the trio of eggs thrown high into the air, caught, cracked and deftly fried all with one hand. Any juvenile girl marching band leader would have sniggered as Bruce Lee broke one of the yolks. Having carefully fried the other two to perfection, he stabbed them through the yolk and mixed them into the rice. The peppermill was thrown skywards, retrieved for a drum roll on the hotplate and only then was it allowed to season the rice. An innocent chicken dish involved sending brandy fuelled flames three feet high. At last, the extraneous scraps of food were shoved down a hole with a final flourish and he was gone. Not before time. Jugglers can wear thin. Remember the fried rice and flamed chicken? They were surprisingly good as were the tempura (vegetables fried in a light batter) and sashimi (slices of raw fish served with spiced soy sauce) which actually came on a plate. If Bond-san also has sake or Japanese lager, then he should contrive to be on expenses or someone else's guest. It's that expensive. Of course, Japanese cuisine is welcome back in Leeds and it's taken a chain from Birmingham and Manchester to do it but, hopefully, there'll soon be less swordplay and greater effort to make Japanese food accessible to more than the target business crowd.

LIVERSEDGE

64 Leeds Road, Liversedge, W. Yorks
☎ *01924 404911*
Mon-Sat 7pm-9.30pm
Lunch: Tue-Fri 12 noon-1.45pm

Lillibets   Restaurant

It is a measure of improved standards that Lillibets, once a top ten Yorkshire restaurant, now feels to be living on borrowed time. This Heavy Woollen stronghold caters stoutly enough for lonely salesmen on textile expense accounts with its duck à la this and its steak à la that. It still gives Liversedge her special night out with its titbits and its cream and brandy sauces. But all this ragging and ruching, pastel prints, pelmets and limed oak in a Victorian villa. . . you can't dress up a burly mill owner to look like a bridesmaid. It's not fair on either. These rooms scream for somebody's personal touch to deliver us from the show-home catalogue. The food brings comparative relief. Carrot and orange soup with coriander was a winner; spinach and mascarpone dumplings an honourable defeat. The cod with parsley crust lifted with a fine curried Hollandaise. A sickly sweet sauce could not deny that the calf's livers were perfectly cooked. Good hearted if galumphing service matched the vegetables. Puddings were mostly gluttonous combinations of toffee, cream, meringue and chocolate but the prices are pushing their luck given the competition just up the A62 in Leeds.

LOW LAITHE

Low Laithe,
Nr. Harrogate, N. Yorks
☎ *01423 780837*
Open: Tue-Sat 6.30pm-11pm

Dusty Miller   Restaurant

During the 1970s when British restaurants took the first tentative steps away from haute cuisine at one end of the spectrum and Berni Inns at the other, a little restaurant called The Kitchen set up in Leeds serving omelettes, proper soups and cakes. It was owned and run by the late lamented broadcaster and food writer Michael Smith. Behind the scenes was a young man, fresh out of catering college, called Graham Dennison. He went on to launch **Millers** of Harrogate (now in the capable hands of Simon Gueller) and ten years running the Dusty Miller and a busy outside catering business have given him experience which is fully reflected in a restaurant of exacting standards. Elizabeth Dennison, glowing fires, polished oak and a touch of brass and copper all combine for a warm welcome. The menu operates in three parts: à la carte, the Proprietor's menu and there's the really bright idea of a cheapish one course late dinner served after 9.30pm. Elsewhere, much pricier. Like £30 excluding wine. Starters, while generous and often stunning, are doubly stunning at around £9. Dennison has taken to heart Michael Smith's lesson to use only the very best ingredients. A plate of hors d'oeuvres was compiled with excellent smoked salmon, rare roast beef and Parma ham. A scallop and lobster tartlet was generously filled, richly sauced and made of the crispest pastry. Nor could the Yorkshire lamb be faulted - boned, sliced and cooked to juicy perfection and served with redcurrant jelly and an expertly reduced sauce. Duck was taken off the bone but its crispy skin was happily presented with a whole baked apple, glistening in a Calvados sauce. Homely sponge puddings are given a light touch. Crème brûlée offered with raspberries and figs - in December - was the only wrong note in a first class meal. The Dennison's also organise a series of gourmet French evenings.

MALTON

14 Newbiggin, Malton,
N. Yorks
☎ *01653 692236*
Open: Mon-Sun 12 noon-
2pm & 7pm-9pm Closed
Sunday lunch

Blue Ball   Pub

What does the post-modern ploughman have for his pub lunch in Malton? Bruschetta with marinated mushrooms and grilled pepperoni or crostini with cheese, anchovies and capers, of course. This is what happens if you're Brian Ray and your chef walks out. Brian takes over the kitchen with his daughter Fleur, applies imagination and progressively knocks spots off the local opposition. The stained glass, lace and Victoriana of the upstairs wine bar may yet be too dainty for the burghers of Malton but they can take more traditional relief in the warren of head-banging bar rooms with cullen skink (smoked haddock and potato soup), kidneys in Madeira sauce, whole poached black puddings with French mustard, fidget pie and stove chicken. The cooking can be soundly recommended even if the stir-fry vegetables served in Chinese bowls with chopsticks had bathed rather than showered in soy sauce. The two puddings change regularly, hopefully averting the awkward dilemma of one lunchtime when the choice consisted of chocolate or chocolate.

MASHAM

7 Silver Street, Masham
☎ *01765 689000*
Open: Fri-Sun 12 noon-
2pm Tue-Sun 7pm-9pm

Floodlite Restaurant   Restaurant

At this end of Wensleydale high quality dining rooms have been like the proverbial bus: nothing for ages then two come along at once. One destination is the first rate **Blue Lion** at East Witton. This one, the Floodlite is expertly driven and conducted by Charles and Christine Flood. Any advance fears that its title means glaring neon are quickly submerged by the pink walls, gilt mirrors and floral watercolours in a prim afternoon tea setting. The à la carte offers wild red deer, wild boar, steak, lamb, chicken and fish - and correspondingly little for vegetarians - but the best value is the set menu at £10.95 where there are well balanced choices at each course. Sardines grilled to a crisp came with ginger and garlic and a salad lightly dressed in a soy sauce. There's lamb's liver, bacon and rich onion gravy for traditionalists; pork tenderloin with minced mushrooms and Hollandaise sauce for richer appetites. Turned carrots and potatoes with courgettes and mangetout kept their crunch and brightness without being raw. Pace yourself for the excellent puddings. A light banana mousse came surfing in on a butterscotch sauce while the blackberry and apple bread and butter pudding floated on a rich fruit purée. Balance and substance are the watchwords throughout.

MENSTON

Acacia House, Burley Road, Menston, W. Yorks
☎ *01943 873688*
Open : Mon-Sat 6pm-10pm

La Rochelle   Bistro

Chef/Proprietors Martin Spalding and Steven Kendell are becoming promiscuous. They can't settle down with one Yorkshire restaurant when there are new ones to be conquered. They've worked their way through the **Box Tree**, Digby's, Maxwell Plum and **Sous le Nez**; they co-own **Paris** (due to relocate to Rodley's Stanhope Arms) and **Leodis**, keeping them in the food guides to which they have become accustomed. Now they've conquered La Rochelle. Not an obvious beauty, this millstone mansion on the Menston roundabout, severely sand-blasted and draped in fairy lights but with two chefs from the Paris/Leodis stable, both food and service has sharpened up no end. One blackboard is exclusively devoted to fish (that Spalding and Kendell touch again). Another has a three course selection pegged at £11.95. The à la carte menu has a dozen choices just for starters. Vegetarians are considered here, but not elsewhere. A roast pepper, wild mushroom and blue cheese tart was no predictable quiche but a sizzling puff-pastry base, a touch soggy on the bottom but with all flavours intact. Seafood tempura, in batter that was more sumo than geisha, typified the generous spirited nature of the food, stuffed with salmon, squid and jumbo prawns. Pigeon breast with bubble and squeak was not pink but ruddy perfection. Poached halibut had been timed to lose its translucence but no more. Moist and delicate and teamed with smoked salmon and a cream and herb sauce, this was exhibition class again. The mound of fresh crab was generous but unnecessary. Except for a slip up with the carrots – virtually raw – the bouquetiere of six different vegetables was well cooked, well seasoned and well herbed. Four hits out of four dishes. Meanwhile, oil filled lamps burn on red damask table cloths. The high ceiling is brought down with a coat of dark burgundy. There are bentwood chairs, wood floorboards, fine marble fireplaces and a hand painted mural that improves with the wine. It dares to be romantic in these cool, self-conscious days. Pudding took two interesting turns. Tangerine terrine set segments in glistening aspic, a sharp counter for the sweet passion fruit sorbet alongside. But even more remarkable was the rosewater ice cream. Scientists say that the smell of food is more significant than the taste and since rosewater turns up so frequently in cosmetics but so rarely in food, there was the uncanny experience of eating your body lotion from a brandy snap basket. It was delicious.

MOULTON

Moulton, N. Yorks
☎ *01325 377289*
Open: Mon-Sat 12 noon-2pm & 6.45pm-10.15pm

The Black Bull   Restaurant/Pub

Three and a half restaurants and a bar rather than vice versa. There are bar snacks too, doubtless splendid, but that would be missing the point for the first time visitor. The Bull is three and a half restaurants' worth of staunch English food. Roast Yorkshire grouse with game chips and bread sauce? Oysters in ice on a silver platter? The Bull does them properly. The Bull is dependable, Conservative with a big and little 'c' and a hardy perennial of all the best guides. The clientele not only dress and drawl as if they own

North Yorkshire, some of them actually do. Their London club is faithfully reproduced in the deeply polished wood panels of the seafood rooms (evening only, no booking), marble tables and a prize salmon in a glass case above the slate-topped bar. Mussels, crab, lobster, oyster, Dover sole? Yes, sir. Trendy fish import? No thanks. African sundowners are conjured up by the Conservatory and its colonial railway coats of arms from when the Empire ran on time. Best is the heraldic hippo rampant, crest of the Lagos Town Council. If Lord Lucan were to surface in a Yorkshire restaurant it would be here. A luscious grapevine sprawls across the glass roof. Service is loyal family retainer style. Finally, nursery train set days come true in the 1932 Brighton Belle dining car. Pullmans now standing in a pub car park may qualify as being naff in 1995 but with authentic lace curtains, period lamps and starched table cloths, the Bull wins the benefit of the doubt. Above all, for the excellence of its food. The ingredients and dishes on the carte are as timeless as tweed and cavalry twill: salmon, scallops, sirloin, Chateaubriand, rack of lamb, seasonal game and English vegetables, but there's absolutely nothing fusty about the cooking, which is classic. Main courses are priced around £13-£16 so the three course prix fixé lunchtime menu is compelling value at £13.75 and a little more risqué. Here are starters of avocado, pickled herring, sour cream and chives or a warm bratwurst, red onion and potato salad; main courses of steamed sea trout with Hollandaise sauce or fried chicken breast with mushrooms and pasta in a tarragon cream sauce. Broccoli, cauliflower and green beans were happy reminders that cooking can benefit vegetables and they don't have to be raw. A soft apple mousse came in a crisp tuile basket. A flawless coeur à la crème was served with a compote of berries and cherry plums from the tree at the back gate. English food at its best.

NORTHALLERTON

Hook House Farm,
Kirkby Fleetham,
Northallerton, N. Yorks
☎ *01609 748223*
Open: Thur-Sun 10.30am-
6.30pm
(Closed January-Easter)

Farmhouse Kitchen

No one's ever made a fuss in the food guides over Farmhouse Kitchen so it's remained one of the North's best kept secrets. Don't come here looking for black pasta or bruschetta. Yvonne Peirson's farmhouse conversion just off the A1 is defiantly untrendy. You could call it plain English food but when the local ingredients and their handling are of this calibre then it should be recognised at a higher level. Here is a no nonsense roast sirloin with all the trimmings, a rabbit casserole with dumplings, a cod and prawn crumble, set up by a parsnip and apple soup or a hot mackerel pot. There is home reared lamb and all dishes come with three or four freshly cooked vegetables, probably from the Peirsons' own organic kitchen garden. For pudding there's a choice of home made fruit cake with Shepherd's Purse cheese or pavlova or banoffee pie or mango cream or chocolate cake or carrot cake or . . . The bread is proved on a restored Yorkshire range. Yorkshire stone flags, rag rugs and old oak furniture complete the farmhouse scene. Yvonne Peirson comes from a long line of highly capable cooks. Her mother was a baker and her grandmother a cook in service at nearby Scruton Hall. Yvonne stages regular gourmet evenings around such themes as French Country Classics, Sea and Surf and The Best of British. The restaurant itself is open all day, expands into a conservatory and is splendid value. On summer afternoons, you can sit dreamily in the garden, surrounded by green fields and the Peirsons' sheep, until RAF Leeming's low flying Tornadoes suddenly swoop by to remind you which age you're really living in.

OTLEY

11-13 Crossgate, Otley,
W. Yorks
☎ *01943 464351*
Open: Tue-Fri 11am-3pm
Sat 11am-4 pm
Sun 12 noon-5 pm
Thur-Sat 6.30pm-9.30pm

Curlew Café   Semi Vegetarian Restaurant

On three nights of the week, this satisfying little café transforms itself into a modestly priced restaurant. Vegetable and nut terrine, feta cheese salad and aubergine paté are offered as starters. Main courses are represented by stuffed peppers, a walnut, celery and Stilton pie, a chicken and asparagus filo and fish of the day. There's no licence and no corkage if you bring your own bottle. Daytime is more strictly vegetarian with regular soups, pastas, filled jacket potatoes and sandwiches. A gratin or a vegetable curry might be the blackboard specials.

PICKHILL

Pickhill, Nr Thirsk
☎ *01845 567391*
Open: Mon-Sun 12 noon-
2pm & 6pm-10pm

Nag's Head   Pub

Look beyond ye olde beams, ye yards of ale and ye regimental tie collection. Look beyond the deep fried brie and other such typical pub grub fare to check out noteworthy seasonal offerings: rod caught wild salmon, casserole of wild rabbit, fresh herring grilled to crisp perfection with a well matched mustard sauce. Cosy enough village pub/restaurant with stone flagged floors and log fire.

PUDSEY

Bradford Road, Pudsey,
W. Yorks
☎ *01274 668818*
Mon-Thur 6pm-11.30pm
Fri & Sat 6pm-midnight
Sun 12.30pm-11.30pm

27 Westgate, Shipley,
W. Yorks
☎ *01274 594660*
Mon-Thur 6pm-midnight
Fri & Sat 6pm-1am
Sun 6pm-midnight

Unit 4, Unicorn House,
Devonshire Place,
Keighley Road, Skipton,
N. Yorks
☎ *01756 790807*
Mon-Sat 6pm-midnight
Sun 6pm-11pm

Aberford Road, Garforth,
Leeds, W. Yorks
☎ *0113 287 6606*
Open: Mon-Thur 6pm-
11.30pm &
Fri-Sun 6pm-11.30pm

Aagrah   Indian

Mohammed Sabir, Kashmiri restaurant owner, is untroubled by false modesty. Asked by this guide to recommend restaurants other than his Aagrah in Pudsey, he thought carefully and came up with the Aagrah in Shipley and the Aagrah in Skipton. Asked the average price of a meal with half a bottle of wine, coffee, VAT and service, he coolly replied £10. That's pushing it but Mohammed knows how to bang the drum, listing all his awards down to the Heartbeat award for his polyunsaturated fats to the commendation from the Bradford Vegetarian Society. Ingredients? Fresh every day from the market. Wholemeal flours only? Tell the waiter with your order. Low fat milk instead of cream, a no smoking area, non-alcoholic lager? The Aagrah turns them all on. Those Kashmiri specialities? 'Carefully compiled using traditional ingredients known only to my family members', observes Mohammed. Well, the dish of Kashmiri vegetables that includes bananas and lychees is certainly original. Aagrah offers not so much a menu as a compendium of sub-continental cookery. Want Balti King prawns just like they have in Chittagong? Got 'em. Want your kebabs as preferred by the Marajans? Top left hand corner of the menu. Want a whole leg of lamb marinated in vinegar, yoghurt, garam masala, bay leaves, fresh ginger and garlic for approximately six hours and then oven baked? A 50% deposit laid down 48 hours in advance and it's yours for £25. The Aagrah has been at or near the top of the pile for a decade. All the effort pays off and it has a consistent word of mouth going for it. Book to be safe. The Pudsey branch is an unmissable white roadhouse with red neon that could have been airlifted from the outskirts of any American city. Interior charm is embodied by bell-encrusted chairs and the complimentary carnation touch. Shipley, the original branch, Skipton and Garforth, the latest, do takeaways as well. The indefatigable Sabir's also offer outside catering.

RIPON

Minster Road, Ripon,
N. Yorks
☎ *01765 603518*

The Old Deanery   Restaurant

Ripon is hard up for decent restaurants but this is one to watch. Eat well without breaking the bank in a lovely old manor house with log fires, oak panelling, deep armchairs and a view of the minster from every window. There are imaginative lighter items at the bar and excellent value fixed

Open: Tue-Fri 12 noon-
2pm & 7pm-9pm
Sat 7pm-10pm
Sun 12 noon-2pm

meals in the elegant dining room. At lunch come grated rösti potatoes with bacon and shallots, mussels in tomato, onion and garlic with black olive sauce, creamy scrambled egg and salmon croissants filled with Wensleydale cheese and grilled steak. Evenings step up a gear in price, formality and main course ambition, exemplified by chicken stuffed with lobster. Prime meat in the shape of venison, beef, lamb, veal and duck is highly regarded here. A warm welcome and attentive service underline a gracious experience.

RODLEY

Oaklands, Rodley Lane,
Nr. Leeds, W. Yorks
☎ *0113 256 9283*
Open: Mon-Sun 12 noon-
2 pm & 6.30pm-11.30pm
Closed Sat lunch

Olive Tree   Greek

George and Vasoulla Psarias briefly became media stars after their appearance on the BBC's Food & Drink programme where they were filmed entertainingly and argumentatively preparing a meal for the leaders of the Greek Orthodox Church in London. They were well chosen. Their Victorian house on the Leeds/Bradford ring road is home to some of the best Greek-Cypriot cooking anywhere and undoubtedly the best in the region. George was born on Paphos. Vassoulla's family had restaurants in Manchester. They married and opened the Olive Tree in 1981. Head chef Andreas Iacovou is also Greek Cypriot but this is a broad not orthodox cuisine, pulling in fringe Mediterranean influences from Turkey, Lebanon and North Africa as well as Greece and Cyprus. Thus, the mixed starters have the time honoured taramasalata, tsatsiki, hummus, meat balls and stuffed vine leaves but also the aubergine and tahini of melintzanoslata and the lightest of prawn filled pastries. Don't overlook the squid or the kleftiko or the familiar lamb, pork and kebab dishes because George's charcoal grill delivers all of them in optimum form. It also does wonders for chicken with oregano and, more elaborately, veal sofrito, with garlic, parsley, white wine and butter. There's often something ambitious and different on the blackboard or for a solid banker settle for a meze, a three course mixture chosen for you. Vegetarians are well catered for with dolmades, tyropitakia (feta cheese pastries with mint) and spanakopitta (an oven baked dish of spinach, cheese and spring onion with layers of filo pastry). Desserts are dripping sweet confections. Kataifi is shredded pastry filled with almonds, cinnamon and the wonderful flavour of rosewater. The Olive Tree special baklava is filo pastry filled with sultanas soaked in orange juice, orange zest and cinnamon. Greek coffee is considerately offered sweet, medium sweet or sugar free. Tuesday's are bouzouki evenings with George Kontargyries on the balalaika and dancing from 9.30pm. Thankfully, no plate smashing but a little Rodley retsina will soon have Shirley Valentine dreaming fondly of the blue Aegean. The Olive Tree's numerous accolades include a Best Loo Award and Leeds Health Inspectors' award for 'scrupulous hygiene'.

SAWLEY

Sawley, Ripon, N. Yorks
☎ *01765 620642*
Open: Mon-Sun 12 noon-
2pm Tue-Thur 7pm-
8.30pm Fri & Sat 7pm-
8.45pm

Sawley Arms

This pub serves better than average food if you don't mind eating your lunch with Fred Trueman. A life size portrait of this professional Yorkshireman only slightly quieter than the real thing hangs over the mantelpiece in one of the many snugs off the bar. One room is only just big enough for a fireplace and two winged chairs, the ideal place for a chin wag on a winter's day after a walk around nearby Fountains Abbey. Other aspects are rather prim and over-restored. There are soups, sandwiches, stuffed pancakes and homely puddings at lunchtime and a more elaborate evening menu with excellent attentive service at both.

SAXTON

Headwell Lane, Saxton,
N. Yorks
☎ *01937 557242*
Open: Tue-Sun 12 noon-
2pm & 6.30pm-10pm
Closed Sun dinner

Plough Inn   Pub

A village inn that makes its own focaccia and does it well is worth noting. Beautifully served with tomato, mozzarella and sprigs of rosemary and the Plough becomes a serious contender among those aspirant pubs that are really now dining rooms with bars attached for an aperitif drink. The dining room, sadly, is the major drawback: Artex walls, melamine mats and glutinous amateur art that stretches polite criticism. Very disappointing for a handsome old building in this upmarket village in the Elmet flatlands between Tadcaster and Sherburn. Still, there are old fashioned virtues in friendly service, keen prices and big, warm helpings of food generally strong enough to blot out the characterless surroundings. Shallot and goat's cheese tart and a weighty seafood parcel completed a flying start. Main courses lost a little ground as salmon with ginger and sesame copped out with the fish too dry and the sesame too spare. Nor did the venison need the help of a misconceived chicken mousse but the roast pigeon with port and mushrooms was masterly. Sauces were rich and generously herbed and a splendid bowl of vegetables included lovely baby marrows. The crème brûlée would have been at home in many more sophisticated joints. A choice of dessert wines comprising 'one that comes in a small glass or one that comes in a tall glass' would have travelled less well but was so disarmingly delivered that it rounded off a satisfying meal perfectly.

SCARBOROUGH

14 Belgrave Crescent,
Scarborough, N. Yorks
☎ *01723 367841*
Open: Mon-Sun 7pm-
9.30pm Closed Tue

Holly Tree   Restaurant

The schizophrenia of modern Scarborough is amply summed up by the fate of the Grand with its magnificent exterior and tatty interior. Once the biggest hotel in Europe, atop the Queen of all Resorts, it is now buttressed by Pleasureland, owned by Butlin's and more likely to set up a cheap handbag sale than a fresh crab sandwich. Tom Laughton's old Royal is more agreeably time warped but has no gourmet appeal. However fine the Georgian terraces still look in a certain light, there's nothing of real culinary interest going on at North or South Bay. The Lanterna restaurant has cropped up in a few guides down the years with familiar Italian dishes but the Holly Tree should succeed as the best rated restaurant. It's beyond the station in what would be a backwater Victorian square but for the loud theme pub on the corner. Tim and Sue Boulton diligently search out fresh ingredients for their changing blackboard menu. It's not easy in Scarborough. Witness Tim driving to Leeds for his fish in preference to what the harbour below can provide. Guinea fowl, wild boar, pigeon and game appear regularly and they always offer two vegetarian dishes. Tim cooks sensible food sensibly. Warm salads of pigeon and stir fry prawns with ginger and spring onions tasted fine but were both let down by a bed of iceberg lettuce. The meat dishes were excellent. Roast lamb was cooked to just-pink tenderness, the fat to a crisp. Roast duck, too, had a well crisped skin fending off a rich plum sauce. Roast standards were further upheld by monkfish with a fennel sauce. All were served with a huge dish of simply and accurately cooked vegetables: leeks, courgettes, carrots, broccoli, cauliflower and potatoes. Desserts of brandy snap fruit baskets, profiteroles and bread and butter pudding had the Scarborough dated feel but the English cheeses were in proper condition. There's an honourable struggle going on here. The rooms could honestly do with a face-lift and it was disturbingly easy to book a table early on a Saturday evening. Maybe Scarborough does not want the Holly Tree but it certainly needs it.

SHEFFIELD

23 Alma Street, Sheffield,
S. Yorks
☎ *0114 272 8195*
Open: Mon-Sat 12 noon-
3pm & 5.30pm-11pm
Sun 12 noon-3pm & 7pm-
11pm

Fat Cat   Pub

A back street pub that devotes half of its menu to vegetarian dishes is a rarity but the Fat Cat is an independent sort of place. David Wickett, polytechnic lecturer turned licensee, has moulded the sort of bar he wanted to drink in: no music, no games machines and, in one particular bar, no-smoking. Out at the back, Patrick Morton brews the real ales for which the Cat is primarily renowned and wins its laurels in the ale guides. Alison Gosling wins praise here for her filling stews and pies and lentil soup or spinach and red beans with pasta. Hearty puddings of gooseberry crumble or apple pie are served with cream or custard. Handily positioned for visitors to the nearby Kelham Island Industrial Museum.

SHEFFIELD

84 Burncross Road,
Chapeltown, Sheffield,
S. Yorks
☎ *0114 246 9004*
Open: Tue-Sat 7pm-9pm

Greenhead House   Restaurant

On arrival at this sturdy detached house in Chapeltown, guests are steered into a small, almost domestic lounge with a lot of Dralon. The door is closed. Neither noise, smell or atmosphere penetrates. It is like waiting to go into an interview. The all inclusive menu leaves no room for manoeuvre. You will pay £28.50 and you will receive nibbles, a four course dinner, a cheese offering and petit fours. It is a full evening and ultimately good value, once forewarned that two quick courses are not an option. The poised (and no smoking) dining room reveals itself to be a superior space to the waiting room. For all the courses, the menu comes down to a sensibly brief selection that changes monthly. A winter's night produced a rich dish of mussels on a bed of spinach in a Roquefort sauce. Next came a lovely sweet parsnip soup. Fillet steak was cooked to perfection. Pudding was an imaginative chocolate and chestnut mille feuille. Finally, there were real farmhouse cheeses: Shropshire Blue, a soft and salty Northumbrian Coquetdale, rarely seen in these parts, and David Reed's reliable Swaledale. Throughout, classy presentation reinforced the all-round assurance of the cooking and the combinations. Greenhead House takes its food seriously but not pompously and its attention to the main purpose made it the Good Food Guide's 1994 restaurant of the year in South Yorkshire. The service was genuine and generous with a foil wrapped parcel of petit fours to take away when coffee was declined. A nice touch, now remembered and honoured in return.

SHEFFIELD

Charnwood Hotel,
10 Sharrow Lane,
Sheffield, S. Yorks
☎ *0114 258 9411*
Open: Mon-Sun 7am-
11pm

Henfrey's /Brasserie Leo   Hotel/Brasserie

Jacket and tie are requested by the management in the traditional Henfrey's hotel restaurant that serves an elaborate four course menu for £25. Brasserie Leo, situated at the front of the building, is more relaxed. The tiled floor and starched white cloths are a reasonable stab at an authentic brasserie as are the late finishing hours. The menu length, however, would be ambitious for the Brasserie Lipp let alone the Charnwood Hotel. It takes in fisherman's chowder at the budget end and a top priced fillet steak at £14.50. In between is a considerable range of fish, vegetarian, meat, light bites and puddings even before a comprehensive blackboard menu. There's talent in the kitchen but it's also one of those tiresome places that hasn't woken up to the fact that most people now know what basil tastes like so that when they order a dish of gnocchi with tomato and basil they don't just want to be impressed with the title of the piece they actually want to taste the basil. Someone should tell the portion controller that basil's not that expensive any more.

MADE IN SHEFFIELD

'If it isn't marked Sheffield then it isn't made in Sheffield.'
Roadside hoarding, Sheffield Parkway, 1994

It is reassuring to record that anyone eating at the restaurants on these pages may well be handling cutlery made in Sheffield. For all the ravages of the steel industry, Sheffield is actually making as much cutlery as before the war, albeit with a smaller workforce and fewer firms. Names as synonymous with Sheffield as Arthur Price now import from Korea; stainless steel floods in from Taiwan and butt-welded knives arrive from Japan but for silver plate and sterling silver, Sheffield still rules the world.

The first cutlers set up in the 12th century. Around the local rivers were the pre-requisites of early steel: ironstone, charcoal, grindstones and water power. Chaucer refers to a Sheffield knife in the Canterbury Tales and by 1624 the Company of Cutlers in Hallamshire were incorporated. Boulsover's discovery in 1743 of Old Sheffield Plate by fusing silver onto copper to achieve the effect of sterling silver was crucial until eventually overtaken by electro-plating.

The industry was also notorious in successive Victorian Royal Commissions for glaring abuses in child labour (six year old girl workers were common), wretched pay and grinder's asthma, one of the worst of killer industrial diseases, caused by flying metal dust. The Dickensian conditions do not have to be imagined. They still exist in the Arundel Street area courtyard workshops of the last 'Little Mesters', hafting, sharpening, polishing, buffing and hardening, not children now but freelance workers, sometimes in their 70s. Nearby, in Church Street is another world. The top echelons of the industry are embodied in the **Cutlers Hall**, the Master Cutlers and their annual Feast which has run for more than 360 years and for some is the most sought after social ticket of the Yorkshire year.

MPs, ambassadors, senior members of the armed forces and captains of industry take up the first 150 seats. The rest are at the invitation of the annually elected Master Cutler, who takes a year off for his duties, is immortalised in a portrait and whose company will foot the catering bill. The 500 guests in white tie and tails (and about 30 women) are greeted by trumpet fanfares and a guard of honour as they climb the richly carpeted sweeping staircase to the galleried Great Hall, the biggest livery hall in the north of England, edged with stout columns of grey marble and dominated by a huge crystal chandelier (another is from the Titanic's sister ship). A portrait of Queen Victoria looks down on guest speakers like Winston Churchill, Lloyd George, Margaret Thatcher and the Princess Royal. Shimmering in the candlelight is the best show of silver the livery company can muster. The Cutlers have a piece of silver for every year since 1773, including the Norfolk Knife, made for the 1851 Great Exhibition, standing two feet high and brandishing 75 blades; a 1974 silver dish by **David Mellor** to celebrate the bi-centenary of the Sheffield Assay Office; and a 1994 silver model of Sheffield's supertram. Elsewhere in the Hall, the Mistress Cutler is hosting dinner for the wives of the Freemen. Other feasts are the Installation Feast in October, when the new Master Cutler is installed after a traditional lunch of steak and kidney pie and in July, the less formal Forfeit Feast, an annual dinner dance. They also hold six lunches a year for the city's 1,000 oldest women and 1,000 oldest men. In 1994 the youngest was 84.

Despite all the pomp, today's Cutlers Feasts pale alongside those of the past. The 1906 menu had 10 separate courses that included turbot, quails, sweetbreads with truffle sauce, saddle of mutton, haunch of venison, grouse, pheasant and partridge and as many different wines and spirits. The feast traditionally began with turtle soup made from a live turtle transported from Liverpool and killed on site for the soup to be brought to the top table in the upturned shell. The shell was then polished, inlaid with a silver crest and presented to the Master Cutler. Turtle shells still adorn the walls of the Cutlers Hall. The public rooms are open Mon-Fri 12 noon-2pm to visitors unless there are functions going on. Conducted tours are by appointment at £1.50 a head, five people minimum. The 1832 Hall caters for everything from dinner dances and weddings to accountancy examinations and the awarding of Royal medals.

Yet the greatest silver plate and cutlery collection in Sheffield is not at the Cutlers Hall but at the **City Museum** in Weston Park. Apart from London's Victoria and Albert Museum, it is acknowledged as the world's finest. For more history, the **Traditional Heritage Museum** reproduces the cutlery office of George Wostenholm, **Shepherd Wheel** at Abbeydale is an authentic 18th century grinding wheel and **Kelham Island Industrial Museum** has a 'working' row of Little Mester workshops. But the real thing is still happening, all the while policed by the Cutlers Company to ensure that the 'Made in Sheffield' mark is not abused by anybody outside Hallamshire.

When King Fahd of Saudi Arabia entertains on his yacht, it is with a £250,000 bespoke 20 place setting with dishes, trays, candelabras, all by Sheffield's **British Silverware**. Their 12 place solid silver setting costs a mere £5,000. **Richardson's**, meanwhile, are Europe's largest kitchen knife manufacturer. The **Egginton Group** have absorbed the old established firms of Wostenholm's and Joseph Rodgers to become specialists in pen and pocket knives. **Hiram Wild**, one of only two forgers left in the city, make cutlery for many of the world's airlines. **Barker and Dixon**, a small family firm celebrating their centenary in 1995, sell traditional decorative pieces from their shop on Glossop Road. David Mellor, a Sheffield born and trained silversmith and outstandingly the doyen of British modern designer cutlers, now operates just over the Derbyshire border in his stunning Hathersage factory (see p134)

To buy Sheffield cutlery the canteens made by British Silverware are at Sheffield's premier jeweller **H.L. Brown**. **Morton's** in West Street and **Don Alexander's** on Ecclesall Road have Sheffield made kitchen knives and reasonably priced stainless steel and silver plated cutlery. **United Cutlers**, of Petre Street, sell 12 place settings in solid silver at £5,060 or in stainless steel for £1,044. They have factory tours, a showroom and a mail order service. **John Osborne**, an old established Sheffield firm, also sell slightly sub-standard or surplus stock from their works in Solly Street. There are serrated kitchen knives, photograph frames and cutlery sets in sterling, silver plate or stainless steel. For real Sheffield bargains visit Hiram Wild, also in Solly Street, where general manager Michael Rodgers will show you the factory and sell sterling silver 'firsts' at £2,000 for a 44 piece set or 'seconds' at £58. No fancy displays here but dusty cardboard boxes and piles of stainless steel seconds to rummage through. You can buy odd pieces and a five place setting. They can't promise to have a full set of seconds but by mixing firsts and seconds you can put together the cheapest set of top quality cutlery in town.

SHEFFIELD

141 West Street, Sheffield,
S. Yorks
☎ *0114 279 6677*
Open: Mon-Fri 12.30pm
& 6.15pm-10.30pm
Sat 6.15pm-11pm

Le Neptune   Fish Restaurant

The West Street area is a great white hope of Sheffield city centre for bookshops and garage cafés, small designer clothes shops and in Le Neptune, a determined attempt to establish a top flight French fish restaurant. It looks good on the outside: Poissons and Coquilles St. Jacques hand painted on a racing green finish. Inside, there's a bright white-tiled Riviera feel but the red plastic chairs and Monet posters are less classy. The real problem was four customers between 20 tables on a payday Thursday evening. Even allowing for the road outside being dug up for the supertram, it must be terribly dispiriting to have a prime site in the centre of one of Britain's biggest cities, win a place in the Good Food Guide and have next to nobody to cook for. 'It will be better when the University gets back', said the waitress. With a starter of foie gras and grape and apple salad at £13.95 and main courses of halibut or fillet steak both touching £16.00, she surely didn't mean the students. 'We get quite a few professors in here', she explained. Good for the professors. To be fair, there are also main course dishes at around £9.00, a 'rapide' prix fixé menu each lunchtime when Sheffield's legal, medical and business community are more available to fill the room and there's 20% off the à la carte between 6pm and 7pm. If Le Neptune needs to compromise on its pricing to win over Sheffield, there's no sign of it compromising on its cooking or its formidably generous servings. An anchovy salad came not only with plenty of well dressed greenery and anchovies but with two large and unadvertised croutons loaded with black olive paste. Red mullet was marinated in citrus juice to a fine edge. Fillet of cod in red wine, herbs and onion string was extraordinary, so rich and intense that any dessert was out of the question. Chef Simon Wild has been criticised as a reactionary for such classically conceived dishes. Actually, there's so much new wave fish cooking about that it was a most welcome surprise, especially done so well. Seafood tagliatelle was less original, with a surfeit of salmon and white fish suggesting a tactical use of leftovers. Puddings are mousses, sorbets and brûlées.

SHEFFIELD

220 Oakbrook Road,
Nether Green,
Sheffield, S. Yorks
☎ *0114 230 4819*
Open: Mon, Thur, Fri, Sat

Rafters   Restaurant

Wayne Bosworth, formerly of the Charnwood Hotel, and his brother Jamie caused quite a stir when they opened up this 40 seater restaurant in 1993, the dog days of eating out in Sheffield. Nether Green was not spoiled for choice and £16 for a three course dinner with a choice of five dishes at each course is not excessive for a respectable quality of cooking. The style is modern without being off the wall: roast parsnips, mushroom and feta cheese served with a basil and butter sauce made an imaginative winter starter. Chicken liver parfait and celery and stilton soup were well, if conservatively, executed. So were the main courses of fish, steak, lamb and chicken. Salmon comes as a medallion, chicken as a supreme, supported typically by sauces of madeira, mustard, red wine and a horseradish jus for the lamb. Vegetarians are promised their own main course dishes on request but when Rafters was put to this test and even notified in advance, the dishes were disappointing. The restaurant takes its name from an upstairs location under the eaves of a corner building, a setting that could benefit from an investment of more modern styling. The sitting out area is awkward and the dried flowers have had their day. Still, the set-up is friendly and at its best the cooking is more than capable.

STADDLEBRIDGE

Staddlebridge, N. Yorks
☎ *01609 882671*
Restaurant: Tue-Sat
7pm-10pm
Bistro: Mon-Sun 12 noon-
2pm & 7pm-10pm

McCoy's — Bistro/Restaurant

McCoy's has been a stalwart of the food and hotel guides since the late 1980s and brothers Tom (in the kitchen), Peter (in the upstairs restaurant) and Eugene McCoy (in the downstairs bistro) continue to serve unfailingly excellent food, seven days a week. The Tontine is set in an old stone coaching inn complex in the crook of the A19 and A172, the tontine referring to the shared subscription behind the original building scheme. Their restaurant and ante-room are generally described as 'eccentric', for their cheerful 30s decor, the escaping springs of the furniture, a coloured parasol, nice old lamps, mirrors, palms and the studiously non-matching crockery. In fact, it's more fun than really eccentric, and infinitely superior to the dead hand of professional interior designers that beset so many posh dining rooms. Don't mistake any casual notes for what has always been a professional and stylish operation. Modern British now best describes the pea and ham soup, the game terrine with pickled vegetables, the fresh crab, the sautéed scallops or the roast grouse. But they venture to more distant shores for ravioli of fresh langoustine with fresh truffle and herbs, artichokes and salt cod purée, foie gras with brioche and grapes in Madeira, boned quail with rösti. Either way, the ingredients taste impeccable, the cooking proves expert and the presentation is unfussy. With puddings like choc o' block Stanley, a chocolate fondant and sponge soaked in Tia Maria and coffee sauce, you might feel like checking in overnight. The menu is constantly changing and updating. Downstairs, soft lights and candles set against the dark wood of the bistro hit just the right tone for a convivial evening. There are variously sized tables, ferns, an enormous fireplace and a matching big blackboard menu that could offer lobster, steaks, oyster, pigeon, polenta or black pudding. It is busy most days and although the bistro claims to be cheaper than the restaurant it's easy to run up a bill to approach the serious prices upstairs. Either way, it's worth saving up for. You can merely admire some restaurants but you can both admire and be fond of McCoy's.

STAITHES

1 High Street, Staithes,
N. Yorks
☎ *01947 840825*
Open: Mon-Sat 1200
noon-2pm & 7pm-9.30pm
Closed Sat lunch
Sun July-Sept 7pm-
9.30pm
Closed mid Jan-mid
March

Endeavour — Restaurant

Amazingly, there are still eating places where a real fisherman will suddenly burst in, wet from the cold North Sea, and slap down a real, legal,wild salmon before the gobsmacked diners. It tends to settle the main course selection. Lisa Chapman's fish restaurant in Staithes is a delight in every respect. Her intimate, wood panelled dining rooms are just right for a fishing village, salty without floundering under seashells and Frank Meadow Sutcliffe. It's friendly, it's more than fairly priced and while there are exemplary meat, vegetarian and dessert dishes, think fish. Lisa cooks supported by Liz Loughran. They cherish the prime local catches which are produced on the table with simplicity and finesse: that unarguably fresh wild salmon, the brown crab, live blue lobster, sea trout and even octopus, routinely thrown out of Dave Hanson's pots before Lisa ordered them to be 'saved' for cooking and serving with a herb and vinaigrette dressing. Dave Hanson is a local fisherman to his roots. His grandfather, the Staithes lifeboat coxswain, died rescuing a drowning boy. His grandmother is the last true wearer of the Staithes bonnet. His father holds a precious North Sea licence for wild salmon heading for the Esk but when he retires the licence is lost. Like all Yorkshire's historic fishing villages, Staithes is not at its best over August Bank Holiday. But on an autumn or winter night when you can feel the sting of the wind round Cow Bar Nab and the dark, little streets are echoing with the footsteps of smugglers and brave sailors of the past, then turn into the Endeavour and burnish the glow at a magical little restaurant in full sympathy with its surroundings.

STOKESLEY

27 High Street,
Stokesley, N. Yorks
☎ *01642 711888*
Open: Mon-Sun 12 noon-
3pm & 7pm-10pm

Chapter's   Bistro/Restaurant

Chapter's restaurant is being progressively swallowed up by its increasingly successful bistro and not always by customer choice. You can think you're booking into the restaurant, arrive to find the back restaurant closed and that you've been booked instead into the bistro at the front of this old brick coaching inn on Stokesley's handsome High Street. The bistro is actually the sensible option in the first place. The restaurant looks starched and impersonal beside the funkier tones of the front rooms with their hotchpotch of old brown tables, mixed school chairs and framed menus from all over the world. A giant blackboard sails off around the globe like the local hero Captain Cook. North Sea bouillabaisse, an impeccable roast turbot with linguine, mussels and shrimp, Milanese salami, a paella Valencia (that lacked the punch Alan Thompson invests in most of his dishes), Indonesian chicken satay, tropical pudding with mango sauce (a sort of South Seas summer pudding) and peach schnapps cheesecake would be entered in the log of a typical voyage of discovery. Keep a weather eye out for odd items like mussels or mango chasing you round the menu. The ingredients are better than average; the cooking and presentation lives up to Chapter's high reputation and the service is guileless. One gripe: now that the restaurant and bistro menus are almost identical (including the prices) how about some vegetables in the bistro? It's not so cheap that they couldn't come inclusive. Apparently, chef will do some if you ask. Perhaps you should, since the kitchen fails to put its usual bravura into the regulation salads that accompany every dish.

THRESHFIELD

Threshfield, Skipton,
N. Yorks
☎ *01756 752441*
Open: Mon-Sat 11am-
3pm & 5.30pm-11pm
Sun 12 noon-2pm &
7pm-10.30pm

Old Hall Inn   Pub

After dodging the packed car parks and singing kettles of Grassington, Threshfield is no more than a petrol pump to most travellers on the road to Upper Wharfedale. But consider the fine looking Old Hall, which challenges the modest standard and ambition of so much Dales pub food with antipasti of roasted red and yellow peppers, marinated mushrooms and onions in a sweet vinegar dressing. Or vegetarian butternut squash, packed with nuts and seeds. Bullseye again. Stouter tastes can confidently take in game casserole, seafood bake, sausage and mash, loin of pork and nursery puddings. You can't miss a mighty Yorkshire range in all its glory but try to turn a blind eye to the repro panelling and dinky stained glass.

WAKEFIELD

Grange Moor,
Nr. Wakefield, W. Yorks
☎ *01924 848385*
Open: Tue-Sun 12 noon-
2pm & 7.30pm-10pm

Kaye Arms   Pub

No passing motorist could possibly suspect that this sprawling roadside pub between Wakefield and Huddersfield holds the most impressive kitchen for miles although plenty of loyal regulars know its secret. That secret is kept further under wraps inside by decor of violently patterned carpet and tourist Yorkshire display plates. But you start realising the quality of what's going on when you see the first food arrive at a neighbouring table. Chef Andrew Quarmby cooks with imagination and real skill. The trio of filo pastry parcels – aubergine and courgette; leeks, goat's cheese and home-made chutney; and spinach and mushroom on a fresh tomato sauce were each ideally executed. A chicken breast, marinated in garlic, white wine, oil and tarragon released a full and intoxicating aroma when its paper cooking parcel was unwrapped at the table. Other notable dishes were pesto, tomato and mozzarella tart; the plate of cured fish and a warm salad of smoked chicken breast with mango. There are plenty more straightforward steaks, lamb chops or gammon and pineapple. The toffee puddings, crumbles and citron tarts went untried but looked up to the standard of all that had gone before. The wine list has the sensationally fair idea of adding a straight £3 to every bottle instead of the usual double mark up. The more expensive the wine, the better the value. In fact, the Kaye Arms is great value all round.

WARLEY

32 Warley Town, Warley, Nr. Halifax, W. Yorks
☎ *01422 831106*
Open: Tue-Sat 7pm-9.30pm
Sun 1200 noon-2.30pm

Maypole Inn — Pub/Restaurant

High marks for effort at the Maypole in the old stone square of Warley. They've bought their Sir Walter Scott books by the yard. They've decorated their fancy candlelit upstairs dining room richly and deeply in contrast to the plainer pub rooms below. They're capable of revealing a misdirected zeal for Austrian folk music backed up by a sound system that works all too well. Nobody could put more effort into a raspberry mille-feuille which was over the top from the first swirl of cream through a thick vanilla sauce to the last cloying feuille. But nobody, regrettably, should expend so much effort in penetrating the tarmac top layer of their crème brûlée only to find raspberry again. Similar repetition saw brie turn up first in an otherwise blameless mushroom soup and then again stuffed in chicken. One expects a certain amount of kitchen clearance in a midweek prix fixé but this was blatant. Careful steering through the main courses of the menu brought soft and succulent calf's liver and a moist, carefully poached salmon. French bread was thankfully crisp and fresh; the vegetables perhaps too fresh in their extreme crunchiness. The tangled ends of the Maypole do properly unravel to display some authentic talent. There's still room for further improvement.

WASS

Wass,
N. Yorks
☎ *01347 868280*
Open: Tue-Sat 12 noon-2pm & 7pm-9.30pm
Sun 12 noon-2pm

Wombwell Arms — Pub

Neither the bland exterior nor the cold porch promise much but the vibes are much better inside: magazines and wine books to browse through, an auctionable malt whisky collection to ponder, unusual smells drifting in from the kitchen. Alan and Lynda Evans are the publican/connoisseurs, an impression smartly borne out by a high kicking orange and ginger dressing for the smoked platter of halibut, salmon, trout and mackerel. Paprika lamb and a leek and Shropshire blue cheese flan were satisfactorily delivered from a full blackboard designed to suit most tastes. More conventionally, desserts were gooey and heavyweight.

WATH IN NIDDERDALE

Harrogate, N. Yorks
☎ *01423 711306*
Open: Restaurant Mon-Sat 7pm-10pm
Sun 12 noon-2.30pm
Bar Mon-Sun 12 noon-2.30pm & 7pm-10pm

Sportsman's Arms — Pub/Restaurant

Cross the little bridge over the Nidd to reach this Sunday lunchtime favourite for all seasons. It doesn't always live up to its long-standing reputation, as the cooking veers uncertainly between modern intentions and homely tradition. Best stick to the local names that have given Nidderdale its culinary reputation: lamb or trout, done simply and generously. The Carter's undoubtedly have firm supporters as the restaurant has been reinstated in the 1995 Good Food Guide. The large dining room with starched napery and fancy flowers is surprisingly proper for a pub . If you can secure a decent table and chair by the log fire, the bar has a better glow.

WEAVERTHORPE

Weaverthorpe,
Malton, N. Yorks
☎ *01944 3273*
Open: Sat, Sun & Bank
Holidays 12 noon-2pm
Mon-Sun 7pm-9.30pm
No food served Tue

Star Inn   Pub

With jugged hare, rabbit pie, pheasant pot roast, pigeon breasts in red wine, wild boar and home made game pie all on the menu, this is not the pub for the anti cruel sports league's annual dinner dance. Vegetarians are, however, catered for with ratatouille and pan haggarty. This is all forthright cooking. Susan Richardson is a strong supporter of local Wolds suppliers and most of her vegetables come from a friend running a market garden. She is also keen on traditional Yorkshire recipes and had Mary Jane's herb pudding featured in the BBC Good Food Magazine. It's an old family recipe handed down from her grandmother, consisting of bread, onion and suet with lots of herbs and served with onion gravy - reminiscent of sage and onion stuffing. The Star has its prawn cocktail and its coq au vin and the dining room would not feature in any style magazines but with two darts teams it hasn't forgotten it's the village pub either.

WETHERBY

Linton, Wetherby,
N. Yorks
☎ *01937 585353*
Open: Mon-Sat 12 noon-
2pm & 6pm-9.30pm

Linton Springs   Brasserie

Linton Springs was once just the Earl of Harewood's local shooting lodge. To the rest of us it looks like a substantial country house with a golf course. As high powered motors scrunch up the gravel, executive trimmings inside indicate a hotel with its sights set clearly on the conference trade. Don't be too put off. The revamped Gun Room offers lunch or dinner at a reasonable price in such evocative surroundings – stag at bay, tartan chair covers, stuffed pheasant – that it slowly dawns that an actual gun room has been expensively worked over to look like a fake one. Further illusions emerged from the kitchen: that separately piled sautéed mushrooms and yellow rice can be called mushroom risotto; that melted butter for the brill was the beurre blanc advertised. Wrong on both counts but both actually tasted rather good. There was more traditional English impotence with the greens but otherwise the menu and blackboard hit their targets with game pies, pot roasts, fresh fish, proper potatoes and old fashioned puddings. Service was smart and friendly and when one waiter spectacularly dropped silver tray, cutlery, cruets, the lot, it became an endearing moment. Under former Linton Springs regimes of pretentious food at unpleasant prices, there would have been a foul smell in the air and the poor lad would have been taken out to be shot. All those with bad memories could give the latest owners a fresh start.

WINTERINGHAM

Winteringham,
Nr. Scunthorpe, S. Humbs
☎ *01724 733096*
Open: Mon-Fri 12 noon-
1.30pm & 7.30pm-9.30pm
Sat 7.30pm-10pm
Closed Mon & Sat lunch

Winteringham Fields   Restaurant

Not many restaurants serve cutlet of goat and win a Michelin star but Winteringham Fields is no ordinary restaurant. If it's possible to win Michelin stars in the remote Western Highlands of Scotland then why not in the no man's land of South Humberside. Swiss born Germain Schwab and his Grimsby born wife Annie have lit up the south bank of the Humber with their extraordinary, perfectionist food. Take their attitude to greens. Their organic garden supplies them with fresh vegetables and herbs all summer and a greenhouse gives 10 different salads, peppers, white aubergines, yellow courgette and melons, grapes, gooseberries and blueberries. Their fish cooking alone has won prizes – most comes from the all-embracing **Jack Smith** on Grimsby Fish Docks. A winter menu had blinis of wild salmon, superb fresh sea bass in a light fish stock and vanilla sauce, cassolette of North Sea fish in tarragon. Game, locally supplied again, is another obvious forte with pigeon breast, pheasant casserole and loin of rabbit baked in pastry with mustard seed sauce. There is a principled and unwavering precision about every dish and component. The service by grave and authoritative young European men is so correct that the whole experience becomes slightly unnerving. If you've ever wanted to shout in church. . . this is high church, however friendly the intent. From the first choice of fresh breads to the last caraway seed accompanying the Munster cheese (one of a memorable trolley of 60 pan-European cheeses in immaculate condition), it is a tour de force, appropriate for the most special of special occasions. The premises are a restored 16th century manor house with a modern stable conversion of bedroom annexes. The appetiser and coffee rooms are all velvety Victoriana; the dining room more starched and gilded. Without going daft on the wine list, dinner for two can approach £100 and the restaurant is regularly filled. Lunch comes vastly cheaper. Still, only the highest of high diners can approach Winteringham Fields, knowing its price and reputation, without some awe. Indeed, nobody would want to be so relaxed as to eat this calibre of food carelessly. It repays full attention.

YARM

104b High Street, Yarm,
N. Yorks
☎ *01642 788558*
Open: Tue-Sat 11.30am-
9.30pm

Chadwick's   Bistro

The cosmopolitan aura given off by terracotta urns, long white aprons and newspapers on poles sits a little incongruously with the Georgian conservatism of Yarm High Street but it's the food that counts and here, at lunchtime, you can count on marinated chicken livers with an onion and leek marmalade, prawns in their shell with tomato chutney, wholemeal sandwiches of brie and gherkins or Parma ham with Jarlsberg. Chutneys and lemonade are made on the premises; the orange juice comes freshly squeezed. Presentation and service are smart informal. Vegetarians are well looked after. The white tablecloths and a longer menu come out for a more formal dinner.

YORK

104 Micklegate, York
☎ *01904 623767*
Open: Mon-Sun 10am-
5pm Fri & Sat 6.30pm-
9pm

Blake Head   Vegetarian Café/Restaurant

'Vegetarian meals which would honour the best hotels in the world', swooned the Yorkshire Post. That's going some but the evening menu is certainly creative, beautifully presented and full of texture and flavour. Blake Head began life as a bookshop and it still is. The dining room is at the back, a conservatory style extension with glass roof, white walls and light ash tables. There's a daytime self service counter with newspapers on sticks. A pianist plays at weekends. The lunchtime menu changes daily. It could be beetroot soup with roll and butter; rice, nuts and herb stuffed peppers or red lentils and cheese stuffed aubergine. All come with a generous helping of four different salads. There are cakes and crumbles for dessert. Freshly squeezed juices include carrot, celery and apple. The evenings have waitress service and a more sophisticated menu. Norimaki-Sushi rolls, shredded spinach and carrot wrapped in sticky rice rolled in seaweed and served with fresh coriander and yoghurt dressing were better than anything the well-travelled man from the Yorkshire Post had eaten in Japan. Main courses include sautéed oyster mushrooms mixed with roasted marinated goat's cheese on a salad with capers, olives, croutons and walnut vinaigrette. For pudding, a crêpe with almond and rum butter cream with apple and cinnamon sauce. Friday nights bring live jazz and a three course meal for only £10. At double the price, Blake Head would still stand out as one of the region's best restaurants.

YORK

Millers Yard, Gillygate,
York
☎ *01904 610676*
Open: Restaurant: Mon-
Sat 10am-4pm (4.30pm in
summer)
Shop: 9am-5.30pm

Gillygate   Vegetarian Restaurant

Like shop (entry p108), like restaurant. Gillygate wholefoods are committed to nutritious food created without meat or the use of artificial flavourings, preservatives or colourings – a co-operative with an enlightened employment policy and extremely tasty food. Start with Chinese stir-fry vegetables, tofu satay or savoury pancakes. Move on to the fennel and tomato gratin, celery and cashew nut quiche or three bean chilli. Round off with hot plum crumble, coconut and raspberry gateau or chocolate dairy cheesecake. Prices are modest even before student discounts. Children are welcome and there are high chairs, changing facilities and even plans for an upstairs playroom.

YORK

Clifton, York
☎ *01904 644744*
Open: Mon-Sat 12 noon-
2.30pm & 6pm-10.30pm
Sun 6pm-10.30pm

Grange Hotel   Brasserie

By definition, a brasserie has a limited menu and liberal hours. The Grange's brasserie has a broad menu and hours as light as a Welsh pub. Never mind. It's only a brisk five minutes from the Minster yet it's off the tourist trail. There may not be much character in the bird prints and bare brick of the basement but the food amply compensates. Between the menu and blackboard, look out for fillets of megrim with basil butter and capers, wild boar sausages with mashed potato, plaice with chives and king prawns and salmon fish cakes in a herb and cream sauce, a fishcake in which, glory be, the salmon has equal billing with the potato. York looks after its vegetarians uncommonly well. As well as dedicated dishes, the main course vegetables are crisply handled.

YORK

19 Grape Lane, York
☎ *01904 636366*
Open: Tue-Sat 12 noon-
2 pm & 7.30pm-10.30pm
Closed Mon

19 Grape Lane   Restaurant

There's no smoking in the Alexanders' perennially popular dining room which is a wise policy because there's barely space to light up let alone exhale. No 19 is intimate in the way sardines would understand the word. It's also warm and friendly and the food - whether the soups, patés or salads that lead at lunch or their inventive way with fish and meat that underpins the more formal prix fixé three course evening menu – shows a steady and dependable touch of class.

YORK

13 Grape Lane, York
☎ *01904 641750*
Open: Mon-Sat 12.30pm-
1.45pm & 6.30pm-
10.30pm

Kites   Restaurant

Don't be deceived by the bare wood floors, the check table cloths, the simply painted brick and the plain upright furniture into thinking that you've stumbled into a 1970s student haunt. This is no throw-back but an up to the minute kitchen with sharp ideas and combinations at every turn. High marks for the mixed crostini of tapenade, aubergine purée and tomato; the honey and sesame dressing on the duck slices and the lamb with lavender. Good old cod is cooked in coconut milk with garlic, tamarind, chillies and fresh lime and orange juice. High marks, too, for a proper commitment to vegetarian dishes with half of the menu meat free. The two fondues feature melted cheddar, white wine and nutmeg on one hand and traditional Gruyère, Emmental and Kirsch on the other. A beautifully perfumed honey and cardamom sauce lifted a mille feuille of strawberry and cream. Doing the simple things well: a lovely green salad and Yorkshire cheeses topping and tailing the meal. It's friendly, small scale, even homely. It would take a hard heart not to have a soft spot for Kite's. With three flights of steep stairs, take care of that heart on the way up and your feet on the way down.

YORK

7 Scarcroft Road, York
☎ 01904 634341
Open: Tue-Sun 12 noon-
2pm & Mon-Sat 7pm-
10pm. Early dinner
5.30pm-6.30pm

Melton's   Restaurant

Walk into Melton's and you might think you had walked into the picture gallery next door. There are fishing boats at sunset and Yorkshire landscapes of varying degrees of accomplishment, worthy originals but no match for the cooking to come. Owners Michael and Lucy Hjort work strenuously to keep the tables filled on two terraced house floors. The early three course dinner (leave the table by 7.45pm) is good value and there are daily themes on top of the main menu: seafood specials on Tuesday, additional puddings on Wednesday and extra vegetarian dishes on Thursday. Nor does vegetarian mean 'we can do you an omelette' but more likely a sweetcorn waffle with roast carrots, parsnips and coriander sauce. There's a vegetarian dish on the menu every night and a note says that no gelatine or meat stock is used although cheese may include animal rennet. It's a tiny but important point, respecting what vegetarians are about. Perhaps it comes from Michael Hjort's Roux Brothers training. He certainly learned how to cook with imagination, style and a refreshing lack of pretension. The Hjort's occasionally write up their recipes in the Saturday edition of the Yorkshire Post. Their house style is eclectic. Continental and oriental influences collide happily with diverse ingredients: try grey mullet with stir fried vegetables in a black bean sauce or lamb with a herb crust and a powerhouse pot of fresh pesto. Yorkshire game is well used. At Christmas, breast of pheasant was stuffed with ginger and served with a pheasant mousse. Terrine came with pumpkin jam. The apparent simplicity of beetroot on blinis and cauliflower soup outshone the hyper sophistication of foie gras in a port and truffle jelly. Puddings lived up to their surface appeal: old fashioned syllabub or Sussex pond pudding contained a luxuriant lemon and butter sauce that flowed out and surrounded the pudding; a sweet white chocolate parfait was encircled by a citrus sharp lime syrup that complemented precisely the sweetness of the parfait. A striking cheeseboard of well kept British and Irish cheese is served before or after dessert. The service is easy going without being too casual. The final bill is medium expensive but mineral water, coffee and service are all included in the price – a simple strategy but a classy one. Why don't more restaurants do it?

YORK

13a High Ousegate, York
☎ 01904 627929
Open: Mon-Sat 12 noon-
2 pm & 6 pm-10pm

Partner's   Restaurant

Chris Kwiatkowski was born to Polish parents in Africa and then brought up in England and France. Small wonder there's a multi-national dimension to his straightforward restaurant, down a narrow alley off High Ousegate. Try kotlety, a Polish hamburger made with minced pork. Or kulebiaka, a Russian fish pie. There's still no comfort for vegetarians in a Hungarian salad of chicken, mushroom and bacon. His French and English years are respectively summed up on the set price menus with moules Provençales and treacle roly poly with custard. Chris's retail past saw him run an exotic greengrocer's in Bishopthorpe which has informed his strong seasonal awareness and he was a founding partner of 19 Grape Lane. But above all, like almost every Pole, he is naturally a great mushroom and fungus fanatic. When he was billeted as a child along with 4,500 post war refugees at Sutton on the Forest, he brought rabbit, pheasant and wild mushrooms home to his tin hut. Today, he knows where to find white truffles in Scotland and the ceps and morels frying gently in butter or garlic off the autumn menu are hand picked and Yorkshire's own.

CLASS COOKERY

F amous name cookery schools are not cheap. The Roux Brothers, Leith's and Cordon Bleu in London will separate you and your money at an alarming rate and cookery holidays in Tuscany can cost £2,000 for a fortnight.

At the other end of the scale every local authority in Yorkshire and Humberside run courses from two hours to two years on everything from boning poultry to creole cuisine. Mighty catering colleges like **Thomas Danby, Roundhay Road, Leeds ☎ 0113 249 4912** are highly vocational, turning out generations of meat technicians, canteen chefs and hospitality caterers. The public can join one day demonstrations by illustrious chocolatiers and visiting TV chefs and taste the students' best efforts in the training restaurants of Millers at Barnsley College; Craven College, Skipton and Harrogate College.

What the region lacks for the serious amateur cook is much in between the hit and miss of the evening class and the public school prices of the London establishments. Most promising is the **Blue Goose Cookery School, Newby, Clapham, N. Yorks ☎ 01524 251520**. It's run by German born Willi Rehbock who propelled the tiny and delicious Blue Goose restaurant in Settle into the Good Food Guide before closing it to concentrate on his cookery courses. His one day demonstrations are on classic themes: dinner party entertaining and preparation for Christmas. With lunch and wine, they cost £24.50. He has plans for longer hands-on courses when he moves to West Yorkshire in 1995.

The **Vegetarian Society, Dunham Road, Altrincham, Cheshire ☎ 0161 928 0793** operates the excellent Cordon Vert School, which proclaims itself as the only such school in the world. The diploma course is aimed at professionals but there are numerous short courses which include: Learning to Demonstrate; Italian Vegetarian Cookery and So You Want To Open Your Own Vegetarian Restaurant. There is something for everyone from rank beginners upwards.

Across another border is the delightful **Eggleston Hall, Barnard Castle, Co. Durham ☎ 01833 650553**. For 20 years Rosemary Gray ran a Cordon Bleu cookery school here before handing over to her son Sir William Gray. Now, one and two day courses offer food, horticulture and antiques. There is an unforgettable walled garden and outstanding visiting chefs of the recent calibre of Alastair Little of Soho and Shaun Hill of Gidleigh Park, Devonshire.

The really serious food student might consider Leeds University's annual symposium of food history, which has attracted in the past such gurus as the seafood scholar Alan Davidson. Theoretically, anyone can go but the subject matter can be arcane in the extreme. The 1991 symposium Traditional Food East and West of the Pennines has recently been published in paperback, edited by C. Anne Wilson who is also the contact for future symposia. Full details from the **Brotherton Library, University of Leeds ☎ 0113 233 5518**.

Finally, getting away from it all, there's a Yorkshire outfit running Cook Around France weekend breaks which offer demonstrations, hands on cooking, market visits and first rate French food in small hotels. Details from **Inntravel, Hovingham, York ☎ 01653 628811**.

13

Books & Cooks

This is a short chapter for learning more about Yorkshire food, its cooking, its literature and its history. While the region can take reflected glory from the continuing successes of Leeds born Marco Pierre White as London's most brilliant chef, Yorkshire lacks a single great name who is indivisible from the vast literature of food. We have yet to find our Jane Grigson or Elizabeth David, even our Delia Smith. Yorkshire Television stolidly mass produced *Farmhouse Kitchen* for more than a decade and the spin-off books are still in print. Apart from the Saturday morning *Nosebag News* on Radio York presented by Anne Stirk, it is difficult to think of any worthwhile contemporary regional broadcasting on food. For modern food writing, Saturday's *Yorkshire Post* has well known regional chefs writing their own recipes, a Feeder's Digest column on local food news and tips and Robert Cockroft's uncompromising restaurant reviews. Martin Dawes of the *Sheffield Star* is best for South Yorkshire. The *Dalesman* and *Yorkshire Journal* have occasional original articles on regional food lore. Yorkshire food has avid historians and the University of Leeds has one of the world's great food libraries. This chapter also includes a select bibliography.

A YORKSHIRE FOOD LIBRARY

'A Book necessary for Mistresses of Families, higher and lower Women Servants, and confined to Things Useful, Substantial and Splendid, and calculated for the Preservation of Health, and upon the Measures of Frugality, being the Result of thirty Years Practise and Experience.'

Elizabeth Moxon, English Housewifery, Leeds, 1769

There are few classics of Yorkshire food writing. Peter Brears is our best food historian and his two books: *The Gentlewoman's Kitchen: Great Food in Yorkshire 1650-1750* and *Traditional Food In Yorkshire* are two indispensable volumes for anyone with a scholar's interest in the region's food. Marie Hartley and Joan Ingilby's masterly *Life and Tradition* trilogy of Yorkshire is full of rewarding detail but has a far broader remit than food. The late great Jane Grigson, who was brought up in Sunderland and had many Yorkshire holidays, wrote affectionately and astutely about Yorkshire food. But it was a Yorkshire Daleswoman, Dorothy Hartley, who in 1954 wrote the delightful *Food In England*, with much Yorkshire anecdote and description.

Charles Dickens and Charlotte Brontë give ferocious fictional accounts of vile Yorkshire institutional cooking in *Nicholas Nickleby* and *Jane Eyre*. The truth that, outside wealthy homes, food in the Ridings has usually varied from plain to foul is also made autobiographically by Richard Hoggart in *The Uses of Literacy* and *A Local Habitation*, politically by E. P. Thompson in *The Making Of The English Working Classes* and journalistically by George Orwell in *The Road To Wigan Pier*.

Gerald Priestland's *Frying Tonight* is the standard work on fish and chips. He read his Fish Friers Review assiduously to unearth this story from 1971: 'Roughly 6,000 visitors thronged the Doncaster frying trades exhibition. The competition to find Miss Hot Chips in Hot Pants attracted 42 entrants, including one female impersonator called Barry.' *Fish 'N' Ships* by John Goddard and Roger Spalding is a more salutary account of the vicious conditions under which Grimsby mariners landed our fish.

There are Dales cookbooks, Brontë cookbooks, Yorkshire pudding books and all manner of collections with spurious Yorkshire connections. One or two give solid information on background and tradition, notably *Yorkshire Fare* by Margaret Slack and *Old Yorkshire Recipes* by Joan Poulson.

For new food books **Waterstones** probably have the biggest selection. Second-hand book shops have the odd gem but there is one man who may have got there first. Tom Jackson is still remembered as the moustachioed general secretary of the Post Office Workers Union. In 1982 he retired for a gentler lifestyle, selling second-hand food and cookery books, by mail order, as **Jackson's of Ilkley, 22 Parish Ghyll Road ☎ 01943 601947**. During school holidays, he travels the country with his daughter and wife (who deals in children's books), scouring for old cook books. He publishes his quarterly catalogue so successfully that the best titles are sold within a week. Elizabeth David was a regular buyer until her death. His most expensive sale was a 1638 edition of *Two Books of Cookerie and Carving*, a bargain, says Tom, at £600. The current lists have books from £5 to £200. His food credentials come from his father and grandfather who ran a bakery in Hunslet, Leeds: 'Now lost somewhere in the Sunblest empire.'

The library is free. Like many before and since, Blanche Legat Leigh's term as Lady Mayoress of Leeds in 1935 might have gone unremembered were it not for the special place she holds in the hearts of researchers and food historians for her remarkable collection of 1,500 cookery books which she presented to the **Brotherton Library, Leeds University**. Her gift inspired the Preston donation of 604 volumes and 47 pamphlets in 1962 and the recent acquisition of the Camden Collection of 1,500 volumes of 19th and 20th century cookery books. Leeds now has the finest food library in the country outside the British Museum.

The earliest titles are a Babylonian tablet dated 2500 BC that contains a diet list and an Egyptian wall painting of 1200-850 BC on plaster and papyrus depicting offerings to the food God Osiris. The main titles begin in 1585 with the anonymous *A Booke of Cookry Very Necessary for All Such as Delight Therein, Gathered by A.W.* with a recipe for larks and a sparrow stew cooked in ale. There are many early first editions: Hannah Glasse's 1747 *The Art of Cookery Made Plain and Easy,* (a first edition recently sold for £6,000) and John Evelyn's garden calendar of 1664, *Acetaria, A Discourse of Sallets* that lists 73 different varieties of herbs and vegetables. Some, such as skirrets, rampion or trip-madame, are virtually unknown today. One W. M., writing in 1655, identified a profitable market with a modern resonance. In *The Queen's Closet Opened*, he promised to reveal untold secrets from the royal kitchens.

Each generation had its favourite cookery book. Elizabeth Moxon was a Yorkshire cook who in 1741 published *English Housewifery Exemplified* which ran to eight editions. Ann Peckham of Leeds, 'for forty years past one of the most noted cooks in the County of York', wrote *The Complete English Cook* in 1773. Her recipe for umble pie contains the umbles or sweetbreads of a deer, mixed with suet, sugar and currants. But this was a modest affair compared with her Yorkshire Christmas pie. In it, a goose, a turkey, a chicken, a partridge and a pigeon were all boned and wrapped, one inside the other. The resulting parcel was wrapped in a pastry crust and topped off with diced hare, woodcock and any other wildfowl available. Some of these pies, served in hotels and inns at Christmas, stood one foot high.

By contrast, Alexis Soyer, the celebrated chef of the Reform Club, who was appointed by the government to run soup kitchens during the Irish potato famine and in Crimean war hospitals, travelled to Yorkshire to learn about the cookery of the poor and was so disturbed by their ignorance that he published the best selling *A Shilling Cookery for the People*.

In 1845 Eliza Acton's *Modern Cookery for Private Families* was the first to set down ingredients, quantities and timings in a coherent manner. It took seven years to write and was mercilessly plagiarised. Almost every cookery book of the late Victorian era, including Mrs Beeton, contained Eliza Acton's uncredited recipes. *Mrs Beeton's Book of Household Management* was published in 1861 when she was 25 years old. When she died at 28, a week after the birth of her third child, it was already a huge best seller. The Brotherton has first editions of both Acton and Beeton. Sadly, it is not committed to a comprehensive modern collection. Volumes can be consulted in the Reading Room, by appointment with the Curator of the Special Collection.

BIBLIOGRAPHY

Acton, Eliza; Ray, Elizabeth. Ed. *The Best of Eliza Acton* , 1968.

Abbey, Ampleforth. *Cooking Apples,* 1982.

Anson, F. Peter. *British Sea Fishermen,* (undated)

Bacon, Josephine. *Exotic Fruit and Vegetables,* 1988.

Bissell, Frances. *The Real Meat Cookbook,* 1992.

Brears, Peter. *The Gentlewoman's Kitchen: Great Food in Yorkshire, 1650-1750,* 1984.

Brears, Peter. *Traditional Food in Yorkshire,* 1987.

Brears, Peter. *Images of Leeds 1850-1960,* 1992.

Burns, David. *The Quaker Enterprise,* 1980.

Calvert, Kit. *Wensleydale Cheese,* 1977.

Chapman, Pat. Ed. *The Good Curry Guide,* 1991.

Christian, Glynn. *The New Delicatessen Food Handbook,* 1993.

Cockcroft, Barry. *Daughter of the Dales,* 1990.

Consumers Association; Jaine, Tom. Ed. *The Good Food Guide,* 1994.

David, Elizabeth. *English Bread and Yeast Cookery,* 1977.

Davidson, Alan. *Mediterranean Seafood,* 1972.

Davidson, Alan. *North Atlantic Seafood,* 1979.

Davidson, Alan. *A Kipper With My Tea,* 1988.

Davidson, Alan. *On Fasting and Feasting,* 1988.

Dowell, Phillip; Bailey, Adrian. *The Book of Ingredients,* 1980.

Ellis, Audrey. *Farmhouse Kitchen,* 1971.

Eyton, Audrey. *The Kind Food Guide,* 1991.

Gear, Alan. *The New Organic Food Guide,* 1987.

Goddard, John; Spalding, Roger. *Fish 'N' Ships,* 1987.

Grigson, Jane. *Fish Cookery,* 1973.

Grigson, Jane. *English Food,* 1974.

Grigson, Jane. *Vegetable Book,* 1978.

Grigson, Jane. *Food with the Famous,* 1979.

Grigson, Jane. *Fruit Book,* 1982.

Grigson, Jane. *The Observer Guide to British Cookery,* 1984.

Hartley, Dorothy. *Food In England,* 1954.

Hartley, Marie; Ingilby, Joan. *Life and Tradition in the Yorkshire Dales* , 1968.

Hartley, Marie; Ingilby, Joan. *Life and Tradition in the Moorlands of North East Yorkshire,* 1972.

Hartley, Marie; Ingilby, Joan. *Life and Tradition in West Yorkshire,* 1976.

Hoggart, Richard. *The Uses of Literacy,* 1957.

Hoggart, Richard. *A Local Habitation,* 1988

Hurst, Bernice. Ed. *Food From Britain: Food Focus 2,* 1989.

King, J. Elizabeth. *The Markets of Yorkshire,* 1989.

Larousse, Librarie. *Larousse Gastronomique,* (English text), 1988.

Leeming, Margaret; Huang Man-Hui, May. *Chinese Regional Cookery,* 1983.

Mabey, David. *In Search of Food,* 1978.

Mabey, David; Gear, Alan and Jackie. *The Organic Consumer Guide,* 1990.

Mabey, Richard. *Food for Free,* 1972.

Mellis, Sue; Davidson, Barbara. *The Born Again Carnivore,* 1990.

Mosey, Don; Ramsden, Harry Jnr. *The Uncrowned King of Fish and Chips,* 1989.

Muir, Richard. *The Dales of Yorkshire,* 1991.

Orwell, George. *The Road to Wigan Pier,* 1937.

Pearson, Gordon. *Hull and East Coast Fishing,* 1991.

Phillips, Roger. *Wild Food,* 1983.

Poulson, Joan. *Old Yorkshire Recipes,* 1974.

Priestland, Gerald. *Frying Tonight: The Saga of Fish and Chips,* 1972.

Rance, Patrick. *The Great British Cheese Book,* 1982.

Rance, Patrick. *The French Cheese Book,* 1989.

Ratcliffe, Roger. *The Bradford Book,* 1990.

Ratcliffe, Roger. *Leeds Fax,* 1992.

Rawlins, Janet. *A Dales Countryside Cookbook,* 1993.

Safe Food, Parents for; Taylor Joan and Derek. Ed. *Safe Food Handbook,* 1990.

Sekers, Simone. *Fine Food,* 1987.

Slack, Margaret. *Yorkshire Fare,* 1979.

Sleightholme, Dorothy. *Farmhouse Kitchen,* 1975.

Smith, Julia. *Fairs, Feasts and Frolics,* 1987.

Specialist Cheesemakers Association, Harbutt, Juliet. Ed. *Guide to the Finest Cheeses of Britain and Ireland,* 1993.

Steerwood, Rob; Machan, Peter. *Made in Sheffield,* 1986.

Tannahill, Reay. *Food in History,* 1973.

Thompson, Michael. *Fish Dock, The Story of St. Andrew's Dock Hull,* 1989.

Thompson, E.P. *The Making of the English Working Classes,* 1963.

Tindale, John. *Fishing Out of Whitby,* 1987.

Wainwright, Martin; Locke Tim. *The Which? Guide to Yorkshire and the Peak District,* 1992.

Walker, Caroline; Cannon Geoffrey. *The Food Scandal,* 1984.

Waterhouse, Keith. *City Lights,* 1994.

Wilson, C. Anne. Ed. *Traditional Food East and West of the Pennines,* 1994.

Wright, Carol. *Yorkshire Country Cookbook,* 1975.

Wright, Victoria. *Brontë Kitchen,* 1984.

Yorkshire Evening Post. *Yorkshire Scrapbook.*

GAZETTEER

Aiskew
Big Sheep & Little Cow Museum *ice cream* 68

Altrincham
Vegetarian Society, The 108, 198

Ampleforth
Ampleforth Apple Orchard, *fruit* 42

Asenby
Crab & Lobster *pub/restaurant* 152

Askwith
Ashdale Cheese *cheese* 56, 68

Badsworth
Brickyard Farm *organic vegetables* 42

Baildon
Bracken Hall Countryside Centre *fungus forays* 45
Conway's *restaurant* 152

Baldersby
Smithy Farm Shop *meat, fish, deli* 110

Barnard Castle
Teesdale Trencherman *smokehouse* 22, 119
Eggleston Hall *cookery courses* 198

Barnoldswick
Stanley's *oatcakes* 74

Barnsley
Armstrong's *restaurant* 152
Charter Market *indoor market* 124
Clamps *cooked meat* 124
Croque Café, Le *baking, café, takeaway* 75, 136
Gosling *tripe* 124
Hirst, Albert *butcher* 24, 124
Kelly's *baking* 75
Mitchell's *fish* 124
Oldfield's Original Pie and Pea Stall *pie and peas* 124
Pickering's *wholefoods* 100
Round Green Deer Farm *venison* 35
Scott's Fisheries *fish and chips* 143
Spencer's *tripe* 124
Superfruits *fruit and vegetables,* 124
Worsbrough Mill *flour* 72

Barrow on Humber
Wheelbarrow Foods *organic vegetables* 44

Barton on Humber
Elio's *restaurant* 153

Beckwithshaw
Windmill Farm *venison* 35

Bedale
Bedale Market *outdoor market* 124
Carrick's *fish, fruit and vegetables* 12, 51, 124
Cockburn & Son *meat and game* 24
Crakehall Water Mill *flour* 72
Cunningham's *preserves* 88
Plummer's *café* 136

Beverley
Beverley Arms Hotel *café* 136
Butler's Parlour *café* 136
Café Within *café* 136
Cerutti Two *restaurant* 153
Ginger's Tea Room *café* 136
Good 'N' Fresh *fruit and vegetables* 51
Jack & Son *delicatessen* 110
Peck & Son *fish* 12
Tea Cosy *café* 136
W.I. Market *baking* 85

Bilbrough
Three Hares *pub* 153

Bingley
Priestley's *cheese* 63
Really Good Food Shop, The *delicatessen* 110

Birstall
IKEA *kitchenware* 134
Oakwell Country Park *historic kitchen* 86

Bolton Abbey
Barden Tower *café* 136
Devonshire Arms *restaurant* 137, 154
Tea Cottage *café* 137

Boroughbridge
Bowley's Home Baking *baking* 75
Cheese & Co *cheese, deli* 63
Sheila's Bakery *baking* 75

Boston Spa
Café Provence *bistro* 154
Hunter's *delicatessen* 110
Wilkinson's *meat* 25

Bradford
Agatha's *West Indian vegetables* 125
Ahmed Foods *Asian fruit and vegetables* 51, 111
Aire Valley Yoghurt *yoghurt* 69
Al Halal Supermarket *Asian supermarket* 110, 111
Ambala *Asian sweets* 96, 111
Bharat *Indian restaurant* 157
Bombay Brasserie *Indian restaurant* 157
Bradford Superstore *Asian supermarket* 111

Dr B's *West Indian café* 164
Dyson's *restaurant* 175
Egg Box, The *eggs* 130
Floyd's Creative Cuisine *baking* 80
Flying Pizza *restaurant* 173
Fosters *game* 130
French Revolution *bakery, takeaway* 80
Glenn's *Caribbean restaurant* 165
Gourmet Foods *Jewish delicatessen* 116
Grain of Sense *wholefoods* 104
Granny's Kitchen *preserves* 89
Granvin's *fish* 16
Great Northern Wine Company, The *olive oil* 115
Grillade, La *restaurant* 173, 175
Habitat *kitchenware* 134
Haley & Clifford *delicatessen* 116, 119, 173
Haley's *restaurant* 173
Hammond Sauce Works *Yorkshire relish* 88
Hansa's *Indian restaurant* 157, 174
Haye's *shellfish* 130
Hereford Beefstouw *restaurant* 174, 175
Hing Fat Hong *Chinese supermarket* 117
Jumbo *Chinese restaurant* 177
Kendal Moore *delicatessen, café* 117, 141
Kirkgate Market *indoor/outdoor market* 129, 130
Kosherie, The *Jewish delicatessen* 118
Leodis *restaurant* 175, 176
Lucky Dragon *Chinese restaurant* 176, 177
Mai Thai *Thai restaurant* 165
Mandarin *Chinese restaurant* 177
Maumoniat's *Asian supermarket* 39, 111, 118
Maxi's *Chinese restaurant* 177, 178
Meanwood Valley Urban Farm *organic fruit, vegetables, eggs* 47
Milan's *Polish restaurant* 165
Nash's Tudor Restaurant *fish and chips* 142
National Rivers Authority 19
Natural Food Store *wholefoods* 104
Natureways *vegetarian outside catering* 150
New Asia *Chinese/Vietnamese restaurant* 165
Nut Shop, The *nuts* 130
Oakwood Fisheries *fish and chips* 142
Oldest Fish & Chip Shop in the World, The *fish and chips* 142
Pasta Romagna *Italian delicatessen* 118
Pinky's *Indian outside catering* 39, 150
Pizza Express *Italian restaurant* 175
Polish Catholic Centre *Polish restaurant* 165
Pool Court at 42 *restaurant* 175, 178
Raja's Tandoor *Indian restaurant* 179
Rakusen's *matzos* 79
Ramsden's *fish* 130
Sala Thai *Thai restaurant* 165
Salsa Mexicana *Mexican restaurant* 164

Salvo's *restaurant* 179
Sang Sang *Chinese restaurant* 177
Shabab *Indian restaurant* 157
Shear's Yard *restaurant* 175
Simply Cakes *cakes* 75
Sous le Nez en Ville *restaurant* 164, 175, 179
Sparrow's Wharf *wine bar* 175
Spice Corner *West Indian vegetables, spices* 130
Stanley *eggs, game* 130
Summat Fishy *fish and chips* 142
Teppanyaki *Japanese restaurant* 179
Thai Siam *Thai restaurant* 165
University of Leeds *food symposium, historic cookbooks* 198, 201
Vinceremos *organic wine* 46
Warsaw Stores *Polish supermarket* 118
Welham *fish* 130
Whitelocks *restaurant* 40
Whittard of Chelsea *coffee* 146
Wildblood *cooked meat* 130
Wilson's of Crossgates *meat* 29
Wing Lee Hong *Chinese supermarket* 118

Leyburn
Carrick's *fish, fruit and vegetables* 17, 53
Cheeseman, The *cheese* 65
W.I. Market *baking* 85

Liversedge
Lillibets *restaurant* 180

Longridge
Kitchenalia *kitchenware* 134

Low Laithe
Dusty Miller *restaurant* 180

Malton
Blue Ball *pub* 181
Delicatessen & Wine Shop *delicatessen* 119
Realfare *wholefood* 105
Simply Delicious *outside catering* 150

Market Weighton
Swain's *fish* 17

Masham
Bowley's Home baking*baking* 80
Brymor Ice Cream Parlour *ice cream* 68
Floodlite *restaurant* 181
Mad Hatters *café* 141
Reah's Gourmet Confectionery *sweets, chocolates, cheese , preserves* 97

Meltham
Lodge R & J *pies, cheese* 37

Menston
Rochelle, La *restaurant* 182

Middleham
Nosebag Tea Shop *café* 141

Middlesbrough
Filbert's *vegetarian café* 141
Cucard, La *restaurant* 164

Morley
Antonio's *delicatessen* 119
Wilson's of Crossgates *meat* 29

Moulton
Black Bull *restaurant* 182

Mytholmroyd
Waites *baking* 80

Nafferton
Green Growers *organic vegetables, eggs* 48

Nantwich
Reaseheath College *cheesemaking courses* 61

Newsham
Shepherd's Purse *cheese* 61, 68

Newton Le Willows
Fortmayne Dairy *cheese* 62

Northallerton
Bellina Chocolates *chocolates* 98
Betty's *baking, chocolate, café, tea, coffee* 80, 144
Carrick's *fish, fruit and vegetables* 17, 53, 131
Cheeseman, The *cheese* 65, 131
Complete Cook, The *kitchenware* 134
Farmhouse Kitchen *restaurant* 183
Lewis & Cooper *grocers* 75, 119, 134
Northallerton Market *outdoor market* 131
Pepper Arden *game pies* 39
Selby's *delicatessen* 120
Trueman's *meat* 29
W.I. Market *baking* 85

Norton
Bakery, The *baking* 80
Fletcher & Son *meat* 30

Norwood
Chocolate Society, The *chocolate* 93

Osmotherley
Swales, Trevor *honey* 89

Otley
Baines Cheese Van *oatcakes, cheese* 65, 131
Bondgate Bakery *baking* 82
Curlew Café *vegetarian café/restaurant* 184
Gloucester's delicatessen *wholefoods* 120
Otley Market *outdoor market* 131
Patisserie Viennoise *cakes, chocolates* 75, 98
Quantrill's *fruit and vegetables* 53
Weegmann's *pies* 39
W.I. Market *baking* 85

Oxenhope
Great Hill House Farm *meat* 36

Penistone
W.I. Market *baking* 85

Pickering
Moorland Trout Farm *trout* 19
Mulberries *café* 144
Standford Hall Farm *organic fruit, vegetables, meat, eggs, mushrooms, herbs* 48
W.I. Market *baking* 85

Pickhill
Nag's Head *pub* 184

Pilsley
Chatsworth Farm Shop *cheese, meat, delicatessen, grocery* 27, 65, 120

Pocklington
Bayernstubl Zillertal *restaurant* 164
Hailey's *fish* 17
Swain's *fish* 17

Pontefract
Trebor Bassett *sweets* 94

Pudsey
Aagrah *Indian restaurant* 157, 184
Craven's *fish and chips* 142

Richmond
Carrick's *fish, fruit and vegetables* 17, 53
King's Head Hotel *café* 144
Swaledale Cheese Company *cheese* 62

Ripley
Hutchinson's *butcher* 30
Hopkins Porter *delicatessen* 120

Ripon
Carrick's *fish, fruit and vegetables* 53, 131
Fountains Abbey Visitor's Centre *café* 144
Fresh Cut *cheese, delicatessen* 121
Great Northern Wine Company *olive oil* 115
Holmes, Ian *cheese* 65, 131
Old Deanery *restaurant* 184
Raw Deal *wholefoods* 105
Ripon Market *outdoor market* 131
Studley Royal Tea Room *café* 144
Warehouse, The *café* 144

Ripponden
Pork Pie Appreciation Society 37
Upperview *café* 145

Robin Hood's Bay
Bay Fisheries *fish* 17

Rodley
Olive Tree *Greek/Cypriot restaurant* 164, 185

Roos
Melbourne's *meat* 30

Smith & Tissington *fish, poultry* 132
Sombrero, El *Mexican restaurant* 164
Thornton's *chocolates* 98
Top Farm Cheese *cheese, delicatessen* 66
Traditional Heritage Museum 146, 189
Turner Designs Mark *cutlery* 134
UK Mama *West African restaurant* 165
United Cutlers *cutlery* 189
Whittington *fish* 132
Wild, Hiram *cutlery* 189
W.I. Market *baking* 85
Wood & Wragg *fish, poultry* 132
Yvonne's *baking* 82

Shipley
Aagrah *Indian restaurant* 157, 184

Skipton
Aagrah *Indian restaurant* 157, 184
Bizzie Lizzie's *fish and chips* 143
Cheese Stall *cheese, baking* 66, 133
Hailey's *fish* 20, 133
Healthy Life *wholefoods* 105
Heber Wines *olive oil* 115
Herbs *café* 147
Priestley's *cheese* 66, 133
Rafters *café* 147
Skipton Market *outdoor market* 132
Stanforth's Celebrated Pork Pies *pies* 39
Whitaker's *chocolates* 98
W.I. Market *baking* 85

Sleights
Botham & Sons, Elizabeth *baking* 82
Egton Bridge Gooseberry Society 52
Radfords *meat* 31
River Garden Café *café* 147

Sneaton
Beacon Farm *ice cream, yoghurt* 69

Sowerby Bridge
Java *Indonesian restaurant* 165

Staddlebridge
McCoy's *restaurant* 191

Staithes
Endeavour *restaurant* 191

Stamford Bridge
Esk Fisheries Association 21

Stokesley
Chapters *restaurant* 192
Stokesley Delicatessen *delicatessen* 121
W.I. Market *baking* 85

Swinsty
Swinsty Tea Rooms *café* 147

Tadcaster
Little Deli *delicatessen* 122

Tankersley
Brooklands *restaurant, Barnsley chop* 124

Thames Ditton
Special Cheesemakers Association 56

Thirsk
Bates *cheese* 66

Thorne
W.I. Market *baking* 85

Thorner
Intake Lane Goat Herd *cheese* 62, 68

Thornton Dale
Hill's *meat, cheese* 31

Thornton Steward
Wensleydale Wild Boar Breeders *wild boar* 36

Threshfield
Old Hall Inn *pub* 192

Tickhill
Taylor's of Tickhill *grocers* 122
W.I. Market *baking* 85

Todmorden
Bailey *tripe* 133
Bear Healthfoods *wholefoods* 107
Crumbly Cheese, The *cheese* 67
Saker Foods *wholefoods* 104
Todmorden Market *indoor market* 133

Tollerton
Stark Farm *organic fruit, vegetables, meat* 49

Wakefield
Asquith *fruit and vegetables* 133
Baig's *Asian fruit and vegetables* 111, 133
Cartwright *eggs* 133
Danka's *delicatessen* 133
Fayre Do's *delicatessen* 122
Hey *tripe* 133
Horne, Stephen *fish* 133
Kaye Arms *pub* 192
Rhodes *eggs* 133
Sutton *eggs* 133
Wakefield Market *indoor, outdoor markets* 133
Winn *nuts* 133
Woods *fish* 20, 133

Walshford
Walshford Farm Shop *meat* 34

Warley
Maypole Inn *pub/restaurant* 193

Wass
Wombwell Arms *pub* 193

Wath In Nidderdale
Sportsman's Arms *restaurant* 193

INDEX

NOTES

NOTES

NOTES

NOTES